Tom Atkins

Tom Atkins joined the Royal Air Force in 1986 and has flown operationally over Bosnia, Kosovo, Afghanistan and Iraq. He is an authority on Second World War aviation and regularly gives presentations to groups, clubs and societies. His historical knowledge and his own military flying background give him a unique insight into the lives, surroundings, and equipment used by his characters, which he uses to full effect in his books. He is married and lives with his wife and son in Newark, England.

DEMONS IN THE DARK

Tom Atkins

DEMONS IN THE DARK

Vanguard Press

A CIP catalogue record for this title is
available from the British Library.

ISBN 978 184386 485 1

Vanguard Press is an imprint of
Pegasus Elliot MacKenzie Publishers Ltd.
www.pegasuspublishers.com

First Published in 2009

Vanguard Press
Sheraton House Castle Park
Cambridge England

Printed & Bound in Great Britain

Dedication

This book is dedicated to all the people who put on a uniform and fight for their country.

The Front Cover

Top scoring Luftwaffe night fighter pilot Heinz – Wolfgang Schnaufer dives away after attacking a 106 Sqn Lancaster bomber over its target. Despite the Lancaster being set on fire during the attack the bombers front gunner fights back and Schnaufer's radar operator enters a "Duel in the Dark" with the wounded bomber.

This Robert Taylor print entitled "Duel in the Dark" is available through The Military Gallery Wendover, England. Or on the Internet at "*militarygallery.com*"

ACKNOWLEDGEMENTS

I needed to do a lot of research before I could attempt to write this book and do the subject any justice. It was very important to me that the end product should be as realistic and accurate as possible, while being an exciting read. Too many times history is spiced up to make it more interesting or politically correct. This usually results in a distorting of the facts and ultimately the truth is lost in the fiction. This is a tragedy because the truth, no matter how unpalatable, should never be erased. If we do that, how are we ever to learn from our mistakes of the past? What should be remembered is, what is not politically correct now could well have been perfectly acceptable then, and we should judge people by the standards of the time and not our standards of the present.

Many people helped me with the writing of this book and they deserve mention, some however, for reasons of their own, prefer to stay in the background. Firstly I would like to thank Arthur Breeze and all the members of the Lincoln Branch of the Aircrew Association. Their combined knowledge and experience of World War 2 bomber operations was invaluable to me. Their Lancaster Bomber Briefing, where they put together a presentation by a full Lancaster crew, taking the audience through a complete bomber raid was inspirational. The Battle of Britain Memorial Flight were particularly helpful, giving me access to their Lancaster and talking me through the finer points of flying and maintaining it. Particular thanks go to Flight Lieutenant "Jack" Hawkins, the Adjutant, Corporal Tim Burrows, one of the ground crew and Squadron Leader "Stu" Reid, one of the pilots. Lastly, but by no means least, is Syd Geater, who was a Wireless Operator flying with 106 Squadron. Syd is one of life's great characters. He has the energy of a man half his age and a great enthusiasm for collecting technical data and facts. His knowledge and vast catalogue of information are a goldmine for anyone researching this subject and he is undoubtedly an outstanding expert in this field. He has been a great help to me and deserves far more recognition than I believe he will get from this book.

1

The sky above was a bright blue, the sun a dazzling white ball. The stratus cloud tops spread out as far as the eye could see. The Lancaster appeared suspended in space, cruising at 210 mph. The aeroplane's upper surfaces were painted a dull brown and green camouflage, its sides and underneath were matt black. The sun reflected from every angle on the aircraft's skin and every piece of Perspex. The flashes of reflected sunlight meant the Lancaster, despite being so small in the great vastness of the sky, was visible for many miles. The crew would have been feeling very exposed if this had been an operational flight but this was an easy transit flight over the UK and, in January 1944, no German intruders dared venture here in daylight.

The Lancaster had taken off from RAF Syerston, the Lancaster finishing school for 5 Group Lancaster crews, and had almost completed its flight. Normally crews were packed off to their Operational Squadrons by train or truck. Sometimes the newly trained crews managed to grab some leave before being thrown into the great unknown of operational flying. But this crew were different. Syerston had recently lost two Lancasters to mishandling by inexperienced crews, as they were rushed through training to replace growing casualties. Another Lancaster was lost to engine failure on takeoff, the time when a tired, overworked engine is most likely to fail and also the time when it is vital that it doesn't. Whatever the cause the result was the same, a wrecked aircraft and a handful of "His Majesty Regrets" telegrams. Replacement aircraft had to be flown in and, as luck would have it, a course of student crews had just completed their training. The powers that be realised that if all the replacement Lancasters available for 5 Group were flown to Syerston, the newly trained crews could ferry them on to the Squadrons, so saving much needed ferry pilots dispersing over the whole of Lincolnshire and they could now be flown back to their base from one airfield instead of several. So this brand new Lancaster with its brand new crew, came to be suspended over Lincolnshire, sandwiched between a bright blue sky and an even brighter white cloud layer, en route to RAF Metheringham and 106 Squadron.

Sitting on the glycol tank that formed the step up into the cockpit in the nose of the Lancaster was the bomb aimer, Sergeant Bob McKenzie from Perth, Australia. At five foot eight Bob was not exactly tall, but he was certainly broad. He was an ideal build for a boxer, and he had trained as an amateur since he was a boy. His fair hair was crew cut, his face tanned angular and chiselled with a powerful jaw and light blue eyes. A former dockyard clerk, Bob had travelled to England to join up when, in his opinion, his own country had dragged its feet in getting him into the action. Like a lot of Australians Bob did not have much reverence for authority, and at twenty-one he reckoned that he had had a lifetime's worth of red tape.

The Lancaster was heading south, it was nearly two o'clock in the afternoon and the sun was almost directly ahead. It lit up every corner of the normally dark nose through the bomb aimer's hemispherical Perspex bubble, which formed the lower half of the Lancaster's nose, and the power operated Frazer Nash gun turret, which formed the upper half. Screwing up his eyes against the glare, Bob pulled up the sleeve of his Irving flying jacket and looked at his watch. By his rough calculations it should be almost time for them to start their descent. Reaching for his map he started to refold it so that it was a manageable size for use in the small nose compartment. It had been a boring flight. They had been ordered to do a navigation exercise en route to Metheringham and normally he could have helped the navigator by map reading his way along the route, calling out significant features on the ground as they went. But they had climbed into cloud shortly after takeoff and, with the exception of a brief glimpse of the ground over the north coast of Scotland, they had been above continuous cloud the whole time. As he punched and folded the reluctant map into the desired shape, he felt a warm glow of contentment. The training was now over, the messing about and hanging around at an end and he was finally going to get a chance to have a crack at some real Jerries. He knelt forward and lay down on his stomach with his head inside the Perspex bomb aimer's dome, sorted out his intercom leads and laid the map in front of him. He squirmed himself comfortable and waited for them to start to descend.

Standing behind Bob on the flight deck was Sergeant Jimmy Wilson, the Lancaster's flight engineer. A year younger than Bob, he looked younger still. He stood six foot four and was powerfully built, but he was a gentle giant who lacked any aggression. He came from North Walsham in Norfolk, where he had been a mechanic and spent his days repairing farm machinery. He liked working on cars and it was his ambition to one day own one, but until then he would make do with his motorbike. His love of all things mechanical made him an ideal flight engineer and while his slow drawling Norfolk accent led some people to think he was slow, they soon had to revise their opinions.

Right now his eyes were watering, as he scanned the dazzling southern horizon from the left 9 o'clock, through the Lancaster's nose, to the right 3 o'clock. Directly outside the right hand side cockpit window, was the number three engine, a Packard-built Rolls-Royce Merlin 28. Along with its three sisters, it was making a deep throaty purring roar, which sent vibrations through the whole aircraft. The three blade de Havilland constant speed propeller looked like a silver transparent disc, the yellow painted tips barely visible as they turned at

1900 rpm. Further to the rear, the sun was reflecting on the upper surface of the wing, showing every rivet. The Lancaster's slightly raised cockpit canopy gave excellent vision to the rear. Jimmy could look along the top of the fuselage, past the D/F loop aerial and astrodome, towards the mid-upper turret and the twin tailplanes and rudders. Further round still, back to the 9 o'clock position, the sun was gleaming just as brightly on the port wing, and, leaning back to look along the rear of the pilot's armoured seat, he could see both the port engines. Jimmy knew of no other heavy bomber that gave the pilot and flight engineer such a good all-round view, except perhaps the Stirling which had now been retired from mainstream bombing Ops. It would be a great help in assessing any flak or cannon fire damage. He shivered, and the hairs stood up on his neck at the thought. His round ruddy face took on a very serious appearance; he hated the thought of operations. He was cursed with a very good imagination and could too easily imagine flames leaping out of the port engines, flaring back in the slipstream and whipping over the top of the fuselage. He quickly brought himself back to reality. Looking down at the instrument panel, he realized that he could not see anything but a blue grey mist. As his eyes adjusted to the dark instrument panel beneath the cockpit coaming, after a few seconds of eye straining and blinking, he could see enough to check the two rows of four dials, 1900 rpm and plus 7 pounds of boost on each engine. This was the recommended boost and the lowest rpm that allowed them to maintain their cruising speed of 160 mph indicated air speed. In this configuration, with the Lancaster lightly loaded, they would get the most efficient fuel consumption and the best range.

An airspeed indicator is only accurate at a certain pressure and, to a lesser extent, temperature. These are set as standard, so the airspeed indicator is accurate at about 3000 feet or below. As an aeroplane gets higher, the air pressure and temperature drop, making the instrument under read, so although the gauge said they were doing 160 mph they were actually doing 210 mph. This did not matter to the flight engineer or pilot, in fact it was quite useful, because as an aeroplane gets higher, it needs to go faster to gain the lift required to stay airborne in the thinner air. An aeroplane with a stalling speed of 60 mph at low level may have a stalling speed of 100 mph at say 20,000 feet but at 20,000 feet the gauge would show 60 mph when the aircraft was doing 100 mph, so as far as the pilot was concerned, the stalling speed was the same. The difference between indicated air speed on the gauge and true air speed through the air only becomes important when it comes to navigation. As far as Jimmy was concerned, that was a black art.

He looked over to his left at his pilot, Pilot Officer Douglas Jackson. His light blue grey eyes were also screwed up against the glare, which made them look almost translucent. They were fixed on the horizon ahead and Jimmy realised that his skipper was finding flying directly into the glare a strain.

Doug Jackson was also twenty, but looked older which gave him some credibility over the other, more baby faced pilots at the training unit. He had thought being an officer would also give him some standing in the eyes of his crew, but this didn't seem to be the case. The sergeants, who made up most of the rest of his crew, called him sir, occasionally, but usually called him skipper or boss. Doug didn't mind but as a very new and junior officer he wasn't sure if it was really the done thing. A vicar's son from Cambridge, Doug was a quiet person with a serious disposition, brought about by the acute knowledge that he had the lives of his crew in his hands. It was the first real responsibility he had ever had, and it weighed heavily on his mind.

Doug was not relaxed. His eyes were watering and aching from staring into the sun and he couldn't scan his instruments because his eyes wouldn't adjust to the darker cockpit before he felt the over-riding urge to look out again. This was partly due to an incident during his flying training when he had had a near miss with another aircraft. Since then he had kept a very good lookout. And partly it was because he knew he was not particularly good at flying on instruments. He was also soaked in sweat; cold was generally a more common problem. However, today the bright sun had turned the cockpit into a greenhouse and he could feel his hair soaking wet under his leather flying helmet. While he was taller than most of the other pilots, he was slim and he was glad he wasn't a big person because the Lanc was not wide, especially when you had someone Jimmy's size beside you.

Doug knew that it must nearly be time to start their descent into RAF Metheringham. He had hoped to see a gap in the clouds by now. The Met man had said that the cloud would clear at midday and whatever cloud was left would be broken with a 5,000-foot base. But there were no gaps. The question now was how low did the clouds go?

The navigator's compartment was immediately behind the cockpit, and separated from it by a black curtain. Sitting in his seat, facing the left side of the aircraft, leaning on his small navigation table, was Ron Dune, a bank clerk from Cheltenham. At twenty-six he was the oldest member of the crew and, as a flying officer, the most senior rank, although Doug, the pilot, was still the aircraft captain. Ron was tall and of average build with dark curly hair and a moustache. After years of bending over desks he had developed a slight stoop and thanks to a tyrannical bank manager, an inferiority complex. He was relieved to be called up for the RAF, if only to escape his bullying boss. Once in the RAF he had become an administration officer and with his experience dealing with paperwork he did very well. Soon he gained confidence, and started to enjoy the respect and power his officer status bestowed on him. But aircrew was where the real power lay. People really took you seriously then and so he applied to train as a pilot. However, Ron was not a natural flyer and a complete lack of hand eye co-ordination meant it would be safer for all concerned if Ron became a navigator. With promotion to flying officer, as a consolation prize, he trained as a navigator and had no difficulties with the course. But, behind his mask of confidence, which often came across as arrogance, Ron was full of self-doubt. In short, he had been bullied and told he was no use for so long he was now ready to believe it.

With this sort of attitude Ron was not popular, and when it came to "crewing up", nobody wanted him in their crew. He had resigned himself to being a replacement navigator and this appealed to him, as he thought he might be placed with an experienced crew and have a better chance of survival. Unfortunately, Doug's original navigator caught flu and was unfit to fly for some weeks. So Ron was put onto Doug's crew, much to the horror of the sergeants.

On top of this, Ron was newly married, and his wife, Janice, was not at all happy about being separated from her husband, or the job he was doing. She made this quite plain in her letters, which were getting angrier and more upsetting. Ron found himself thinking about his marriage problems more and more. Ideally he wanted the same as she did: he didn't want to fly. He wanted the status of being aircrew, without the danger or inconvenience, and if he could just get through the thirty trips of this tour, he would never fly again.

All the other crews graduating from Syerston had short transit flights to their new bases. But because of Ron's arrogant and condescending attitude, his sergeant navigation instructor could not resist a parting chance to get his own back on his irritating student. So Ron's crew had a 1,000-mile final navigation exercise en route to their new station, a flight of over six hours. The instructor knew it was petty but he had grown to really hate Ron, and he pitied the crew that got stuck with him. Not that he was a bad navigator; he wasn't, although he was very under confident. The real problem was the fact that he would never fit in with a crew and become part of a team.

Five feet further to the rear of the aircraft, sitting on the left side facing forward, was the radio operator, Sergeant Harry Duke. Another twenty-year-old, he was an electrician from Lewisham, south London. He had lived through the Blitz and was keen to give some of it back. He was short and wiry, with very blond hair, pale skin and bright blue eyes. He possessed a rapier-like wit and the gift of the gab. Always cheerful, Harry was rarely seen without a cheeky grin on his face and he often had the crew in stitches with his throwaway one-liners.

At the moment he was busy getting direction finding or D/F radio bearings from various ground stations for Ron, who would use three or more of them to fix the Lancaster's position. Harry had to work closely with Ron but didn't like him. Ron had insisted that Harry take multiple passive bearings with the D/F loop aerial, which took time and was not particularly accurate. A better method would have been a ground station D/F fix. It would be more accurate and only take three minutes. But this would mean asking the ground for help and Ron did not want to admit he needed help. Not that it should be anything to be ashamed of. They had not seen the ground for 400 miles and they were about to descend through cloud, which could go down to the ground, and an accurate position would be vital. Harry repeatedly tuned his R1155 receiver to the D/F frequencies then got out of his seat to reach the rotating gear of the loop aerial, above his radio set. He turned the aerial until he found the null point in the signal and passed the bearing to the navigator before sitting down to retune the receiver for the next beacon. All the time he muttered under his breath but the droning roar of the Merlins kept this hidden from Ron.

Much further to the rear of the aircraft, sitting in his sling seat suspended from either side of his turret, was Alex Stuart, a nineteen-year-old Scot from the fishing port of Peterhead. As the mid-upper gunner he sat with his head and shoulders above the top of the fuselage in his round Perspex Frazer Nash dorsal turret. His all-round view was terrific; the only area he could not see was below. His hands rested on the turret controls, two pistol grip handles, with the tops of the handles leaning towards each other at 45 degrees and pivoted in two planes. The handles were slightly more than shoulder width apart, just outboard of the breeches of the two Browning .303 machine guns. Twisting the handles right rotated the turret to the right, the further he twisted the handle the faster it rotated and the same applied in the opposite direction. By twisting the tops of the handles towards him he could elevate the two machine guns and by twisting them away from him he depressed the guns. Alex loved this crew position. It gave him a far better all-round view than the tail turret, and his five-foot-eight lean frame seemed to fit the turret perfectly. He didn't even mind the intense cold of the turret. If he could live through a Peterhead winter, living in a turret would be easy. Cold was one thing Alex knew a lot about. He had been a fish porter on Peterhead fish quay and the ice-cold north winds were relentless. Even in the summer a fog would descend on the town, cutting out any sunlight and all the time the wind was there, cold enough to cut you in two. Carrying boxes of fish packed in ice around Peterhead fish docks was probably the best training a person could have to prepare them for the freezing temperatures experienced in a Lancaster's turret.

Alex was more Scottish than Rob Roy. He had an accent so broad that many Scots had difficulty understanding him. His short black hair and dark brown eyes only succeeded in making his skin look even paler and like many nineteen-year-olds he was plagued with acne. Despite this, women loved him! He seemed to know all the right things to say and they seemed to want to mother him. The rest of the crew could not understand his success, but they couldn't help but admire him for it.

At the moment Alex was scanning the sky above and behind the Lancaster. This was for two reasons. Firstly, if they were attacked it was likely to come either out of the sun, or from the rear. Secondly, he had been staring into the sun for most of the last two hours and his eyes needed a rest. Despite the lack of any form of comfort in his turret Alex was a happy man. He had always wanted to fly but never thought he would have a chance. Now he was fulfilling a dream.

The final member of the crew was the rear gunner, Sergeant George Coates, a coal miner from Spennymoor, a mining and iron and steel town, in south Durham. At twenty-five George had been a miner for ten years and he had hated every minute of it. Physically he was ideally suited for working in the dark eighteen-inch high coal seams. He was only five foot four, lean and muscular, but mentally, George hated the dark wet humid and claustrophobic environment. He had always been interested in aeroplanes and although, as a mature twenty-five-year-old, he was well aware of his life expectancy as a rear gunner, he reckoned that it was better than spending the rest of his life in an underground hell. Getting into the RAF had not been straight forward because coal mining was a reserved occupation, so George had lied and told the recruiters he worked in an ironmonger's. The recruiter hadn't believed him, because the second finger of George's left hand had been amputated at the first joint. It was all too common for miners to lose fingers, working with heavy machinery in the dark, but he had allowed him in anyway.

As a result of spending all his working life underground George had a pale skin. His brown hair was side parted and Brylcreemed, while his blue eyes were always darting around and missed nothing. Like many short people George made up for his lack of height by being prepared to fight anyone who crossed him. However, until he was crossed he was a very placid amiable character. His Geordie accent was mild and soft, until he had had a few drinks or he got angry. Then it became hard and aggressive, but George was a solid character and a steadying influence with a dry sense of humour. The rest of the crew felt secure with him in the rear turret.

George was bored out of his mind and his legs had gone into cramp. He slowly swung his turret from side to side quartering the sky for the enemy aircraft that he knew would not be there. It was so bright he had had to turn the brightness right up on his reflector sight. His turret controls were similar to Alex's and so was his gun sight, a projector pointing upwards through a lens onto a sheet of glass at 45 degrees directly in front of the gunner's face. The gunner looked through the glass at his target and his sight appeared superimposed on the sheet of glass. A red dot was where the bullets from his four Browning .303s would go and there was a ring to help him judge the range to the target. Most sights were set so that a German night fighter would be at 400 yards when its wing tips touched both sides of the circle, providing the fighter had a fifty-four-foot wingspan, which the Messerschmitt 110, the main German night fighter, had. The other common German night fighter, the Junkers 88, had a sixty-five-foot wingspan, and so when its wingtips touched each side of the circle it would be nearer 500 yards away. George had the ring and bead as bright as possible to show up in the sunlight; normally it was a barely visible glow in the dark. For what must have been the thousandth time that flight he screwed up his eyes, forced himself to concentrate and peered into the glare, for the fighters he knew weren't there.

Back in the cockpit Doug flicked the rotary switch on the front of his oxygen mask to transmit and held it to his mouth.

"How long to top of descent, nav?"

Ron had been waiting for this question and he wished he knew the answer. The H2S ground mapping radar had packed up just after John O'Groats and the GEE navigation system hadn't worked when he switched it on. He had had to fall back on radio D/F bearings. He had just finished plotting the last D/F bearing and the three lines formed a triangle with 20-mile sides and they could be anywhere inside it. By dead reckoning he believed they had three minutes to the top of descent, but he hadn't had an accurate fix now for some time and the Met man had been wrong about the weather, so he was probably wrong about the winds. That meant they could have been blown miles off course. His own efforts to determine the wind direction and strength had been confusing, indicating drastic changes in wind direction and strength. In the end he had given up and gone with the forecast winds and placed his hopes in an accurate fix before descent. Now that this had failed, he felt himself start to panic. It started as butterflies in the stomach and then turned to a feeling of nausea, which worked its way up his throat. He started to feel flushed and a cold sweat broke out on his face and down his back. He thought he had made a mess of things and was about to be found out. It was just like being back in the bank, waiting for the inevitable rain of abuse and public humiliation from the manager. He stared at the map for inspiration but nothing came. His mind was now numb with panic; he had to say something, but what? "Three minutes, skipper." What would it matter? They would soon recognise something below the clouds. He folded his map with his trembling hands, drew back the curtain to his right and with eyes screwed up against the glare stood behind the pilot's seat.

The clouds still extended to the horizon in all directions.

"It's no good, Jimmy!" shouted Doug, his head close to the flight engineer's ear so he didn't have to use the intercom. "I can't see the instruments and keep a lookout. I'm going to start flying on instruments now ready for the descent. You keep a good lookout!" Then on intercom, "Where's the nearest high ground, Ron?"

"The Peak District, well to the west," Ron answered vaguely. Please God, let us be on track, he thought. His mind was now in such a panic he would rather risk descending into the side of a hill than admit he was not sure of their position.

"Okay," replied Doug. "That's three minutes. We're starting our descent now," he announced for the benefit of the rest of the crew. Then he reached forward with his right hand and brought the throttles back to zero boost, let the airspeed fall to 140 mph on his airspeed indicator, then lowered the aircraft's nose to maintain that speed, trimming the Lancaster as the speed stabilized. In this attitude the Lancaster would descend at about 400 feet per minute. The white carpet got closer, wispy semi transparent tendrils of cloud whisked past. A shadow flashed across the cockpit as they clipped the top of a slight ridge of cloud breaking through again into sunshine, then the world went brilliant white as the Lancaster was enveloped in cloud.

It was almost as bright inside the cloud as flying above it. Only now all around them was white. No up, no down, not even any real idea of how far you could see. The only thing that told them they were the right way up was the artificial horizon on Doug's blind flying panel, showing a nose down attitude. To its left the airspeed indicator looked glued to 140 mph, below that the altimeter slowly unwound. To its right the gyro compass was steady on one eight five degrees and to the right of that the turn and slip indicator confirmed a straight course. Above this, the last of the blind flying instruments, the climb and descent indicator showed a steady descent at 400 feet per minute. Doug's eyes flicked from the artificial horizon to one of the other instruments, then back to the artificial horizon. Then to a different instrument, then back, constantly scanning as he had been taught. How he hated instrument flying! It was okay for short periods of time at this height but, as the ground got nearer, he always felt its presence and wanted to pull the nose up. He had once unthinkingly done this and the airspeed had slowly dropped close to stalling and only the last minute selection of emergency boost had saved them. After that Doug had dreaded having to fly on instruments. The inside of the cloud had now lost its brilliance and was a dull grey. Water droplets collected on the windscreen and moved upwards and outwards in the slipstream. Down and down they went. They had been in the cloud now for almost ten minutes and were descending through 3,000 feet on the altimeter, which was set to the QNH. Altimeters work by measuring atmospheric pressure and if they are set to an incorrect pressure they will read an incorrect height. With the correct QNH pressure, forecast by the Met man, set on the altimeter it will read the aircraft's height above sea level, Of course you would still fly into the top of a 3,000 foot mountain with 3,000 feet showing on your altimeter. So it's vital to know the height of the ground you're flying over and for that you need to know where you are.

So much for a 5,000 foot cloud base, thought Doug, "How high's the ground around here, Ron?"

"300 feet maximum."

If we're where we should be, he thought.

"What about that bloody great cathedral in Lincoln?" asked Harry from behind his radio set.

"We're well south of that, sergeant," replied Ron, angry that anyone should question him.

2000 feet came and went. By now the cloud was dark grey and the wing tips were only visible through a fog. As 1,000 feet approached Doug started to get the urge to pull the nose up, but resisted. Then at exactly 1,000 feet there was a sudden lightening of the cloud. Then they were out.

The fields 950 feet below them looked wet and although they were not in a rain shower at the moment they could see showers of rain falling on both sides of them and ahead of them. Visibility was about two miles but would drop to less than half that in a rain shower. It was a typical dark grey miserable English winter's day.

"I love the bloody weather in this country!" moaned Bob, from the aircraft's nose.

"Never mind that, does anyone recognise anything?" asked Doug.

Nobody answered.

Doug selected the RAF Metheringham frequency on the short-range VHF radio telephone or RT to his left. This would allow him to speak to Metheringham from up to 40 miles away.

"Coffee Stall, Coffee Stall, this is Hadnone F for Freddy, do you read me, over?" Coffee Stall was the call sign of RAF Metheringham. Hadnone was the call sign for 106 Squadron and F was this aircraft's identification letter.

"Hadnone F for Freddy. This is Coffee Stall answering, you are loud and clear, runway two zero in use right hand. QFE niner niner two, circuit clear. Call airfield in sight, over."

"Runway two zero right hand. QFE niner niner two. Wilco, Hadnone F for Freddy." Doug reached forward with his left hand and turned the knob next to the altimeter until 992 was set on the pressure setting scale. Now the altimeter would read zero feet as the Lancaster touched down at Metheringham, which was sixty-three feet above sea level. They were now flying level 100 feet below the clouds, 850 feet above the ground and their altimeter showed 837 feet, or it would if any pressure altimeter could be read that accurately. It was very easy to get confused and had caused the deaths of many aircrews.

"Airfield dead ahead!" called Bob as the airfield, barely visible, emerged from the grey haze.

"That's it! Right on the nose!" said Ron, his confidence restored and scarcely believing his luck.

"Coffee Stall, Coffee Stall, this is Hadnone F for Freddy, airfield in sight over."

"Hadnone F for Freddy, Coffee Stall answering, you are clear to land, over."

"Roger, Coffee Stall, we'll come straight in." Then on intercom to Jimmy, "Before landing checks, quick!"

The airfield was getting close, but they were in a good position to make an approach if they were quick with the checks.

"Auto pilot control cock," challenged Jimmy.

"Out," responded Doug, as he checked it.

"Superchargers."

"Low ratio."

"Air intake."

"Cold."

"Brake pressure."

"In limits."

"Flaps."

"20 degrees." Jimmy lowered the flaps to the 20 degrees mark.

"Undercarriage."

"Down." Jimmy slid the safety bolt to one side and moved the lever to the down position.

"Skipper! That's the wrong airfield!" yelled Bob.

"No, it isn't," snapped Ron, desperate for it to be the right place. "The runways are all in the right directions."

"But it's covered with Yank Dakotas," replied Bob.

"Are you sure?" asked Doug.

They were nearly at the airfield boundary and Doug knew that at less than 300 feet he could not afford to be distracted now, but he was not going to land at the wrong airfield.

"I can see the bloody white stars, skip!"

Doug pushed all four throttles to the gate giving plus 9 pounds of boost to the engines and pulled back on the control column to raise the nose but maintain 140 mph. The engines roared but the Lancaster felt sluggish. It wouldn't maintain 140 mph and climb, something was wrong! They weren't getting full power and he needed to do something quickly. Should he close the throttles and try to land anyway? The speed was starting to drop, don't stall it!

"Rpm, skipper!" said Jimmy, pointing at the gauges.

Bob's call of wrong airfield had interrupted his checks before he could put the propellers into fine pitch and now they were doing the aerial equivalent of trying to accelerate away in fourth gear. Doug's hand shot to the pitch levers increasing the propeller rpm to 2850 and the Lancaster accelerated forward, its speed not falling below 120 mph and its height not falling below 100 feet.

"Does anyone know where the hell we are?" asked Doug shaken by his forced error. At the same time he turned the Lancaster to the left to clear the American airfield's circuit, which was fortunately empty.

Ron's mind was in a whirl. "Er, we must be off track." He was now sweating profusely and a complete panic.

"The Yanks have some bases near Grantham," said Bob.

Doug thought for a second while he settled the Lancaster into a gentle climb and selected the undercarriage up, steadying on a heading of east. "If we're near Grantham we can head east and see if we can recognize something. If we don't, we'll hit the coast and pick up a landmark there."

"Yes, head east," blurted out Ron. "We're sure to see something then." He was desperately shuffling his map trying to find Grantham but he was all fingers and thumbs and his eyes weren't focusing properly.

The Lancaster was now level at about 800 feet above the ground. 200 feet below the clouds Doug set it up to fly at low speed. Landing gear up with the flaps at 20 degrees, bringing the revs back to 2650 and plus 2 pounds of boost the speed reduced to 130 mph. The stalling speed would be about 100 mph and they would now have more time to spot things on the ground in the worsening visibility.

"Hadnone F for Freddy, Hadnone F for Freddy, this is Coffee Stall, are you still making a straight in approach? We can't see you, over," crackled over the RT.

Damn, thought Doug. What the hell was he going to tell them? "Coffee Stall, this is Hadnone F for Freddy, negative... We're repositioning for another approach."

From Bob, "Big building at 11 o'clock."

"Looks like a stately home," said Alex, who had turned his turret forwards to try to help spot things.

The building was huge, made of red bricks with white sandstone pillars and facings. The centre section had a grand pillared entrance and a high domed clock tower, while large wings extended out either side.

"That's College Hall at RAF Cranwell," said Doug.

"Gotcha!" said Bob triumphantly. "Metheringham is northeast of here."

Doug turned left again onto northeast, so that they passed College Hall on their right-hand side, staying well clear of the grass airfield to the south of it, although it was unlikely that any of the student pilots being trained there would be airborne in this weather.

"Eight miles to Metheringham," said Ron, who had found Cranwell at last.

The visibility was definitely getting worse. It wasn't yet three o'clock but the light was starting to fade and a shower of rain closed in on them from their 2 o'clock.

Alex strained his neck from side to side, as he slowly swung his turret to try and get a better view of the countryside below. He could see Harry's head in the astrodome behind the cockpit doing the same thing. Out of the corner of his eye something moved, which in itself was not unusual when looking forwards from an aircraft doing 130 mph. But this was a movement that was not relative to the movement of the aircraft. His eye instinctively flashed to the movement. At first he thought it was just a darker patch of cloud or a sheet of rain. Then he instantly knew what it was! His right hand shot to his intercom switch and before it got there his air gunner trained eye had assessed that the relative bearing between them and the shadow about to emerge from the rain shower had not changed and they were therefore on a collision course.

"Break left! Aircraft! 2 o'clock!"

The loud and urgent shout made Doug jump and he instinctively looked right to the 2 o'clock position. The Spitfire was emerging from the rain shower heading at 90 degrees to them, crossing their nose from right to left in a slow descent. It took Doug two seconds to see the Spitfire and assess the situation. In that time they had got 300 yards closer. It took another second for him to push the throttles to the gate and he remembered this time to select fine pitch on the propellers. At the same time his left hand threw the control wheel as far left as it would go and pulled back to keep the nose up, a manoeuvre so violent he would never have tried it in a bomber if he had had time to think about it. The Spitfire was now very close, the pilot plainly visible looking directly at them, his eyes wide above his oxygen mask. Dark soot marks stretched back along the sides of the nose from behind the exhausts, covering the green brown camouflage paintwork; Doug could even see the rivulets of water streaming round the sides of the cockpit canopy. Then the Lancaster finally responded to the controls and started to roll quickly left. The G force increased as Doug pulled the control column back with both hands to keep the Lancaster's nose from dropping and the engine noise increased to a tortured howl. The Spitfire disappeared below the edge of the cockpit. Even Alex in his turret could no longer see it, as it was now behind the right wing but surely it must now slam into the underside of the Lancaster. They were now pulling three G and Ron, who normally weighed thirteen stone, now weighed thirty-nine stone and, standing behind Doug's seat, his legs could not take the strain and he collapsed on the cockpit floor. In the astrodome Harry had nothing to hold on to and he fell backwards to the floor beside his seat banging the back of his head hard on the main wing spar, where it bisected the fuselage. Jimmy used his massive arms to hold on to the back of Doug's seat and the side of the cockpit to help support his weight against the G. The others braced themselves for the terrible impact that must come any second. They waited. Nothing. Fractions of seconds that seemed like lifetimes. Vivid memories flashed through minds: thoughts of families, friends, girlfriends, a wife. Still nothing. Doug levelled off and throttled back. They had turned through 90 degrees and were now heading northwest.

"Did anyone see where he went?" asked Doug.

"Rear gunner, skipper, he disappeared into the clouds going up like a lift. He must have missed us by bloody inches!"

Doug brought the Lancaster slowly round to the right back onto northeast.

"Is everyone okay? Check in front to back."

"Bomb aimer okay."

"Flight engineer okay."

"Nav okay," said Ron pulling himself up off the cockpit floor.

There followed a pause.

"Harry?" asked Doug.

Jimmy looked back and saw Harry lying on his back on the floor.

"Harry's hurt, skipper. He looks unconscious, I'll go and check him."

"No, Jimmy, I need you here. We'll be landing in a minute. George, come up and see what's the matter with Harry. I take it you and Alex are okay."

"Well, I'm okay, skipper, but I can't speak for that jock twat. I'll come forward now."

"Seeing as the Geordie bastard doesn't know, I'm fine, skipper, but my underpants are a bit shitty," came the reply from the mid-upper turret.

"Should have stuck to wearing a kilt then, shouldn't yer," retorted George as he opened the rear doors to his turret and lifted himself out backwards, disconnecting his intercom leads before Alex could return his abuse.

"Airfield 2 o'clock," said Bob.

Doug dipped a wing to get a better look. "Is that Metheringham?"

"Yes," replied Ron too quickly.

"Sure?"

"Yeah, skip, there's a railway line running north south to the west of it and it's covered with Lancs," came the confident reply from the bomb aimer's compartment.

"Right," said Doug turning left on to north to give himself plenty of time to complete the before landing checks, and at the same time joining the down wind leg for a right-hand circuit. Jimmy had to move behind Doug's seat to let Bob through the cockpit to his landing position behind the main spar. For obvious reasons, Bob did not consider the bomb aimer's compartment a safe place to be on takeoff or landing. While he had stayed in the nose occasionally for takeoff and landing he felt safer behind the main spar. The checks completed, Doug called Coffee Stall to make sure they were still clear to land.

"Affirmative Hadnone F for Freddy, you are clear to land, the circuit is still clear and we have you in sight now."

Doug brought the Lancaster round in a sweeping curve and lined up on the main north south runway. It was easy to tell this was one of the new wartime airfields. It had the same A-shaped pattern of three intersecting runways but no main accommodation site or row of hangars and the grass either side of the runways was churned up, rutted and covered with mud and standing water where heavy machinery had obviously been. They were now well established on the approach and everything looked good for a landing.

"Stand by for landing, everyone."

Jimmy looked round. Ron was back in his seat looking pale. Behind him George was bending over Harry while Bob stood the other side of the main spar. Not being on intercom they would not have heard the warning. Jimmy nodded at Ron to turn round and warn them to be ready for landing but he just stared back at him blankly. Jimmy pulled off one of his gloves and threw it over Ron's head hitting George in the back. George looked round and Jimmy signalled with his hands that they were about to land. George put his thumb up then, with Bob's help, lifted the small radio operator, who was now starting to come round, over the main spar where they all sat on the floor with their backs against the spar for landing.

The landing was smooth and uneventful with flying control telling them to turn left at the end of the runway and follow the taxiway to their dispersal. Doug taxied slowly. He was shaking slightly and all he wanted to do was get out of the aircraft without further incident. The two inner engines were throttled back and he steered the big bomber by increasing and decreasing power on the outer engines. They passed some dispersals with Lancasters parked on them. Ground crews were swarming over them. Crossing the end of one of the secondary runways, they saw a group of men waiting by a dispersal. One walked towards them and held up his hands to indicate that he would marshal them into the parking area. Doug followed his signals and the Lancaster swung neatly into the dispersal. The shutdown checks were carried out and one by one the big engines were silenced. Finally, with all systems shut down, the marshaller signalled that the wheel chocks were in place and Doug released the brakes. His head buzzed from the sudden lack of noise. He listened to the hissing and clicking of the hot engines and the buzz of the gyros as they ran down. Beside him, Jimmy finished scribbling some figures on a bit of paper and made his way aft. Behind him he could hear others picking up their bits of specialist equipment and parachute packs and making their way to the rear door between the mid-upper and rear turrets. Doug took a deep breath, undid his seat harness and followed them.

At the rear door Bob was passing kit bags and suitcases to Alex outside on the tarmac. Doug squeezed past and climbed down the short ladder to the ground. George was looking at the cut and huge bump on the back of Harry's head.

"Are you alright, Harry?" Doug asked.

"I'll be fine, boss. I just need a pint to take this headache away."

"I reckon he'll need a couple of stitches, skipper," said George. "I'll take him over to the doc's as soon as we've stashed our kit."

"Sorry I threw it around a bit back there." Doug looked at the ground and shuffled his feet.

"No problem, boss, we're all still in one piece," said Harry, taking out a packet of cigarettes and offering one to Doug.

Doug shook his head. He didn't smoke, his father did not approve of it. He noticed Ron was standing by himself at the tail smoking his pipe. Doug didn't like the way Ron didn't mix. Turning he walked to where Jimmy was standing under the wing by the right main wheel, talking to a tall slim man wearing a sleeveless leather fur-lined jacket over dirty grey-blue overalls. The man's hair was black and receding, covered in grease and combed back. As Doug approached he turned towards him and smiled.

"Hello, sir, I'm Sergeant Green. Welcome to Metheringham, and believe me, you're welcome to it."

"Hello, sarge, I'm Pilot Officer Jackson. What do you mean?"

"Well, I hope you're not too fond of home comforts, sir. The RAF has just taken over this place and it's a dump. The billets are crap, freezing cold and always damp, worse still they're scattered all over the place. If you don't have transport you spend most of your time walking between sites and with all this bloody mud it's like a route march around the Somme. On top of all that the water and electricity keep failing. If we all weren't so bloody good we'd be right in the shit I can tell yer. Your flight engineer tells me you've got a good aircraft, sir."

"Yes, but I don't know who will be flying it regularly."

"You will, sir, it came through on the grapevine this morning, and these reprobates are your ground crew," he said pointing at the half a dozen men who were removing engine cowlings and checking tyres.

"Oh, I thought this aircraft would go to another crew."

"Usually it would, sir, but you've struck lucky."

A wagon pulled up behind them and a WAAF driver put her head out of the window. "Pilot Officer Jackson?" she smiled.

"Yes."

"I've to take you and your crew to Ops then on to your accommodation."

"Right," he said. "We had better load up."

The bags were soon aboard and Doug made to follow the rest of the crew as they climbed over the tailboard, when the WAAF stopped him.

"Captains travel in the cab," she said.

"Oh, right." I'll never get used to this, he thought.

2

As the truck drove around the perimeter track, Doug stared out of the side window, lost in his own little world. The WAAF driver watched him out of the corner of her eye. She decided that he had a kind face and was probably one of the nice sort of officers who wouldn't look down his nose at other ranks. Most officers were alright but some could be real snobs. This one looked tired and his eyes stared into space.

The truck hit a small bump and jolted Doug out of his daydream. They had followed the perimeter track back the way he had just come in the Lancaster and were now approaching the first set of dispersals, each one with a Lancaster parked on it. As they drove past the first one, Doug noticed the empty bomb trolleys by the side of the dispersal. Passing the aircraft's nose he could see into the open bomb bay, which was full of bombs. He turned to speak to the WAAF driver but she beat him to it.

"Ops are on, sir."

Doug was surprised. "The weather's pretty bad," he replied.

"The Met man says it will clear a bit by five o'clock and then improve through the night. It's a long trip so they won't be back until the early hours. It should have cleared up by then," she smiled.

"You seem very well informed." Doug took his first real look at the WAAF. She was in her early twenties with a pretty round face, hazel eyes and what appeared to be dark auburn hair. This was up in a hair net and almost completely hidden under the WAAF hat pushed to the back of her head. She was small and slim, wearing baggy blue overalls, which didn't hide the fact that she had a good figure.

The WAAF hesitated. You had to be very careful with some officers, they could turn nasty at the slightest thing. Now that he was looking straight at her with his blue-grey eyes, she was nervous. But she was a good judge of character and she was sure that this one was alright.

"That's the best thing about being a driver, you get to go all over the camp and poke your nose into things, sir," she smiled shyly.

"How do you know it's going to be a long trip? The crews won't have been briefed yet."

"No, but the fuel bowser drivers told me that they were loading a lot of fuel, the same amount they took the last time they went to the big city."

"The big city?"

"Berlin, sir." She knew she was right about him.

Now they crossed the end of the main runway and turned towards the control tower, a green two storey building with what looked like a small greenhouse on the flat roof. To the left of the control tower was a hangar. They turned left off the perimeter track before they got to it and stopped outside a Nissen hut.

"This is the crew room. The corporal inside will have your lockers ready. I'll wait here while you drop off your flying kit, sir."

"Thank you…"

"Leading Aircraftswoman Patterson, sir."

The corporal had their lockers ready and they stripped off their heavy fur-lined flying kit and put it in their lockers. This took the gunners longer than the others as they also wore electrically-heated suits to stop them freezing in their turrets. They gave their parachutes to the corporal then returned to the wagon dressed in their working blue, battledress tops now worn over shirts and ties rather than sweaters. The sergeants wore forage caps at jaunty angles on their heads, while the two officers wore flat SD hats. Doug's was very battered where he had tried to make it look less new while a little worse for drink after his first solo flight and gone a bit too far. The wagon continued to the end of the road then turned left on to what had obviously once been a country lane, but was now closed to the public since the airfield had been built. An almost immediate right followed by another left brought them to another group of buildings.

"Ops and admin site," Leading Aircraftswoman Patterson said.

They stopped outside a hut with an armed RAF policeman outside. Duck-board led over the mud from the road to the hut.

"Briefing room," said Patterson. "Wing Commander Baxter, OC 106 Squadron should be in there. He wants a word with you all before I take you to your billets, sir."

"Why's that?" asked Doug nervously.

"Some things even I don't know, sir." She smiled. "I'll wait here for you."

Doug climbed out of the wagon. "Everyone out, leave your stuff. The Wing Commander wants to see us."

The inside of the hut was lit by a row of five yellow light bulbs; the windows were painted over white. The white corrugated iron walls curved from the cold bare concrete floor in an arc over their heads and down again to the floor. There were rows of tables and chairs across the width of the room with an aisle up the middle. The room was cold, colder than outside, and smelled damp with a faint whiff of new paint. At the far end of the hut was a low stage with a lectern to the right-hand side of it, a table on the left-hand side and a large curtain covering the back wall. To one side of the curtain was a blackboard with names on it which Doug took to be the names of the aircraft captains. To the other side was a map of the airfield. Six men were looking down at something on the table but as Doug walked in with his crew behind him, they all looked up. One of the men turned, jumped down off the stage and walked towards them.

"Hello, chaps, I'm Wing Commander Baxter OC 106 Squadron. Welcome to the Squadron." He was not a tall man, but he had a powerful voice and a presence that seemed to emanate confidence and strength. His dark eyes flashed a quick glance at each of them and while his smile was without doubt warm and genuine it was also obvious that he was sizing up this new crew.

"I thought I'd just have a few words before everyone arrives for the briefing; take a seat." He indicated the front row of chairs. "This is a good Squadron. My predecessor, Wing Commander Searby, was only in command for a couple of months but the Squadron Commander before that was Guy Gibson, of the Dam's fame. The word is that if he hadn't formed a special Squadron for that show he would have taken this one. So we have pretty high standards and a good record. It's a maximum effort tonight so there won't be many of the chaps around but you'll get to meet them all soon enough. We've just moved here and the station is a bit rough and ready. The Station Commander is Group Captain McKechnie and he's real old school. He's sorting things out in short order I can tell you and we're going to have FIDO here which should be useful when the fogs start."

Doug had heard of FIDO, Fog Intensive Dispersal Operation, but had never seen it. All he knew was that basically lots of fuel was pumped down pipes either side of a runway and set on fire. The tremendous heat generated burnt off the fog so that aircraft could land. It was supposed to work very well.

Wing Commander Baxter had walked over to the airfield map and was now pointing out various items of interest. The runways were a typical "A" layout of three runways, the main runway being almost north/south, two zero/zero two. Runway numbers corresponded to their magnetic heading to the nearest 10 degrees, so landing on runway two zero you would be heading two zero zero degrees on your compass and zero two zero degrees is the opposite of two zero zero. The main runway was 5700 feet long and 150 feet wide, a good length, but a fully loaded Lancaster would still use up most of it. The two secondary runways, zero seven/two five and one three/three one, were both 3800 feet long but still 150 feet wide. FIDO would only be installed on the main runway. The perimeter track wound its way round the outside of the airfield crossing the end of each runway. At various locations around the perimeter track were dispersals. These were of the spectacles type, which were new to the RAF and much easier to taxi a heavy bomber onto. The bomb dump was to the northwest of the airfield outside the perimeter track in a small wood. A revetted area with mounds of earth piled up into walls to deflect the blast should the hundreds of bombs stored there explode, either as a result of enemy action or by accident. To the northeast of the airfield, near the threshold of runway two zero, was a copse of trees. Doug did not like the idea of there being trees so close to the runway but there was nothing he could do about it. There were three hangars, one off the perimeter track to the east

31

of the airfield, one near the control tower. This, the Wing Commander said, was "A" flight, to which they would belong. The other hangar to the west of the airfield was "B" flight's hangar and their dispersals were off the perimeter track beside the bomb dump. Doug was grateful he was to be on "A" flight.

The domestic arrangements for the airfield looked a nightmare. Altogether there were ten separate sites spread around the south and southwest of the airfield. Site one was the technical site on the edge of the airfield, where they had left their flying kit. It also held the fire section, armoury, guardroom, flight and squadron offices and flying control as well as a host of other buildings. Site two, where they were at the moment, held the operations block, station headquarters, intelligence block and, of course, the briefing room. Site three to the north was the sick quarters while site four to the south was the communal site with a gym, barber, tailor, education block and NAAFI. Sites five and six were west of site four and were officer and sergeants' accommodation. Site seven was well to the south of the airfield and was airmen's accommodation. Site eight to the south of the airfield was the officers', sergeants' and airmen's messes. Site nine was considered by many to be the most important site as it was the WAAF accommodation. Finally site ten was another set of airmen's accommodation. It was easy to see that what Sergeant Green had said was right; if you didn't have transport you were going to spend most of your time walking between the far flung sites.

Baxter turned back towards them after pointing out the last site on the map.

"This is a satellite station of RAF Coningsby as is RAF Woodhall Spa down the road. Metheringham supports the Squadron for all administration and supply. We have our own ground crew for first line daily maintenance, Metheringham supports any second line damage repair while any third or fourth line maintenance and overhaul work is done at Coningsby. That's about it really, chaps. We'll be briefing in a minute so get yourselves settled into your quarters and report to the Squadron Adjutant at 08.00 tomorrow in the Squadron office. He'll sort you out from there. Young Sally Patterson knows where your accommodation is and I dare say she can probably answer any questions you have better than I can so I'll see you tomorrow."

Thanking the Wing Commander they were getting up to leave when Baxter said, "By the way, chaps, did you have any problems on your way here?"

Doug was surprised by the sudden question and was unsure as to what to say. What did the Wing Commander know? How could he know what had happened to them? Should he admit what had happened, but how would that look to their new boss? On the other hand if he did know something and Doug was caught lying.

"No sir," Doug replied a little nervously relying on the old Air Force adage of when in doubt deny everything.

"That's alright then," said Baxter slowly. "It's just that we got a message from an American at Fulbeck saying a Lancaster nearly landed there but overshot at the last minute and they thought that it may have had this Squadron's letters on it. Apparently it nearly collided with one of their Dakotas. Then the Squadron Commander of 438 Sqn phoned from RAF Digby to ask if one of my Lancasters had nearly had a collision with one of his Spitfires. He wanted to know if they were alright... But as it wasn't you it doesn't matter." He smiled and turned back to the map. Doug and his crew left.

Baxter returned to the stage and one of the men by the desk turned towards him. He was an older man than the Wing Commander, possibly in his mid forties, but only a Flight Lieutenant and he wore the old single winged observer's flying brevet.

"Do you think it was them?" he asked.

"Oh yes," smiled Baxter. "Did you see the look on their faces?" They laughed and returned to the desk and maps.

With the door shut behind them, Doug stood outside with his crew. "Christ! Do you think he knows it was us?" asked Ron.

"He knows, sir," said George, "How many other Lancasters will be flying around in this weather, with a maximum effort on tonight?"

"It could have been one on an air test before being bombed up," offered Harry.

"Yeah, but that's a long shot and you can bet your bottom dollar that he'll be watching us from now on," said Bob.

Leading Aircraftswoman Sally Patterson had been talking to the policeman outside the briefing room. Now she walked slowly back to the wagon listening to the crew talking and trying to piece together what had happened.

Doug walked behind the rest of the group. Not only had their arrival been a disaster, he had been caught out lying to his Squadron Commander. Things couldn't get much worse. Then the two people walking in front of him stopped. It was Alex and George. They had obviously hung back. The rest of the crew were already getting into the wagon.

"Sir," George began slightly hesitantly, "if someone in the crew screwed up, you would want to know so that it could be put right, wouldn't yer?" He was looking Doug straight in the eye while Alex was looking down at his feet and looking very uncomfortable.

"Yes," replied Doug looking from George to the guilty-looking Alex.

"Well, Alex here saw that Spitfire before anyone else and called the break, right, sir."

"Yes," said Doug, wondering what on earth Alex had done wrong.

"Then nothing happened for a couple of seconds before we broke." He paused. "Next time, sir, when someone calls the break you don't look, you just break, okay sir?"

Doug stared back in shock.

"That's all, sir," said George and he and Alex turned and walked to the wagon.

Doug felt like he had been slapped. He was angry that a sergeant had talked to him like that, especially one from his crew. But he was angrier with himself because he knew George was right. He had made a mistake that could have got them all killed. In fact, forgetting the propeller pitch controls was also a dangerous mistake. That was twice in a simple transit flight that he could have killed his crew. How on earth was he going to get them through a tour of thirty operations alive if he wasn't even competent enough to fly a simple transit flight safely? It was a very subdued and unhappy pilot officer that sat next to Sally as she drove him to his billet. Sally could feel the tension but she knew when to keep her mouth shut.

The wagon came to a stop and Sally pulled on the hand brake.

"This is your billet and your navigator's, sir. The ablutions are in that hut there," she said pointing to another Nissen hut at the end of the row of accommodation huts.

"Thanks," said Doug, surprised that there were no ablutions in his billet but too depressed to say anything. He got out.

"We're here, Ron!"

Ron clambered out of the back of the wagon and the rest of the crew passed them their bags.

"See you both tomorrow," the sergeants shouted as the truck drove away.

"The skipper's okay," said Bob.

"He did nae break when a told him tae," growled Alex.

"He will next time," replied George firmly.

"He can certainly throw a Lanc around when he wants to though," said Harry feeling the lump on the back of his head. "It's that bastard Dune I can't stand. He's the nav. It's his fault we nearly landed at the wrong place."

"Considering how far we flew and the weather, that was really a pretty good bit of navving. But why the hell didn't he get Metheringham to give us some help before we descended? They could have given us a good fix or a heading for base," asked Bob.

"Search me. He never asks for any help, the arrogant git," replied the small radio operator.

"The thing that worries me is that he was in a complete panic when we got below the clouds," said Jimmy. They all nodded in agreement. Even those that hadn't been able to see Ron had heard the panic in his voice and it did not bode well for the future.

Doug and Ron stood outside the Nissen hut that was to be their home until they completed their tour. It was built on a concrete base, the corrugated iron structure and brick end walls painted a dull green. Two square four-pane windows flanked the door in the end wall. Doug hoisted his kit bag on to his shoulder, picked up his suitcase, walked along the duckboard over the sea of mud and, with his free hand, opened the door. He was greeted by a smell of damp and the same chill that had been present in the briefing room. He found himself in a narrow hallway with another door immediately in front of him. On opening the second door he entered the main part of the hut. He stood in a short corridor with a door on either side; one marked Flt Cdr the other Sqn Ldr Bell. Walking to the end of the corridor he entered the main part of the hut. It had a narrow iron framed bed in each corner and the bed heads were against the corrugated iron walls. A black-leaded pot bellied stove stood between the two beds on the left side of the room, while a fifth bed occupied this place on the right side of the hut. Four square windows identical to the ones in the end wall let light into the room and two yellow bulbs hung on two-foot flexes from the ceiling. Doug walked slowly into the room, his soft footsteps still audible on the bare concrete floor. The beds were all made. Rough grey RAF blankets pulled tightly around the thin mattresses. The windows had condensation on them and the room smelled damp and airless. The stove was on but at less than six feet from it Doug could only just detect its heat. At the opposite end of the hut was another corridor identical to the one through which they had just entered. Ron stood behind Doug.

"If I'd wanted to live in these sort of conditions I would have joined the army!" he said.

As he spoke a small frail-looking man in a white jacket emerged from a side door in the short corridor at the other end of the hut and Doug realised that this must be the room belonging to the batting staff. The white-haired man advanced towards the two officers.

"Good afternoon, gentlemen, I'm Goddard, we've been expecting you. Let me take those, sir," he said taking Doug's suitcase and placing it on the bed in the far right corner of the room. "This will be your bed, sir, and this one's yours, sir," he told Ron taking his case and placing it on the bed in the far left of the room, directly opposite Doug's.

"Would you like a cup of tea? We've no sugar of course, but we have plenty of milk, one of the advantages of being in the country, sir."

Doug couldn't help but smile at the kind and slightly fussy Goddard. "Yes, we'd love a cup of tea, thank you, Goddard."

"Well, if you gentlemen would like to settle in I'll put the kettle on. Your lockers are through there." He indicated the door opposite the one from which he had entered. "I'm afraid I don't know your names so I haven't been able to label them yet but they are the two on the far right," he called as he disappeared into his batting room.

Doug sat on his bed. He laid his kit bag on the floor and started to open his suitcase. Opposite him Ron was doing the same. Folding wooden chairs were propped against the walls beside their beds and for the first time Doug noticed signs of the other occupants of the hut. Shoes under beds, an alarm clock on a chair by a bed. They would be briefing now, off to the big city. After the day he'd had he was glad he wasn't going with them.

Sally drove her wagonload of sergeants to the guardroom. There they signed for their three hairy grey blankets with two light grey lines lengthways down the middle, and the bolster-type pillow. Normally they would have also been issued two white sheets and a pillowcase, but they were told that these were out of stock and they would have to do without. Then Sally drove them to their billet. It was slightly south of the officers' accommodation but made up of rows of the same Nissen huts. They looked identical to the officers' huts but the door opened directly to the inside of the hut, with no lobby to help keep out the cold draughts. Eight beds were down one side of the hut and six down the other side. A plasterboard wall screened off one corner of the hut. A label on the door proclaimed that this room belonged to Warrant Officer Dexter. The ineffective potbellied stove stood in the centre of the hut. There were no lockers, only rails to hang clothes from. These were suspended from wooden shelves attached to the corrugated iron walls beside each bed. Like all the others, the hut was cold, damp and devoid of any home comforts. Five beds at the near end of the hut appeared to be unused so they dumped their kit on those. Other beds showed signs of ownership, a kitbag leaning against the wall, boots under a bed, clothes hung on rails. It looked like they would be sharing with at least one other crew. George and Harry dropped their kit on their beds and went straight back to the wagon where Sally had said she would take them to the sick quarters so that the doctor could look at Harry's head. Bob, Jimmy and Alex started to unpack their kit in silence. They had arranged to meet up with George and Harry at the sergeants' mess later. Eventually Bob spoke.

"How the hell can it be bloody colder inside than it is outside?"

"Concrete floors. They suck the heat right out a yer," replied Alex.

"Well, let's stoke up the stove and get the place warmed up."

"It won't make any difference. There's nae insulation. The heat will just go straight out the roof."

"We're going to freeze in the air and on the bloody ground," moaned Bob. "Christ, I wish I'd stayed at home."

The unpacking done, the three made their way up the road towards where they had been told the sergeants' mess was. Although there had been showers of rain all afternoon it was now fine and looked like it might stay that way. It was still cold, the sort of damp cold that gets into your very bones. The wind had dropped and was now a gentle breeze but it still added to the chill in the air. They all wore their great coats as they walked briskly towards the mess with thoughts of warmth and maybe a beer. Dusk was drawing in and it was starting to get difficult to see the puddles in the lane. Then a Merlin engine started, swiftly followed by another. They were a long way away but none the less completely unmistakeable.

"Let's go and see them off," said Jimmy. They all grunted in agreement and hurried off towards the airfield.

George and Harry had just left the sick quarters when the first engine started. The doctor had stuck a plaster on Harry's head and given him two aspirins, which was what he did with most patients who hadn't been shot. Harry wasn't impressed, but he wasn't surprised either. As more and more engines fired they looked at each other and set off to the airfield.

Doug and Ron had also been on their way to their mess when they heard the engines. Doug had suggested watching the Squadron leave but Ron wasn't interested so Doug went to the airfield and left Ron to go to the mess alone. As Doug walked through the technical site along the road they had driven down earlier that afternoon, he could see the dim blue lights that marked the edges of the perimeter track. The earth was very dark now with the sky a couple of shades lighter, so that although he could make out the shapes of the trees on the other side of the airfield silhouetted against the sky, anything below the horizon was almost invisible. Faint red and green navigation lights moved on the other side of the airfield as the Lancasters taxied towards the end of the runway. The dark shapes of the aircraft themselves were almost invisible in the darkness. Doug was now on the perimeter track beside the hangar he had seen earlier. The aircraft were all manoeuvring on the other side of the airfield and they would be taking off on runway two zero. He quickened his pace not wanting to miss any of the takeoffs, bearing left as he crossed the perimeter track heading for the control tower where he could just make out a group of people. As he approached the small group, the white runway lights came on. A few seconds later the engine noise at the far end of the runway changed from a deep rumble to a throaty roar as the first Lancaster started its run. The throbbing beat of the engines rose and fell rhythmically as the four Merlins strained against the weight of the heavily loaded bomber. As the aircraft gathered speed the rise and fall of the engine notes quickened. He could see it emerging from the dark, its tail up, swinging slightly from side to side, all the time getting faster. Its green navigation light on the starboard wing tip contrasted against the blue exhaust flames which, despite the flame dampers, lit the sides of each engine. The blue light barely reflected off the Perspex cockpit but Doug was too far away to see the figures of the flight engineer and pilot. One had his eyes on the engine instruments while his left hand held the throttles fully open in emergency boost. The other was looking straight ahead keeping the big bomber straight with his feet on the rudder bar, both hands on the control column, easing it back, feeling for when the Lancaster was ready to lift off. It roared past him, now barely 100 yards away, the last light of the winter's evening reflecting off the mid-upper and tail turrets. The throb of the engines could now be felt more than heard and Doug's lungs vibrated inside his body. Still the Lancaster didn't lift, there was less than 200 yards to the end of the runway and the bomber was doing over 100 mph. Doug found himself willing the Lancaster into the air. Then almost reluctantly it rose from the runway and staggered over the perimeter fence clawing for height, its engine noise fading into the dark. Immediately it was replaced by another roar as the second Lancaster started its run. Again and again the performance was repeated until the seventeen aircraft the Squadron were fielding that evening were airborne. The last engine noise faded into the dark and the runway and taxiway lights snapped out.

"Hello, skipper," said a voice in the darkness.

Doug looked around and made out the shape of a small man with his arms wrapped around his body. The silhouette combined with the London accent gave away the owner of the voice.

"Hello, Harry, are you alright?"

"Yeah, skipper, just bloody freezing." Harry and George coming straight from the doctor's were still wearing their battledress.

"Did you see the doc?" Doug asked.

"Yeah, he's a proper quack!"

"Soon sussed you though, didn't he, you malingering little git." George emerged from the dark followed by the rest of the sergeants.

"I'm a casualty of war," insisted Harry.

"It's a pity you're not a Yank, they'd give you a purple heart for that!" laughed Bob.

"It's a pity he's not a Yank, he could get us a jeep," said Jimmy. "We're going to spend half our lives walking around this mud hole."

They all mumbled their agreement when another voice came from the darkness. "I may know someone who could help you there."

The stranger was tall and thin with a public school accent. He was well wrapped up against the cold in a greatcoat. What appeared to be a scarf was wrapped around his neck and his SD hat was pulled hard down on his head. He held a pipe in the corner of his mouth but still managed to speak clearly out of the other side.

"You're the new crew just arrived today, aren't you? I'm Flight Lieutenant Forrester, Nigel Forrester, Squadron Adjutant." He reached out and shook Doug's hand. "I believe Sergeant Green may be able to get his hands on some bicycles. Tell him I sent you. You could of course put in a request through stores but you'll probably finish your tour before they arrive that way. Far better to do it unofficially," he said tapping the side of his nose. "Are you going to the mess now?" he asked Doug. "I'm going that way myself, can I offer you a lift?"

Doug said goodnight to his crew and walked with the Adjutant to an Austin 7 parked nearby. A short drive brought them to the officers' mess, a prefabricated building with a corrugated roof. Doug could not make out any other detail in the dark but at least it wasn't another Nissen hut. Hanging their hats and greatcoats in the cloakroom, they went through into the bar where Nigel bought Doug a half of bitter. They sat in two old but comfortable leather chairs by a fire.

Doug had now recognised Nigel as one of the men on the stage in the briefing room that afternoon. He was in his mid forties, tall and slim with grey hair combed back. His face had wrinkles around his brown eyes and across his forehead and he had a strong jaw with a prominent chin. His arms were strong and he had big hands. He clenched a small straight pipe in his mouth, only removing it to drink. It suddenly struck Doug that Nigel was the spitting image of Popeye the sailor and he had to suppress a laugh. Looking at Nigel's observer's wings he asked how long he had been in the RAF.

"Oh I'm a regular. I've been in twenty-six years. I started on nine acks in 1918, flew a few trips over the trenches before it all ended, then spent most of my time in the Middle or Far East bombing rebellious wogs." He smiled. "Some people just don't want to be civilized." The warmth of the fire was starting to thaw out their cold limbs, making them tingle, and their faces started to glow. "There's been some changes since those days. Flying in cloud or at night was a real adventure then, now it's routine. Covered cockpits, radar, powered turrets, computerized bombsights, electronic navigation systems. We thought we were lucky if we had a radio."

"Have you flown Ops in this war?"

"Well, I flew Whimpeys on leaflet raids in 1939. What a bloody waste of time that was! Then I became a navigation instructor for a while before doing some intruding in Mosquitoes out of Malta. Then I had a crash and they said I was too old and too broken to fly any more and I've been the Squadron Adj ever since. Wing Commander Baxter lets me fly on the occasional air test but nothing operational. I have been to Berlin once, on what I refer to as the longest air test in history." He winked. "But don't you dare tell Baxter." He finished his half of bitter. "Well, I'm going to get a few hours' sleep before the boys come back. I wouldn't wait up for them if I were you. We've got an area familiarisation flight planned for you and your crew tomorrow morning so I'll see you at 08.00." With that he said goodnight and left.

When Doug got back to his hut, Ron was sitting up in bed in his red and white striped pyjamas. He had his knees up, with his suitcase resting on them as a writing desk.

"I'm just writing to Janice," he explained.

Doug told Ron about the flight the next morning, the Squadron Adjutant and the possibility of getting some bicycles. Ron did not seem interested and the mention of bicycles met with a look of disapproval. Eventually Doug gave up trying to have a conversation with him and went to bed himself.

Something woke Doug. He had no idea what but he was instantly wide awake. He lay still, his ears straining in the total darkness listening. He heard a car door slam shut and voices. Eventually the car drove off and then he heard singing, "Hurtling down the runway throttles open wide, see the mighty Lancaster she sways from side to side."

The hut door burst open and the light came on. Doug screwed up his eyes against the glare.

"Sorry, chaps, didn't think anyone would be in. We're the first back you see."

Doug forced his eyes open to see two Flying Officers in battledress with whistles attached to their collars. Both wore a heavy white woollen sweater instead of a shirt under their battledress. One was a pilot, one a navigator and they were staring at him and Ron.

"You must be the new boys that brought that Lanc in yesterday. I'm Charlie Clark and this is Taffy Williams. Welcome to the Squadron." They both shook Ron and Doug's hands.

Charlie was about five foot ten medium build, in his early twenties with a fresh youthful face; his hair was ruffled where it had been flattened under a flying helmet. Taffy was short and chubby and spoke with a soft Welsh accent. They both had red lines over their noses and down their cheeks from their oxygen masks. They were celebrating, they explained, because they had just flown their twentieth trip and were two thirds of the way through their tour. Charlie had just been told he was to be promoted to flight lieutenant. They talked as they got ready for bed in the opposite two corners of the room. It had been a lively trip with lots of flak but they thought that they had hit the target and rumour had it that the full moon in the start of February would curtail Ops for two weeks and they would get leave. That was over a week away however and they thought that there would be time to get another three or four trips in before then.

"That's good, I'd like to get in a couple of trips before there's any breaks," said Doug.

"Oh, I don't know if you'll get in any trips as a crew before then," Charlie said. "They will want to send you as second pilot with someone else first to get some experience and they will have you doing area familiarisation before that so that you can find your way back."

He smiled and Doug wondered if he had somehow heard of their trip the day before. Doug was disappointed but Ron breathed a silent sigh of relief. With a final request that they try not to wake them in the morning when they got up Charlie and Taffy turned off the light and went to sleep.

Later that night the sergeants had a similar experience but without the singing as seven sergeants came crashing into their billet.

"Sorry, boys," said an Australian voice. "We knew old Dexi wasn't back yet," he nodded towards the Warrant Officer's room, "but we didn't know we had company. I'm Digger Jones and this is my crew."

"Bob McKenzie," said Bob, shaking hands, glad to see another Australian. As it turned out there were three Australians in Digger's crew and a lot more on the Squadron.

"Good trip?" asked George.

"We're back, aren't we?" was the short reply.

"What's it like on a raid?" asked Harry.

"Depends," said Digger, as he and his crew started to get ready for bed. "On a quiet trip it's like any other night flight. You might see a bit of flak and a few searchlights. Then at the target you see the target indicators and you drop your bombs on them then come home. On a bad trip you see lots of flak and searchlights, bomb the indicators then come home. But you might have a few holes in your plane. Or you might not come home at all." He gave a mischievous grin.

"What do the target indicators look like?" asked Bob.

"Very pretty. Bright yellow, red and green balls of fire in the sky, with waterfalls of flame falling from them."

"So they're easy to see?"

"They're bloody impossible to miss!"

"Can you see other aircraft?" asked Alex.

"You don't want to," was the reply. "If you see any of ours it's because they're too bloody close for comfort or they're on fire and if you see any of theirs they're attacking you."

"Have you seen any night fighters then?" pressed Alex.

"Too bloody right!"

"Did you shoot at them?"

"Christ, no! If you see any night fighters and they haven't seen you, you sneak away in the dark. If they have seen you, you corkscrew like hell to throw them off. Shooting back only gives your position away and pisses them off!"

Alex looked horrified.

"Look," said Digger quietly. "We've got pissy little 303s. We're sitting on tons of fuel and bombs and the only armour we have is the back of the pilot's seat. They have 20 and 30 mm cannon and loads of armour. Your best chance is to hide, not fight! That really is a last resort. We won't be getting up till late morning, so don't wake us up." And with that they turned off the lights.

Someone was shaking him, Doug realised.

"It's me, sir, Goddard. It's 07.00, sir, and here's your tea." He placed the tea on the chair by the bed. The hut was dark, the only light coming from the open door to the batting room. It cast a light across to the other side of the room where Goddard was waking Ron. It was freezing and the last thing Doug wanted to do was get out of his warm bed. He had laid his greatcoat over his blankets for extra warmth. He wrapped his hands around the cup of tea, sipped the hot liquid and steeled himself for the gigantic effort it would take to get out of bed. Eventually he could put it off no longer and quickly got out of bed and went shivering to the locker room to get dressed. Ron came in yawning.

"Morning," he whispered, not wanting to wake Charlie and Taffy. Ron grunted a reply as Doug picked up his wash kit and left the hut for the ablutions block. There was a frost on the ground, which was good in that the mud was frozen and he could walk on it. His breath left his mouth like fog as he hurried along. There was a faint ribbon of lighter sky in the east as dawn started to break, but above the sky was still pitch black with stars showing the lack of cloud cover that had allowed the frost to form. With any luck it would be a good day for the area familiarisation flight.

A row of toilets filled one wall in the ablution block with urinals on the opposite wall and two rows of sinks facing each other in the centre. There was only cold water, and this was so cold it actually hurt to touch. Doug made do with a quick rub over with a flannel before starting to shave. The cold razor stung and he cut himself several times. Splashing water over his face to remove the last of the lather and drying his face, he longed for a room in an officers' mess with a sink in it and hot water. He returned to his hut hating the fact that for the foreseeable future every day was going to start like this, and wondering what had happened to Ron. He found the light on in the hut and Ron sitting on his bed shaving with a bowl of hot water on a chair in front of him.

"Where the hell did you get that?" Doug asked.

"Goddard boiled a kettle up for me," Ron replied.

"And you couldn't have asked him to boil some for me as well, could you?"

"You didn't ask," said Ron indignantly.

"Look, chaps," interrupted Charlie lying awake in his bed propped up on his elbow. "Taffy and I were up most of the night and we will probably be up most of tonight and we would appreciate you not waking us up."

Doug apologised. Charlie and Taffy were not happy.

"It's alright," said Charlie patiently, "but if you're going to shave in the hut, and this is the only hot water available, so I suggest you do, do it in the locker room and leave the light off in here. And for God's sake keep the noise down. If you wake any of the Squadron leaders," he indicated the rooms behind him, "there will be hell to pay."

He was now looking at the empty bed between his and Doug's. "What time is it?" he asked.

"07.20," said Ron.

"Oh," replied Charlie quietly looking from the empty bed to Taffy who was also looking at the bed. "We might get another couple of hours' sleep before we get called."

He rolled over and pulled the blankets up around his head.

Doug and Ron walked to the mess for breakfast in silence. The mess was very quiet with only a few officers around. Then they walked to the Squadron Office in silence. For days Doug had tried to make conversation with Ron but got nowhere and he had now given up. It was a long walk from the hut to the mess and an even longer walk from the mess to the Squadron Office. By the time they got there it was after eight o'clock and the sergeants were already there waiting for them.

"Good afternoon, gentlemen," said Nigel sarcastically but with a smile as they entered.

Doug apologised.

"That's alright, just don't make a habit of it and get your transport sorted out with Sergeant Green and remember to tell him I sent you. You'll need to sign as having read these." He handed out copies of Squadron Orders, Station Standing Orders, Group Air Staff Orders and Officers Confidential Orders. "At 09.00 a wagon will take you to station headquarters so you can do your arrivals. It will then take you anywhere else you need to go to get signatures. Then you can plan a quick familiarisation flight; I suggest you concentrate on the coastline and then various routes from prominent points on the coast to Metheringham. Check out any prominent features in the area until you're happy. It's an excellent day so make the most of it I'll see you when you get back.

By the time they had read through the mountains of paper, or rather skimmed through it and signed as having read it, it was almost 09.00 and the wagon was waiting. Once again Sally was the driver and she was well informed.

"Another good raid for the Squadron last night, sir. Two of the Squadron had direct hits on the target indicators. It's a shame about D for Dog though. They only had five more trips to do and it's the Squadron's first loss for weeks."

It was the first time Doug had realized that the Squadron had lost an aircraft that night. "Does anyone know what happened to them?"

"No, sir. That's usually the way. They just don't come back. Sometimes we hear that they're prisoners but that's months later. Rumour has it Ops are on again tonight."

"How do you know that?"

"Signals have just started to come in and I know one of the girls in the office."

"So where are they going?"

"Don't know yet but my bet's on the big city again."

"Why's that?"

"Full moon's coming, so Butch will want to hammer Berlin as much as possible before then."

"You shouldn't be a driver, you should be in intelligence," said Doug smiling at Sally's ready use of the aircrew nickname for Air Chief Marshal "Bomber" Harris, the head of Bomber Command.

Sally laughed as they stopped outside station headquarters.

Inside, the arrival procedure started. They were all given a card with various sections of the station listed on it and spaces next to the section for signatures. They had to fill in their details on the top of the card then visit all the sections to be processed. At each section, after the appropriate paperwork had been completed, the card was signed and when the last signature was collected they were officially a part of the station. Without completing their arrivals they would not get mail, they would not get paid and their next of kin would not be informed if they went missing. In fact, as far as RAF Metheringham was concerned, they would not exist. Today the arrival procedure went remarkably smoothly and, at 10.30 they were in operations, planning their familiarisation flight. They took Nigel's advice and planned to concentrate on the coast and routes from there to Metheringham, looking at any prominent landmarks as they found them. By 11.00 they were at the aircraft with Sergeant Green waiting for them by the nose of F for Freddy.

"Good morning, sarge," said Doug as he and Jimmy walked up to him. The rest of the crew made their way straight to the rear of the aircraft and started to climb in.

"Morning, sir. Your flight engineer knew what he was talking about when he said this was a good aircraft. We've been all over it this morning and we can't find a single thing wrong with it except the H2S and GEE not working and that was just a blown fuse on the GEE and a loose wire on the H2S. They're both working fine now. I've never had an aeroplane delivered to a Squadron in such good nick in all my years, not a single one."

He led Doug and Jimmy to a small shack by the dispersal that looked like it had been made out of junk, which it had. The roof was corrugated iron and the walls looked like they had been cobbled together from some sort of old packing crates. Inside were half a dozen old chairs of various types against the wall and a packing case table in the centre. On the table was a primus stove with an old tin kettle on it, a Tilley lamp and half a dozen half pint mugs. At the other end of the hut was a desk made out of two 50-gallon oil drums with two planks across the top. The shack was dark and cold and smelt of oil and new timber. On the desk was F for Freddy's F700, the aircraft's log book. In this would be kept the lists of faults, repairs, servicing etc. Any technician working on F for Freddy would sign for every repair made and, where necessary, a supervisor would sign as having inspected the repair. By looking through the various sections of the F700 you could find out all about F for Freddy. From serviceability to persistent faults and how much fuel it was carrying. Additionally if any technician bodged a job he could be traced by his signature. Doug and Jimmy looked through the F700 and when they were satisfied that the GEE and H2S had been repaired and checked, Doug signed for the aircraft. He was now responsible for F for Freddy until he signed it back after the flight. "Will you be long, sir?"

"A couple of hours at the most, sarge."

"Right O, sir. It's just Ops are on, so we'll be busy this afternoon bombing and fuelling up."

"We'll try and keep out of your way. Oh, by the way, you wouldn't know where we could get our hands on some bicycles, do you?"

"Bicycles, sir?"

"Yes. Flight Lieutenant Forrester, the Squadron Adj, said you might be able to help us."

"Oh, right, sir. Yes, we have seven bicycles stored out the back here. The last crew left them here. Do you want them when you get back?"

"Yes, please, sarge, if the other crew doesn't want them any more."

"Alright, sir, we'll have them ready for you." Doug and Jimmy walked out to F for Freddy. "If the other crew doesn't want them any more! Why the hell would you want a bike when you've got a pair of wings and a bleeding harp?" said Sergeant Green sarcastically, half to himself and half for the benefit of some of the other ground crew who were hanging round the flight hut.

"I thought we were going to swap those bikes with that sergeant from stores for some electric heaters for our billet, sarge," one of the ground crew said.

"I was. But I can't do it now Popeye knows about them, can I? What do you think he'd do to us if he caught us selling dead men's bikes?" He walked to the hut door and watched Doug and Jimmy doing their external walk around checks of F for Freddy. "Well, you can have them, but I reckon we'll get them back eventually."

"They might make it through their tour."

"The last one of mine to make it through a tour was Wing Commander Gibson nearly a year ago."

"Oh yeah, you didn't like him, did you?"

"He was an arrogant sod but it was that bloody dog of his I hated."

"Nigger was alright, he didn't mean to wreck your bike."

"Didn't mean to! The great black bastard ripped both tyres off it and mine wasn't the only one either! Now let's get these blokes on their way, then we can have a brew and a wad before we have to start bombing up."

3

An hour and a half later, F for Freddy had travelled the Lincolnshire coastline from the Humber Estuary to the Wash. The crew had noted the main features of the various towns, Boston's large square church tower, Tattershall's unusual red brick castle, Lincoln's huge cathedral high on the hill, dominating the surrounding countryside. But while these were good daytime landmarks they would not be much use at night, with the whole country blacked out. For that they took note of the rivers. They would stand out like silver ribbons in the dark, especially in moonlight. The best of these was the River Witham, in the south of the area near Boston. It had long straight sections with sharp angular bends where it had been artificially straightened to help drain the surrounding fenland. Splitting in two in the north the two rivers flowed parallel to each other less than a mile apart, right up to the outskirts of Lincoln. In the west of the area was the large River Trent meandering northward to the Humber Estuary. If they ever reached this they would have overshot Metheringham by some sixteen miles. Railways were another good feature to use at night and these covered Lincolnshire, so that the problem would not be so much finding them as deciding which was which.

By 12.30 they had seen everything they wanted to see and Doug decided to practise his landings with some circuits of the airfield. It was a lovely day for flying. The wind was light and the visibility excellent. F for Freddy had just turned onto its downwind leg to make its third landing when flying control called them on RT telling them to land off this circuit. Puzzled they landed and taxied back to their dispersal. Before shutting down F for Freddy's engines the marshaller indicated that Doug should open the bomb doors. Opening the bomb doors with the engines stopped took thirty minutes of hard pumping on the manual system and Doug thought the ground crew must want to check the bomb bay because F for Freddy had never carried bombs before. Sally was waiting in her truck by the edge of the dispersal. They all clambered out of the aircraft with their parachutes and flight bags and walked over to Sergeant Green who was talking to Sally.

"What's up, sarge?" asked Doug.

"I've to take you all over to the Squadron office, sir," said Sally.

"Do we have time to pick up our bikes?" asked Bob.

"I'll keep them if you like," Sergeant Green told him.

"We'll take them," said George firmly as he slung his parachute into the back of the wagon and disappeared behind the shack to collect his bike.

With the bikes loaded and everyone aboard, the wagon set off to the Squadron Office.

"Do you know what this is about?" Doug asked Sally.

"Nobody's told me anything," Sally said evasively.

"Nobody tells you anything, but you always know what's going on, don't you?"

"Whatever are you trying to say, sir?" asked Sally, the picture of innocence.

"Come on."

"It's not for me to say, sir."

"We're not in trouble, are we?" Doug was still worried about lying to the Wing Commander.

"Not that I know of, sir."

"But you do know what this is about?"

"I can guess, sir."

Doug slumped back in his seat. He could see he would get nothing out of Sally, which was frustrating. But the most annoying thing about it was that Sally probably knew no more than he did but she, a lowly leading aircraftswoman, had put it all together to form a big picture and worked out what was going on, whereas he, a commissioned officer, was still in the dark. He looked across the cab at Sally, fixed her with his blue eyes and smiled.

"What?" she asked nervously.

"Nothing," replied Doug, smiling all the more. He wished he had asked Sergeant Green why he had wanted the bomb doors open. Collecting his bike had distracted him. It could be a routine check or it could be to load F for Freddy with bombs. Maybe another Lancaster had gone unserviceable and another crew was taking F for Freddy on the Op tonight. If that was the case maybe he could get his second pilot trip in. The faint fluttering of butterflies started in his stomach announcing his rising excitement as the wagon arrived at the Squadron Office.

As a group they walked into the Squadron Office to be met by Nigel and Wing Commander Baxter.

"There you are, Jackson," said the Wing Commander. "We have a bit of a problem." Baxter looked down at the desk in front of him and paused, as if unsure how to proceed. This is more than just another crew taking our aircraft, thought Doug.

"You see, under normal circumstances we would give you all a few days to settle in. Then send you on a trip with an experienced crew to show you the ropes before sending you all on an Op on your own. But we've been put in a bit of a spot." He shuffled some papers.

"Tonight is another maximum effort and we're a crew down. We've always managed seventeen aircraft on maximum efforts before and the Station

47

Commander insists that if we have seventeen crews and seventeen serviceable aircraft we send seventeen aircraft on the Op tonight." He looked up at Doug and his crew. "So I'm afraid you're all to be thrown in at the deep end. You're all going on the Op tonight. Specialist briefings at 14.00 in the respective leaders' offices so you've got an hour to get yourselves fed and sort yourselves out. Main briefing at 15.30."

Nigel, standing slightly behind and to the left of the Wing Commander, did not look happy and Doug got the impression that he did not agree with the decision. Baxter himself was obviously uncomfortable with the decision and had probably put up quite a fight against it, but inevitably lost to a superior ranking officer. Doug felt he should say something but all he could come up with was, "Right, sir, we'll see you at the briefing."

They left the office in silence, but once the door was shut they erupted in a babble of voices.

"Jesus! That's not much warning!"

"We're ready as we'll ever be, why shouldn't we go!"

"Wonder what the target is?"

"It's not fair that they should drop this on us like this," complained Ron.

"I'd rather have it like this," said George. "It's better to get the first one over with and this way we have less time to worry about it."

"Who's worried?" said Alex. "It's the Jerries who should bloody worry!"

Doug didn't know what to think. The butterflies in the stomach and tingling in the hands told him he was more excited than worried. Sally was leaning against the side of her wagon.

"You're going then, sir?" she asked, as she straightened up and saluted, a slightly worried look on her face.

"Are you ever wrong?" asked Doug smiling and returning the salute. "Is it the big city?"

"I think so. You'd better hurry if you want to sort anything out, get your pre-flight meals and I'd get some chains and locks for those bikes if you want them to be here when you get back."

"We can use the locks off our kit bags today and get chains tomorrow," said Alex.

"Sod the bikes, it's eggs for us, boys," yelled Bob as he unloaded his bike from the back of Sally's wagon.

"Have any of you blokes noticed how the Adj looks just like Popeye?" asked Harry.

Armed with the enthusiasm of youth and the knowledge that nothing bad would happen to them they took the news that they were going to the most dangerous target in Europe completely in their stride. And, like all the crews before them, laughed away any fears that were lurking in the recesses of their minds.

Dropping off their flying kit in the crew room, they cycled back to their messes. The sergeants' dining room was empty when the five sergeants walked in but it soon filled up as all the other NCOs who were flying that evening filed in. There were usually at least five NCOs in each crew, so they tended to all sit together to eat. Occasionally two crews would sit at the same table if there was space, but most sat at individual tables. The meal was always the same and had almost become traditional. Bacon, a fried egg, and fried bread or fried potatoes. Not exactly a feast but in war rationed Britain anyone not flying was only allowed one egg a week. Each table had a small bowl on it with tablets in it.

"What are these?" asked Alex.

"I've just asked one of those sergeants that," said Harry. "They're called Wakey Wakeys. They're to stop you going to sleep on long trips."

"Right, I'll have one of them," said Alex.

"Me too," said Jimmy.

They passed them round and swallowed one each with a gulp of tea, except for Harry. "He also told me not to take any before take off," he said smiling.

"Why?" asked George.

"Because if the mission gets scrubbed I can still get a night's sleep. You're all going to be awake now no matter what!"

He roared with laughter.

"You complete Cockney bastard," said Bob with real feeling, but George was smiling.

"What are you smiling at, George? You took one as well."

"Oh, I'm just thinking of all the different ways we can get our own back on him," said George with a gleam in his eye.

"Right," replied Bob, flashing a demonic grin at Harry.

"You've got to take your chances while you can," laughed Harry, tears of laughter running down his face, completely unworried by the threats.

They cycled back to their billet to pick up any odds and ends of kit that they felt they might need on an Op. Ahead of them they could see Doug and Ron cycling back to their hut, although Doug and Ron were riding in silence, whereas the sergeants chatted and joked.

Entering their hut Doug and Ron almost walked into two RAF policemen coming out. The policemen were carrying a kit bag and a suitcase.

"Excuse us, sir," said one of them as they squeezed past in the corridor. Doug was a bit bemused then on entering the main room he noticed the bed between his and Charlie's had been stripped, leaving just the bare mattress. He stood and looked at it, at last realising why Charlie and Taffy had been staring at it that morning. He walked over to the locker room and looked in. One locker door was open and the locker empty.

Ron stood behind him, also looking at it.

"I'm going to write a letter," said Ron.

"Me too," replied Doug.

The sergeants entered their billet in a much more boisterous mood.

"Eggs for us from now on, boys!"

"You and your bloody eggs, Bob," said George throwing a pillow at him.

Bob caught it. "Fighting men deserve to be well fed."

"Who wants to do any fighting? I would rather just sneak in, get rid of the bombs and sneak out again," said Jimmy.

"Where's your spirit of adventure? Don't you fancy a tussle with the old Hun then, Jimmy boy?" teased Bob.

"Has anyone seen my extra socks?" Alex asked, his head inside his kit bag.

"Has anyone noticed that Warrant Officer Dexter is no longer with us?" asked Harry, staring at the door to the room that was partitioned off. Warrant Officer Dexter's nameplate had been removed.

"Oh shit! That has to be a bad omen," said Jimmy.

"Bollocks!" said George. He had noticed the missing nameplate but hadn't said anything. "He was just unlucky. Anyway he's only missing, he could still turn up." He busied himself sorting out clothes that didn't need sorting, anything not to stare at the door like the others were doing.

"Yeah," said Bob. "He'll probably turn up in a day or two."

"I'm going to write a quick letter," Jimmy said.

"Me too," said Alex.

One by one they all sat on their beds and started to write.

At 13.50, with hastily written letters in their pockets, they rode back to the Squadron Offices to meet their respective specialist leaders who would brief them in detail on the aspects of the mission pertinent to them. They all wore heavy white woollen sweaters under their battle dress tops and thermal vests under the sweaters. They had long johns under their heavy woollen uniform trousers and at least two pairs of heavy woollen socks on their feet. Pedalling their bikes along the country lane they were starting to sweat despite the chill of the crisp winter's day but they all knew that they would be glad of the heavy clothing later that night.

Bob arrived at the bombing leader's office at the same time as a lot of other bomb aimers. Most were sergeants, a couple were flight sergeants and one a naval sublieutenant. The bombing leader was a flight lieutenant with a large moustache. To Bob he looked old with wrinkles around his eyes and grey hair at his temples. As Bob entered the office the bombing leader spotted him.

"Hello, you must be Sergeant McKenzie, I'm 'Swampy' Marsh. Welcome to the Squadron." They shook hands and Bob was surprised at the older man's strong grip.

"Pleased to meet you, sir."

"Ah, another of our colonial friends," smiled Marsh, Bob's origins betrayed by his accent. "You seem to be taking over the Squadron, there's Aussies everywhere and a few Canadians in the woodwork too. Take a seat."

"Better make sure he doesn't take them all!" said an English voice behind him to a roar of laughter. Bob smiled. He was getting a little sick of the Australian convict joke. But it was unlikely to be forgotten because two Australians on the Squadron had recently been caught stealing coal for their billet stove and the old joke had been rejuvenated.

The office was not large and by the time the seventeen bomb aimers had squeezed in, they were sitting shoulder to shoulder round three of the bare magnolia painted walls, their flight bags between their feet or tucked under their chairs and note pads and pencils at the ready. Marsh started proceedings at exactly 14.00 with a roll call, each of the bomb aimers answering "Sir" as his name was called. Marsh stood behind a desk, which had seventeen piles of papers on it. Behind him was a blackboard and easel. The roll call complete, Marsh turned the blackboard around to reveal a sketch map of a built-up area which was obviously a large city. The map showed the extent of the built-up area in yellow with railway lines in red and rivers and lakes in blue. All the other bomb aimers let out their breath in unison.

"Yes, chaps, Berlin again," said Marsh. "I know you went there last night but it's a different aiming point and tonight ground visibility should be good so we're going for a Newhaven with a Paramatta back up."

Each type of target marking had a different name. Mosquito Pathfinders, equipped with "Oboe" did the most accurate target marking. However, "Oboe" relied on electronic beams being transmitted from England to the target and these beams, travelling in a straight line, could only be received at long range by high flying aircraft, because of the curvature of the earth. Mosquitoes, flying above 30,000 feet, could still receive the beams over the Ruhr valley but at far off Berlin, even the nimble Mosquito could not fly high enough to detect the beams. For this reason various other methods were developed for marking the aiming points of distant targets.

The best of these was the Newhaven. This consisted of Pathfinder bombers, manned by experienced crews, dropping brilliant parachute flares over the target to illuminate the ground. These were known as illuminators. Then more Pathfinder aircraft would mark the target visually by the light of these flares using coloured target indicators. These would burst at about 5,000 feet over the target in bright red and green waterfalls of flame and the main force bomber crews would aim at these markers.

If the target could not be located visually due to poor visibility or the pall of smoke which hung over many cities, the attack became a Paramatta. During this type of attack the Pathfinders would drop their target indicators using H2S ground mapping radar which was not as accurate as dropping them visually.

Good results could still be achieved using H2S marking but only when there were ground features in the area that stood out well on H2S, like coastlines or rivers and lakes. Built-up areas also stood out well, but Berlin was such a big built-up area, which part of it did you aim at?

The last method of target marking was a Wanganui; this was used when a target was completely covered with cloud. The Pathfinder aircraft would find the target through the cloud using H2S, then work out the wind and drop parachute flares to hang above the clouds in such a position that if other bombers were to aim at the flares their bombs would fall on the target below the clouds. Obviously it was very difficult to position these flares accurately to allow for the trajectory of the bombs and as soon as the flares were dropped they were blown away by the wind. Wanganui attacks rarely produced good results and were only used as a last resort, if a target was unexpectedly covered by cloud.

Tonight the aiming point was a large factory making aircraft parts in the northeast of the city. But, as it was considered pretty good to get your bombs within a mile of the aiming point, a factory had been picked in the middle of the industrial area of the city. Target indicators, or TIs as they were known, placed visually, would be red. TIs placed by H2S would be green.

Next came the bomb loads. F for Freddy would carry one 4000-pound high capacity high explosive bomb known as a Cookie, sixty 30-pound incendiaries and 1,140 4-pound incendiaries. The theory was that the Cookie would land first, explode on impact, and being a thin cased bomb with a lot of explosive in it, would create a massive blast wave that would demolish any buildings in the immediate vicinity. Additionally it would blow in the windows and remove the roofs of many more. The incendiaries, landing shortly afterwards in the same area, would go through the removed roofs, setting fire to the building interiors. With no windows the air would be free to circulate and feed the flames. In this way large firestorms could be started.

The bombing height was to be 18,000 feet and Marsh emphasised the need to bomb the TIs, not the resulting fires, and to guard against creep back. All raids tended to move away from the aiming point as crews dropped their bombs slightly early so that they could get out of the target area quicker. The predicted wind speed and direction was briefed. This would affect the bombs as they fell and would have to be allowed for by the Lancaster's bombsight.

Finally, Marsh handed out the seventeen piles of papers on his desk. They were reconnaissance photographs of the target and large-scale maps of the area. He then talked the other bomb aimers through what they should see on approaching the aiming point. First he described the aiming point in relation to the other large features of Berlin, so that they would be able to find the general area of the factory. Then he concentrated on the smaller features that might be visible once they had found the general area. There was a large wide road south of the factory running east to west and that might be visible in the light of any fires. The factory itself consisted of long narrow buildings also running east to west, on a square site. With luck the aiming point would be a mass of red TIs. But, in case the marking went wrong, or they arrived at the target when there was a gap in the marking, if one load of TIs burnt out before the next load was dropped, all the bomb aimers should be able to find the target on their own. This shouldn't happen, but lots of things that shouldn't happen during a bombing raid do. Marsh finished his briefing with a last warning against creep back and "Any Questions?" As there were none, the bomb aimers put their papers in their flight bags and, with a casual air, amid light chatter, they slowly filed out of the office and made their way to their aircraft.

F for Freddy, being on the other side of the airfield, was a mile and a half away and it took Bob the best part of ten minutes to cycle out to it. When he got there he saw Alex, Harry and George standing by the ground crew's hut smoking, their bikes lying in the ground beside them.

"Been here long?"

"A few minutes, Jimmy and the boss are inside going over the 700. Any sign of Ron?" asked George.

"Haven't seen him."

"I think this is His Highness coming now," said Harry his eyes screwed up looking at a lone figure cycling along the perimeter track towards them.

Bob ducked inside the hut. Doug, Jimmy and Sergeant Green were going through the 700 at the oil drum and plank desk.

"Ah," said the ground engineer looking up at Bob. "You'll be wanting to check your bombs then." Doug and Jimmy had evidently finished with the 700. The sergeant slid it along to Bob who checked the bombs loaded against what he had been told at the briefing. The heavy Cookie would have been centrally positioned in the bomb bay as close as possible to the aircraft's centre of gravity, so that it wouldn't upset the aircraft's trim when it was released. The incendiaries would be carried in small bomb containers, each holding up to twenty-four 30-pound incendiaries or 236 4-pound incendiaries. This would mean twelve small bomb containers, six in front of the Cookie and six behind. Bob checked the entries in the 700, signed for the bombs and then followed Doug and Jimmy outside. Ron had just arrived and they all walked over to F for Freddy. Doug and Jimmy started their external check of the aircraft while Bob ducked under the open bomb bay doors to walk underneath the Lancaster the length of the bomb bay. Alex and George followed him. Together they checked the Cookie and small bomb containers were secure in their carriers and the safety pins and locking wires had been removed from the release gear. The Cookie was a large cylinder, looking for all the world like an elongated 50-gallon oil drum with three small propellers on the end. The propellers would rotate as the bomb fell, unwinding themselves until they had removed the safety pins from the bomb's fuses; at that moment the bomb would be live. The reason for three propellers was because the bomb had three fuses in case any failed. Despite this, a large proportion of the bombs dropped did fail to explode. A thick locking wire, known as a fusing link, passed through a hole in the propeller shafts to prevent the propellers from turning. The other end of the fusing link was passed through an electromagnetic clamp on the bomb carrier. If it was ever necessary to jettison the bombs they could be dropped unarmed by not applying power to the electromagnetic clamp. Then when the bombs were dropped the fusing links would fall with them preventing the propellers from turning and the bombs from arming. Under normal circumstances an arming switch in the aircraft would be selected, applying power to the electronic clamps. They would then grip the fusing links and when the bombs fell the fusing link would stay attached to the aircraft. The other end of the link would be pulled from the hole in the propeller shaft allowing it to turn and arm the bomb.

The Cookie was held in place by two hinged semi circular grabs that fitted through a suspension lug on the top of the bomb, holding it securely in place. When an electrical current was applied to the grab it would open, releasing the bomb. Bob made sure that this was tight but not over tight as that could cause the bomb to hang up. The small bomb containers were long narrow light alloy boxes which on receipt of an electrical current would spring open to discharge their loads of incendiaries. Again Bob checked that the locking wires were removed and the containers were all secure. Then they gave the bomb bay itself a quick inspection before ducking back out under the bomb bay doors near to the rear entry door.

Doug and Jimmy had finished their external checks and were climbing up the short ladder into the rear entry door. Bob followed them into the light green painted interior. It was chilly inside the fuselage, hidden from the winter's sun. The metal surfaces were cold and wet with condensation and the air smelled of oil and fuel. The only light came in from the entry door and the rear turret far off to his left. As Bob's eyes adjusted to the gloom, he turned right to follow Doug and Jimmy up the fuselage towards the nose. He ducked around the Distant Reading Gyro-Magnetic Compass Master Unit which hung from the ceiling to the right of the door and seemed to be deliberately sighted to bang the heads of the unwary. Then he bent down to make his way under the mid-upper turret which protruded from the ceiling almost halfway to the floor. Not much of an obstacle at the moment but it would be far worse later, when he would be dressed in his bulky leather flying jacket and carrying his parachute as well as his bomb aimer's canvas bag. He was held up in front of the turret by Jimmy checking the emergency escape hatch in the roof. He then had to step up two feet on to the top of the bomb bay; this made the ceiling too low to stand up straight. Crouching, he moved up the narrow fuselage to where a horizontal bar halfway between floor and ceiling bisecting the fuselage barred his progress. Bending forward he put his bag on the floor on the other side of the bar and swung his leg over as if climbing over a gate. The bar was the wing rear spar carry through. The wing main spar carry through still lay ahead. A rest bunk half filled the left side of the fuselage between the two spars. Jimmy had just finished checking the second escape hatch in the ceiling between the two spars. The main spar carry through was bigger and more difficult to negotiate than the first, because once over you were in the radio operator's area and the left side of the fuselage was filled with the radio operator's seat and equipment. At least it was now light. This compartment had a window in each side and the large Perspex hemispherical astrodome in the roof. Squeezing past the radio equipment, Bob came to the navigator's area and sliding past the rear of the navigator's seat he emerged into the cockpit and could once again stand up straight. Jimmy was standing in the small space behind the pilot's seat on the left of the aircraft so that Bob could get past into the bomber's nose. Doug was already in his seat as Bob went past, pushing his bag through into the nose. Then sitting down on the cockpit floor he slid under the right-hand side of the instrument panel feet first into the bomb aimer's compartment which was two feet below the level of the cockpit floor, over the front of the bomb bay. His compartment was, by comparison with the rest of the crew positions, spacious.

Now he started his internal equipment check. Opening his bag he took out his flying helmet and oxygen mask. Putting the bag to one side behind the mark 14 bombing computer on the left of the compartment, he put on the helmet and plugged it into the aircraft's intercom and oxygen systems sockets on the right hand side of his compartment. First he checked the oxygen. Holding the mask against his face and turning on the supply, he breathed deeply. The cold dry oxygen smelt of rubber from the mask but there was no doubt that it was working. Static suddenly filled his ears as Harry switched on the intercom and Bob checked the rotary switch on the front of his oxygen mask was switched off so that the rest of the crew would not have to listen to his breathing as he carried out the rest of his checks. Now he crawled forward to the front of the compartment and looking up slid himself upwards until he was standing upright with his torso in the front gun turret. His oxygen tube and intercom leads were now at full stretch and he would have to be careful he didn't pull them out of their sockets. A swivel seat was behind his back, pivoted on either side just above his hips and he rotated it underneath himself and hoisted his bottom up onto it making himself comfortable. The turret's twin Browning .303 machine guns were directly in front of him, shoulder width apart, black, solid, angular and loaded. He reached forward and lifted the breech cover off the right-hand side Browning; lifting the ammunition belt out he closed the breech cover then did the same to the left Browning. Then, pulling back the cocking handles on the sides of the weapons until they clicked, he cocked both guns. Reaching for the turret controls, outboard of each Browning's breech, he pulled first one trigger then the other; the double click sounded solid and positive. Then he lifted the breech covers and reinserted the ammunition belts. All the while he had been listening to Doug and Jimmy's voices in his earphones as they went through their engine pre-start checks and now they were ready to start the engines.

"Check in front to back ready for engine start," crackled Doug over the intercom.

Bob flicked on his intercom switch. "Bomb aimer ready."

He could see two ground crew below and to his right standing beside a large wheeled fire extinguisher and to the left of the nose, Sergeant Green was looking up at Doug, watching for his signals to start the engines. Bob could not see the other ground crew who were standing on steps built into the sides of the main undercarriage legs immediately above each main wheel. Their heads and shoulders were inside the wheel bays where they could prime each engine before it was started, then continue to prime during the start until the engine was running smoothly.

The rest of the crew had checked in as ready to start and Doug yelled, "Ready start number three!" out of the cockpit side window.

Sergeant Green put up his thumb and looked across at the number three engine which was always started first. Doug yelled, "Contact!" The starter whined and the propeller slowly and jerkily started to turn. The ground crewman was now priming for all he was worth and after about five seconds, the engine fired, with a loud cough, spluttered, then ran smoothly. Doug and Jimmy now moved on to engine number four.

Bob could now get on with more of his own checks. The number three engine powered the hydraulic pump, which powered the front turret, so Bob now took hold of the turret controls, which were identical to Alex's in the mid-upper turret. He spun the turret fully right until it stopped, short of the arc of the number four propeller: a safety device to stop him accidentally shooting himself down. He then did the same to the left, fully elevating and depressing the guns. He checked that the turret would rotate at all speeds. Then turning on the gun sight he adjusted the brightness to his satisfaction and returned the turret to facing straight forward.

Folding away the turret seat he climbed out of the turret and knelt beside the mark 14 bombing computer unit. This was a large black box two feet long by two feet high by one foot wide; it was powered by a vacuum pump from the port inner engine and electricity direct from the aircraft's main systems. He would enter the target's elevation above sea level, wind speed and direction and the terminal velocity on the bombs into this box. The aircraft's own speed altitude and heading would be fed in automatically directly from the aircraft's instruments. The computer would then work out the appropriate aim off angle and set it into the bombsight. He adjusted the input settings and checked that the dials were satisfactorily illuminated so that he would be able to see them later as they approached the target. As he did this, he heard the hydraulic rams behind him moving as Doug closed the bomb bay doors. This would also operate a safety interlock preventing any electricity entering the bomb bay and dropping the bombs accidentally.

Moving to the extreme nose of the aircraft, he lay down on the black leather-padded floor cushion and looked out through the Perspex bomb aimer's bubble. The sky was still a clear blue and while the aircraft was facing north and the sun was out of sight in his 8 o'clock he could tell by the Lancaster's long shadow that it was low in the sky and dusk was not too far away. The bottom 30 degrees of the bomb aimer's hemispherical bubble was a circle of optically flat Perspex so that the bomb aimer's view of the target would not be distorted as he looked through the bombsight. The bombsight was basically a large reflector sight, like those in the turrets. But the sheet of glass was angled away from Bob instead of towards him so he could look down through it at the target. The glass was longer and thinner than the glass in the gun sights and was protected by a cast iron guard that had to be swivelled out of the way to see the glass. A spring-loaded lever on the left of the sight could be pushed forward to alter the angle of the torch-like projector, which, unlike the gun sights, was mounted on an arm above the bombsight. The sight was mounted on a circular bowl-shaped unit, which held a gyro to keep the sight level and on receiving instructions from the bombing computer the sight would allow for the aircraft's drift and throw forward of the bombs. Now, looking through the sight, Bob turned on the red light, which projected the aiming reticule on to the sheet of glass and adjusted its brilliance. The reticule was known as the sword and looked like an inverted T. The aiming point should move down the upturned T until it reached the crossbar of the sword's hilt and then Bob would release the bombs. He pushed the spring-loaded lever forward so that the angle of the projector changed and looking through the sight the sword appeared superimposed on the grass by the edge of the taxiway. Then releasing the lever it retuned to the computer-set bombing angle and the sword now appeared to be on the concrete in front of F for Freddy's nose.

Rolling on to his left side, Bob checked the sixteen bomb arming switches to the right of and just behind the Perspex nose cone were set safe. Then moving to the rear of his compartment he checked the "window" chute on the right side of the compartment. This was where he would drop the paper bundles of metal foil from the aircraft to fool the German radars. The bundles had to be dropped at regular intervals. This could be anything from rate "G", which was five bundles a minute but generally taken to mean as fast as you could over the target, to rate "A", one bundle every two minutes; he would find out the rate to be used at the main briefing. When he was busy on the bomb run Jimmy would come down into the nose to take over dropping the window. The window had not yet been loaded but on his return from the final briefing the rear of his compartment would be filled with hundreds of paper parcels, each slightly smaller than a house brick. Finally he pulled back the leather-padded cushion on the floor to reveal an escape hatch. He turned the handle and the hatch clicked inwards so that he could lift it off into the aircraft. This was the primary bale out hatch and Bob was always slightly nervous that he was lying on top of it for a large amount of the time. It was irrational, he knew, because it had to be lifted inwards so he couldn't possibly accidentally fall out but he couldn't help thinking about it. Still he took comfort that if it came down to it he would be the first to bale out. As he secured the hatch, the roar and vibration from the engines seemed to lessen and Bob realised that Doug and Jimmy had finished their checks and were now throttling back the engines.

"Check in front to back with any unserviceable equipment," ordered Doug.

"Bomb aimer fully serviceable," replied Bob. The rest of the crew replied the same.

With that Doug and Jimmy started to shut down the engines and as the last engine fell silent, to be replaced by the whirring of running down gyros, Bob put his helmet back in his bag and followed the others outside.

"Everything alright, sir?" asked Sergeant Green.

"Fine, no problems at all, thank you."

"It's a good one this one, you mark my words, sir. It'll look after you."

"I hope so, sarge, we'll see you after the briefing." The crew all got on their bikes and rode back to the main briefing room. As they rode they talked about the aircraft, how well everything was working and how good it would be to get this first Op out of the way. Only Ron, riding at the back, was silent.

By 15.20 F for Freddy's crew were all waiting outside the briefing room, most smoking cigarettes, Ron smoking his pipe and Doug standing with his arms folded and aimlessly looking around. Their newly acquired bikes were firmly padlocked and leaning against the side of the hut. They stood out as a new crew by the lack of whistle on their battledress collars and, in their eagerness not to be late, they had arrived at the briefing room far earlier than all the other crews.

The sun was low in the west now and Bob could feel the cool of evening approaching. He hated the cold in this country. It seemed to chill you right to the bone. Even now he could feel the cold damp ground sucking the heat out of his feet through the soles of his boots. The others didn't seem to notice the cold like he did but he supposed that it was because they were used to it. After all, they had never had to put up with the heat of a Perth summer. If he ever made it home he promised he would never complain about the heat again. At that particular moment Bob's home seemed a very long way away. As he was starting to feel homesick a car drove up and out tumbled five officers, all very loud and boisterous.

"Hello, Doug, I heard you were on the show tonight, bad luck them not giving you time to settle in. Still you'll feel a lot better with the first Op out of the way."

"Thanks, Charlie, any tips?" Doug replied.

"Yes, always keep your number of landings the same as your number of takeoffs, old boy!" he smiled. "Don't fly straight and level for more than a few seconds while you're over enemy territory, keep weaving and make it varied. If you get caught in a searchlight dive like the devil straight towards it, that usually throws them off, and if a fighter sees you, corkscrew as hard as you can and he'll usually go and find someone else to bother. Other than that just remember what you've been taught and you'll be fine." With that he went into the briefing room.

"Well, I suppose we should go in," said Doug and carrying their canvas bags of specialist kit, they all filed into the briefing room. Three briefing officers were busy at the front of the room and the curtain was still across the wall map hiding their destination, although by now the word had been spread from all the specialist briefings and everyone knew their target. As they took their seats three rows from the front on the left, George and Alex sat on the far left. As gunners most of the brief would not concern them. Then came Harry, Ron and Bob who would all work closely together on the navigation. Finally came Doug and Jimmy who would work together in the cockpit. Doug liked to sit next to Bob to crib his target maps and reconnaissance photographs as he thought it would help him as he approached the target. Other crews started to come in and take their seats. Suddenly there was a voice close behind them.

"I'm sorry, chaps, but you're in our seats."

They all looked around to see a tall thin flight lieutenant and what appeared to be his crew staring at them.

Doug was about to apologise when Bob spoke. "Your seats, sir?"

"Yes," said the flight lieutenant a little taken aback.

"There weren't any names on them." Bob's belligerence was coming to the fore.

The flight lieutenant's eyes glared and it was obvious he was not going to back down. It is a fact of service life that right or wrong you can usually tell who is going to come off best in an argument by a quick glance at their respective ranks. In this case, a sergeant showing open defiance to a flight lieutenant, Bob was in for one hell of a beating.

"It's alright, Bob, we'll move," said Doug ushering Bob out of the way and trying to defuse the situation as they all moved back a row.

"All the rows are the same anyway," grumbled Bob.

"Then you won't mind moving," said one of the incoming sergeants.

Bob was about to make something of it when Doug touched his arm to hold him back.

By 15.30 the briefing room was full and a general buzz of conversation filled the air. Only Doug's crew seemed silent. Doug himself had noticed F for Freddy and P.O. Jackson chalked on the blackboard to one side of the curtain and an F for Freddy label stuck on their dispersal on the airfield map. His name in the captain's column made the butterflies in his stomach take flight. Suddenly a voice came from the back of the room.

"Attention!"

Everyone stood to attention as the Station Commander, Wing Commander Baxter and Nigel Forrester walked in. Baxter took a seat in the front row and the Station Commander jumped straight up on to the stage.

"Sit down, chaps! Roll call please!" Nigel called the roll with each captain answering for his crew. With all crews present, Nigel nodded to the Station Commander.

"Curtain please!" boomed the Station Commander. The curtain was drawn back to reveal a large map of Europe with a red ribbon from RAF Metheringham out across the Lincolnshire coast north of the Wash and following the north Norfolk coast east. Then out in a straight line over the North Sea to the Dutch coast. The ribbon passed well to the north of Amsterdam then at the Zuider Zee it turned southeast as if heading for the industrial Ruhr valley. North of Essen it turned slightly north of east heading between Munster and Dortmund, then just short of Hanover it turned east to Magdeburg before jinking northeast again to its destination, Berlin. The jinking course was to confuse the German fighter controllers to keep the target a secret as long as possible. But by now the Germans were becoming very good guessers. The route home was less complicated. Northwest to the north of Hamburg hitting the German coast south of the Danish border. Then west over the North Sea back to Lincolnshire, a round trip of about 1200 miles.

"Well, gentlemen," the Station Commander continued, "Berlin again. I know I don't need to emphasize the importance of this target but I will emphasize the importance of a concentrated attack. Berlin is a huge target but there is no point scattering bombs all over it. That would be like trying to kill an elephant with a pin. We must keep our attacks concentrated and devastate individual areas of the city bit by bit!"

The Station Commander, Group Captain McKechnie, was a big powerful man with a long stern face and large moustache. He spoke in a deep confident voice, which Bob imagined a generation before would have led young men over the top into the mouths of machine guns. Doug noticed the George Cross among his medal ribbons which he had been awarded for pulling a fellow student pilot from his burning aircraft when he was a cadet at the RAF College at Cranwell. McKechnie himself had been burned in the rescue, but there were no traces of the scars. The Station Commander was in every sense of the word a formidable man.

When he'd finished, the Station Commander sat down in the front row and the Met man took the stage. He slid the aircraft captain board to one side to reveal a chalk-drawn cross-section of the weather expected at Metheringham from takeoff to 06.00 the next morning, which was long after any aircraft would have run out of fuel. He talked about wind speeds and directions for takeoff and landing, icing levels and cloud cover. The main things of interest to Bob were the wind speeds and directions and any expected cloud cover at the target. There didn't look like there would be any significant weather to affect them, so he just noted that the expected winds in the target area had not changed since the previous briefing. Beside him Ron was frantically scribbling, noting the expected wind velocities at various heights and checking the coordinates of the changes of course. Bob took out his own map and pencilled in the expected track to and from

Berlin. He would look for prominent features along the route and work out approximate timings later.

Next came the Flying Control Officer with the engine start and taxi times and a plea to stick to them unless there was a hold, which would be signalled by a red flare. A green flare would be the signal to start engines while red or green Aldis lamp signals from the runway control caravan would tell them to hold or take off as necessary. The Station Signals Officer, who gave the details of all the frequencies in use for that evening followed him. Group Met frequency for the transmission of updated wind velocities, emergency frequencies, D/F beacon frequencies, GEE navigation stations in use and finally the identification colours of the day.

Last in the line of specialists came the Station Intelligence Officer. He outlined the composition of the raid, a 500-strong all Lancaster force with intruders from 100 Group patrolling the enemy night fighter bases, trying to catch the German night fighters as they took off. He then talked through the route pointing out the large fighter base at Leeuwarden, north of their crossing point on the Dutch coast. Yellow ground marker flares dropped by Pathfinder Lancasters would mark the turning point north of Essen as this turn was critical if they were to miss the flak around Munster and Dortmund. He pointed out other known concentrations of flak along the route, other fighter bases and then concentrated on the target. There was to be a holding point west of Berlin where any bombers arriving early would orbit until they could see the Pathfinder markers. 106 Squadron would orbit at 19,000 feet if necessary but nobody would want to spend any time over Germany flying in circles, so they would all do their best to arrive on time. Window was to be dropped at rate "A", or one bundle every two minutes, from ten miles off the enemy coast, increasing to maximum rate "G" over the target. Yellow marker flares, again dropped by Pathfinders, would signal when to start maximum rate window dropping to confuse the radar-guided searchlights and flak in the target area. And more yellow flares would signal them to go back to rate "A" dropping as they left the target area. Finally the Intelligence Officer talked the crews through the route home again, pointing out areas of flak and fighter stations. Once out over the sea, he advised the crews to descend below 5,000 feet to get below the German ground radar coverage, so that enemy night fighters would have to search for them without the aid of the ground controllers.

After the Station Intelligence Officer each specialist leader stood up and gave a quick run through of what he had already briefed at the earlier specialist briefings. This was for the benefit of the other crew members and helped bring together all the different aspects of the mission.

When the last leader had finished, Wing Commander Baxter got up and stood with his hands on his hips scanning his Squadron crews.

"Right, chaps, most of you have been there before so I don't have to tell you what it's going to be like. Keep your eyes peeled and don't forget, aim at the TIs, not the fires."

He then returned to his seat and the Station Commander got up again.

"Wing Commander Baxter is right. We must keep this attack concentrated and that means aiming at the target indicators. You must also stick rigidly to your timings and not allow yourselves to wander off track. Our route takes us close to a couple of large fighter bases and some large concentrations of flak. Anyone straggling will be a sitting duck so stay alert. Time check." This last remark was directed at the Squadron Navigator Leader. The Squadron Leader stood and gave a countdown to 16.05 and all the crews set their watches.

The briefing now broke up into individual crews checking they had all the mission details correct. Bob pulled his target photograph and sketch maps from his bag and started to study them with Doug. Harry checked his list of frequencies; Jimmy started to juggle his fuel figures and asked Ron for some timings to reach the target and the ETA back at Metheringham. Ron, who was frantically working his Dalton computer and circular slide rule to calculate courses to allow for the winds and ground speeds didn't yet have the answer and bit Jimmy's head off so that he retreated behind Bob and Doug. George and Alex took a quick look at the target photograph although from their positions in the aircraft they would only see it if they were well out of position or they had passed it. They then committed the route to memory as there was no room for maps in their turrets, and although there was always a chance they might spot a good navigation feature along the route, their main job was to look for fighters.

Gradually the crews started to leave until there was only Doug's and one other left. At that point Wing Commander Baxter walked up to them.

"How's it all going then, chaps?"

"Almost ready, sir," replied Doug.

"Good, take your time. All of these chaps have done it before so they're bound to be a bit quicker. Don't let that rush you, you'll find you've got more time than you think. Do another thorough aircraft check when you get to your dispersal and if you're not happy with anything, don't go! See you when we get back." He slapped Doug on the shoulder and left.

"Well," said Doug looking around his crew. "Are we all ready?"

There was a general rumble of agreement and they followed the other crews outside where cars were driving away and crews on bicycles were riding off. It reminded Doug of school breaking up for the summer. They collected their bikes and rode off after the rest of the Squadron. When they got to the crew room, there was a hold up as the crews in front collected their kit. When they finally got to their lockers the first thing they did was empty their pockets of any personal items. Then Bob took off his black service boots and put on his leather fur lined flying boots, followed by his flying jacket. He went to the counter where a corporal gave him his parachute, parachute harness, yellow Mae West life jacket, escape kit, revolver, thermos flask of coffee, sandwiches and a bar of chocolate. He had to sign for the parachute, harness, Mae West and revolver. The Mae West went over the leather jacket buttoning up the front and tightening at the waist. The parachute harness went over the top of this, a strap over each shoulder clipping into a circular locking box which was fitted to a piece of canvas which came around from his back under his left arm so that the locking box sat in the middle of his stomach. A loop of strap made of the same material as the shoulder straps, hung down from the back of the harness. Reaching between his legs, Bob pulled it up over his crotch. The two lap straps of the harness were passed down through this loop then lifted up and plugged into the locking box with a solid click. Now he adjusted the straps until he was comfortable and the locking box sat in the centre of his stomach. There were two spring clips on the shoulder straps onto which the parachute pack would be clipped in an emergency if he should need to bale out. Only Bob took a revolver. He checked it then slid it inside his flying jacket and turned to look at George as he pulled on his electric suit.

"Why didn't you want a gun?"

"It's uncomfortable enough in a turret without havin' a bloody great lump of metal freezing itself to yer. Besides I don't like guns."

"You don't like guns? You're a bloody gunner! You sit behind four Browning .303 machine guns that can fire twenty rounds a second and you say you don't like guns!"

"Yeah, but I can't accidentally shoot meself in the foot with a Browning, can I?" George replied.

"What are we going to do with these?" asked Harry holding up his newly written letter.

"Give them to me," said George. "I've got a big envelope here and we'll seal them in and give it to Sally."

Finally, loaded down with bulky clothing and kit, they walked outside. Most of the other crews had already gone and only two wagons remained waiting for their crews. Sally stood at another wagon cab talking to the driver. She wore a greatcoat over her overalls and a knitted scarf around her neck. She had obviously been through this many times before and was dressed for the occasion. The sun had almost gone and the day, which had never been warm, was now very cold.

"It should be a nice clear night tonight, sir. You won't have any problems finding your way back," she said to Doug as she walked back to her wagon at the same time saluting.

"I hope not," replied Doug, his mind really elsewhere, while Ron as the senior officer present returned Sally's salute.

They all clambered in and set off round the perimeter track. As they passed other dispersals they saw crews standing beside their aircraft having a last cigarette or chatting with their ground crew. Doug made a mental note to get to know his ground crew better as after all their lives depended on their work. At F for Freddy's dispersal the ground crew were standing around the door of their shack holding pint pots of tea cupped in both hands to keep them warm. The wagon stopped and they all got out.

"Thanks, Sally, see you lat…"

But she cut him dead. "Don't tempt fate," she said firmly looking him straight in the eyes.

"Right." A cold shiver ran down his spine and the hairs stood up on the back of his neck.

She smiled. "Good luck."

"Thanks." He smiled, then turned and walked over to Sergeant Green.

There was a tap at Sally's window which made her jump. She turned and opened the window.

"Sorry," said George. "Can you hold on to this, just in case?" He handed the envelope through the window.

"Of course I can, sarge."

"If we don't…"

"Don't worry, sarge, I know the drill." She smiled as she put the envelope on the dashboard.

"Right, bonny lass," George winked and followed the rest of his crew towards the shack.

Doug and Jimmy went straight into the shack to check the 700 and, when they returned, Doug looked over to the edge of the dispersal but Sally's truck had gone. They chatted with the ground crew for a while. It was hard work because they were too keyed up to really think of anything other than the Op. Apparently the ground crew were all going to the camp cinema after seeing F for Freddy off. It had just opened and none of them was sure what was showing that evening but on a wartime airfield in the middle of Lincolnshire in the winter anything was better than nothing.

Fifteen minutes before engine start time, with all the cigarettes finished, Doug decided it was time to get aboard. They carried out the same checks that they had carried out in the afternoon except for the bomb bay, which was now closed, and they stopped short of starting the engines. Only now everything was more difficult because of the bulky clothing, life jackets and parachute harnesses. On top of all that it was now well and truly dusk and inside the fuselage was dark. Soon what little light was left would also be gone.

A car drove around the perimeter track, came into F for Freddy's dispersal and stopped beside the shack. Doug was too engrossed in his checks to pay any attention to it. It was almost time to start engines and he wanted to be absolutely sure he had done everything possible to make this mission a success. He looked at his watch, one minute. All the training had led up to this moment. Then from flying control a green flare arced slowly into the air, its intense light piercing the gloom of the evening and leaving a trail of grey smoke behind it against the dark sky.

4

With F for Freddy's engines throttled back to a deep rumble, a low frequency vibration ran through the airframe. It seemed an especially violent vibration to Bob as he lay on his stomach in the nose. It vibrated him up and down and shook his lungs inside his body. They had taxied out of their dispersal and were waiting for another Lancaster to pass before moving onto the perimeter track to queue up for takeoff. The other Lancaster moved slowly past from left to right, its green navigation light bright on the right wingtip in the growing gloom. As it moved ahead Doug released the brakes and increased the power to the outer engines until F for Freddy moved forward following the other Lancaster. Bob could see the rear turret moving from side to side as the gunner checked his controls but the gunner himself was merely a dark shadow behind his Perspex. The tail was moving from side to side as the Lancaster manoeuvred along the narrow taxiway, the pilot trying to get a better view of the route ahead over the aircraft's nose. Small blue lights at regular intervals marked the edges of the taxiway. Their glow reflected off the Perspex of the rear turret of the Lanc in front as it passed each one. If a Lancaster this heavily loaded strayed off the concrete it would instantly bog down blocking the taxiway for all those behind it.

Bob could feel F for Freddy weaving from side to side as well as speeding up and slowing down as Doug kept station with the other aircraft. Moving at jogging pace they wound their way towards the threshold of runway two zero. About halfway to the threshold the taxiway took a sharp left turn and crossed the threshold of runway two five, one of Metheringham's shorter secondary runways. The perimeter fence was close on the right-hand side and two young boys, probably about eleven or twelve years old, sat on a gate waving at the bombers as they passed. Bob waved back, then as the boys disappeared behind the starboard wing he again looked towards the front in time to see the white runway lights come on and the first Lancaster start its takeoff run. He could not hear it over the noise of F for Freddy's engines as it accelerated down the runway but he knew that the engines would be straining to overcome the inertia of the heavily loaded bomber.

"If you want to leave the nose before takeoff, now's the time Bob," Doug crackled over the intercom.

"No thanks, skipper. I'll stay here." Bob had decided that when the Lancaster was loaded with bombs and fuel one place was pretty much the same as another if they crashed. The resulting explosion would probably flatten anything within at least 400 yards. Three more bombers had taken off and now the aircraft in front of them was lining up on the runway. The red and white chequered runway control caravan sat fifty yards from the threshold of runway two zero on the opposite side of the runway. It was a large four-wheeled vehicle with a raised glass box section in the roof where the runway controller and his assistant sat. They would clear each bomber for takeoff with a single long green flash of their Aldis light and log the takeoff times. Beside it a collection of vehicles and a group of people gathered together, all wrapped up against the cold, waving each bomber off. Bob saw the green light and the other Lancaster started its run. Now it was their turn.

Doug moved F for Freddy slowly into position on the runway centre line, then ran forward a few feet to ensure the tailwheel was straight and throttled back, waiting for the green light. Now that they were closer to the caravan Bob recognised Sally's wagon and he could see her standing beside it waving for all she was worth. The other bomber was airborne now, slowly climbing away, its white tail-light all that could be clearly seen of it. Then it went out, signalling that it was clear of the airfield. Immediately the green light came on in the runway caravan.

Bob both heard and felt the massive increase in power, as the throttles were opened to maximum boost. The noise was a terrific low-pitched deep roar, which rose and fell rhythmically. The vibrations shook his chest cavity and he could feel the Lancaster pulling to the left as the slipstream from the four 1,460 horsepower engines wrapped itself around the fuselage and pushed the tail to the right. Doug was correcting this and Bob looked straight down the runway as the initial swinging of the nose was straightened out and they settled on to a straight course. The white lines of the runway centreline were moving past directly under them, faster and faster. The dim white lights marking the edges of the runway stretching out before them.

"30!" said Ron, calling out the aircraft's speed. The tail started to rise and again the Lancaster started to swing.

"Tail up!" said George from the rear turret. Again Doug corrected it but Bob could now feel a strange sensation as if they were bobbing up and down slightly, like a small boat in a long rolling swell.

"60!" Bob could now see the end of the runway in the distance slowly getting closer and this always made him nervous. Bob knew how the slow approach of the end of the runway would suddenly seem to accelerate, as it got closer. If an engine failed now they could still probably stop in time.

"90!" Now there was no chance of stopping before they ran out of runway. The end of the runway was plainly visible, with its white piano keys and upside down 02 now racing towards them at an alarming rate. If an engine failed now they would hurtle off the end of the runway, smash through the perimeter fence and shoot over the country lane. Their main wheels would bog down in the wet heavy Lincolnshire soil and collapse, leaving the heavy bomber to crash down onto its bomb load at about 100 miles per hour. The bombs and fuel would explode and all that would be left would be a charred hole in the ground. Bob was suddenly aware that his heart was pounding so hard inside his chest that he thought it might burst free. No more than 300 yards to the end of the runway.

"100!" Five more miles per hour to the recommended lift off speed for a heavily loaded Lancaster and less than 300 yards to do it in. Then they still had to clear the boundary fence. Lift, you bastard!

"105!" Slowly F for Freddy rose into the air and clawed for height. Then Doug held it level at about ten feet and selected the wheels up to reduce the drag and help them accelerate. But long before the wheels got into their bays the end of the runway shot underneath them and they were out over the flat Lincolnshire countryside and slowly climbing away. Once they were established in a slow but steady climb, the ground falling away beneath them, Bob released his grip of the bomb aimer's padded cushion, realising that he had been holding on so tightly his knuckles had gone white. Now he reached for his map and started to map read his way to the coast.

Behind Bob in the cockpit Doug set the course of one zero zero degrees compass for the coast, which Ron had passed to him and then waited until they had climbed through 500 feet before retracting the flaps and retrimming. He scanned the instruments and everything appeared to be well. He hadn't expected to get that close to the end of the runway before lifting off but then again he hadn't flown an aircraft this heavy before. There was still a ribbon of light defining the western horizon but ahead to the east, it was dark and the first stars were starting to appear in the clear sky. The bombers still had their navigation lights on and red green and white lights were visible all around as streams of aircraft took off from airfields all over Lincolnshire. Although the sky was clear there was only the smallest sliver of a new moon and the night was dark. This wasn't a problem while all the aircraft had their navigation lights on but when they got to the coast and turned all their lights off, there would be a very real risk of a collision.

"Pilot to crew, keep your eyes peeled and call out any aircraft that gets close." Doug had now had two very near mid-air collisions and they frightened him more than anything else. But his first fright of the night was to come from inside the aircraft, not outside.

A large powerful hand landed on his shoulder making him jump. Turning around as far as his shoulder harness would allow he found himself looking into a pale face framed by a flying helmet, with an oxygen mask hanging down from the right hand side. The dim green light from the instrument panel showed the deep lines around the eyes and the face was grinning from ear to ear.

"What the hell are you doing here?" he shouted over the engines.

"Thought you might like some company on your first trip, old boy!" Nigel shouted back.

"The Wingco will kill us both for this!" yelled Doug.

"He'll have to catch us first and as both he and the Station Commander are flying tonight, so long as we get back before them they need never know."

"And if we don't get back before them?"

"They'll kill us both!"

The thought of getting on the wrong side of the Wing Commander did nothing for Doug's nerves, but it would be good to have someone along who knew the ropes. Besides what could he do about it now? The coast was ahead, hardly visible as the last light had now gone from the sky and with only a few stars out there was little light to reflect off the sea's calm surface. They crossed the coast at 6,000 feet, switched off their navigation lights and continued their long slow climb up to 20,000 feet.

"Bomb aimer to navigator, crossing the coast now, at Wainfleet."

"Roger, navigator to pilot, on track and on time."

They flew on. No other aircraft were visible now but they were there, five hundred of them converging into a stream. Suddenly Doug saw two parallel red dotted lines in his low 11 o'clock shooting away to the north, then another two lines from the same place. Someone was shooting; surely there wouldn't be any German night fighters this far west? Then he realised that it was only another bomber testing its guns.

"Gunners, you're clear to test your guns."

This caught Bob by surprise as he was lying in his bomb aimer's position trying to spot the Norfolk coast to the south of them and at the same time keep a lookout for other aircraft. As he clambered up into the front turret he heard the sharp rattle of Alex's twin Brownings. He squirmed up behind his guns and his intercom leads got caught on something so he had to reach down and free them. He couldn't see what he was doing in the dark and with all his bulky flying kit on there was no space in the turret. Everything seemed to have hard sharp angular corners and by the time he had freed his leads and got onto his swivel seat Alex and George had both finished their checks and reported back that all was well. Finally Bob swivelled his turret to the left and angled the guns down. He checked the sight, turning down the brightness of the reflector sight, so that it was a dim glow that would not obscure his target, felt the twin triggers under his forefingers, eased on the pressure, and then gave a positive squeeze. Nothing! Shit! He had forgotten to cock the guns. Reaching forward he stretched out for the cocking handles, but with the guns fully depressed he couldn't reach. Bringing his hand back, he elevated the guns, cocked them and was just about to fire when Doug called over the intercom, "What's the matter with your turret, Bob?" Bob reached for his microphone switch, at the same time trying to think what he was going to say, when his elbow caught his intercom leads and the static in his ears stopped. Damn! He'd pulled his intercom leads out of their socket down in the bomb aimer's compartment. Just get the guns checked, then reconnect the leads and report in, he thought. He glanced through the sight and squeezed the triggers. The half-second burst lit up the turret with its yellow flashes and the twin lines of tracer streaked away from him.

Then he saw the Lancaster entering the left-hand edge of his gun sight and his heart stopped. The dim shadow was difficult to see and he might not have seen it at all but for the briefest of glints of starlight on the cockpit canopy. Even now when he looked directly at it the Lancaster disappeared, but searching with the corner of his eye it was visible with his twin lines of tracer heading for its nose. Please God, no! Time seemed to stand still. Then the twin red lines swept past the other Lancaster's nose and headed out into the darkness to land somewhere in the North Sea. Jesus Christ! Bob's heart now started to hammer away like a pile driver, trying to make up for the beats it had missed. He traversed his turret to face the front with the smell of the cordite fumes sour in his nostrils. He climbed down into the bomb aimer's compartment and reconnected his intercom leads, wondering if anyone else had seen him nearly shoot down a friendly aircraft.

"Front turret fully serviceable, skipper. Sorry, my intercom leads came out."

"Roger."

Obviously nobody had seen. Bob was hugely relieved; his credibility in the crew if anybody had seen would have been zero and he would never have been allowed to live it down. Mind you, if he had hit the other Lancaster he would have been court-martialled. As he lay down in the nose shaking slightly and sweating he wondered what the sentence would be for shooting down a friendly aircraft. Maybe they would have had him shot.

The Norfolk coast was now invisible as it curved away from them to the south and they headed out over the North Sea.

"10,000 feet, everyone onto oxygen and check in," said Doug. Bob held his oxygen mask over his nose and mouth with his left hand and locating the press-studs with his gloved hand pulled them towards where his right hand had located the other half of the press-studs on the side of his flying helmet. Then came the usual fiddly operation to get them to click into place without trapping his flying glove in between. Finally the press-studs clicked and he breathed in the cold, rubber smelling oxygen and turned on his microphone.

"Bomb aimer on oxygen."

The rest of the crew checked in on oxygen, their voices now even more muted and robot-like on the intercom. It was now noticeably colder as they climbed ever higher and the stars seemed brighter. There were certainly more of them now. With the complete lack of light in the bomb aimer's compartment, Bob could see the millions of stars stretching across the whole sky. It was a beautiful crisp clean winter's night. With his head in the bomb aimer's bubble looking straight ahead, Bob couldn't see any of F for Freddy. Real flying, he thought. "Third star from the left and straight on till morning." When he was a child, his mother had read him Peter Pan and from then on he had always wanted to fly. Now here he was flying off to kill people and his mother was far away on the other side of the world. Would he ever see her again? His eyes moistened. You dozy bastard! Thoughts like that get you killed! he scolded himself, shaking off the feeling of melancholy and concentrating on a square search of the sky ahead.

The Lancaster droned on and on, climbing up and up until it finally levelled off at 20,000 feet. Bob turned his attention to the bombsight. A small spirit level was fitted to the side of the sight and by adjusting a knob on the side of the sight he could adjust the sight so that it was perfectly level. Now it was really cold and Bob tried not to move on the padded floor, so that he would warm a part of it up to a comfortable temperature. Then he noticed a faint horizontal line below and in the distance. When he looked directly at it, it disappeared but again, when he looked slightly away from it, it appeared again. He reached to his right and pulled the small Anglepoise lamp towards him. As he did he slid over slightly onto a cold patch of cushion. Bugger! He turned the light on and looked at his watch. The glow from the light was barely visible through the layers of paper Bob had put over it to dim it down and protect his night vision. The time was about right, so he turned off the light and looked again. Yes, that was it alright.

"Bomb aimer to crew, enemy coast ahead."

"Roger, we're ten miles off the coast now," replied Ron.

"Okay, I'm starting to drop window now, skipper."

"Roger."

Lifting himself up Bob crawled to the rear of the nose and dropped a bundle of window from the chute. He noted the time as he did so, then crawled back to his bomb aimer's position. The coast slid closer and Bob noticed that to the right, down the coast to the south, there were white lights twinkling in the sky. They were pretty to watch and Bob wondered what it was. He knew he should be keeping a lookout but his eyes kept being drawn back to the twinkling lights. They were almost over the coast and Bob edged forward so that he could tell Ron the second they crossed it. Directly in front of them multiple green lines of tracer suddenly shot up from a point in space. It was difficult to judge the distance but it was undoubtedly close and in the first second Bob couldn't tell if the tracer had been fired towards them or away from them.

Then it became obvious that it had been fired in front of them from slightly below and at a shallow upward angle in the same direction that they were flying, because the short green lines hit a bomber, invisible in the darkness, about half a mile ahead of them. The silent explosions caused a shower of yellow flashes along the underside of the left wing and revealed the bomber in their vivid light. Other tracer rounds that had missed the bomber continued their upward path, eventually losing their momentum and arcing back downward far beyond their target. Sparks flew from the two port engines. Four lines of red tracer flew from the bomber's rear turret arcing down, a pause, then another red burst.

Another burst of green tracer, longer this time, reached out to the bomber, hitting the same wing and the underside of the fuselage, the last two flashes being on the extreme tail. Brilliant yellow flames leapt from the two port engines, flaring back in the slipstream and spreading rapidly over the whole port wing. At the same time, a duller red glow to the right told of another fire in the fuselage. A final short burst of green tracer struck the doomed bomber in the starboard wing, causing flames to flicker from the starboard inner engine. But it wasn't necessary; the bomber was already beyond saving and started its final plunge. No more return fire came from the rear gunner, already dead in his turret, torn apart by two 20 mm cannon shells. The mid-upper gunner could not see the fighter below him and now it was too late. He was desperately trying to get out of his turret into the fuselage lit by flames from a fire in the bomb bay. The bomber's nose dropped further, until it was going down at a 60-degree angle. The yellow mass of flames engulfed the rear of the aircraft, so that only the starboard wing and cockpit were not on fire. Slowly the starboard wing rolled over the blazing port wing, twisting the dying bomber into a vertical dive and, like a meteorite, it hurtled earthwards getting smaller as it descended. Three yellow parachute flares detached themselves from the bomber and they hung in the air illuminating the scene with a sulphur yellow glow. Finally, now only visible as a mass of flames, the bomber hit the ground and exploded, spreading yellow flames and green target markers over the ground in a fan pattern just inside the Dutch coast.

"Pathfinder," yelled Nigel to Doug as he looked down out of the cockpit's side blister at the flaming wreckage and green target markers. "Turn right and give those flares a wide birth. You don't want to silhouette yourself against them and I would start to weave now if I were you, and we should log the position for the debrief."

"Navigator from pilot. Pathfinder shot down in flames this position." Doug hoped that his voice didn't sound emotional but he certainly felt it. The Pathfinder crew hadn't had any chance to bale out and he had just witnessed the deaths of seven men.

"Are we over the coast yet?" asked Ron from inside his curtained-off compartment.

"Yes," replied Doug.

"Thank you for telling me, bomb aimer," said Ron sarcastically.

Bob, who was supposed to be the navigator's main eyes, had been distracted by the regular window dropping and the drama outside. He had forgotten to tell Ron they had crossed the coast. Now he felt them enter a right turn and saw the horizon tilt in front of him. They passed the flares on the left and turned back on to track. Now they flew through the heading by 20 degrees before turning back towards it again. Each time they turned with 45 degrees of bank which was far more than normal. Bob realised that it was to allow the gunners to see below them and to make it more difficult for a night fighter to approach into an attack position.

He shuffled to the rear of the compartment. Opening the window chute he took another bundle of window, opened the packet, and dropped it through the chute. Individually the bundles of window would have little effect but the combined window from 500 Lancasters flying in the stream would swamp the German radar screens.

"Bomb aimer to pilot, permission to arm bombs?"

"Go ahead, Bob."

Bob checked four groups of four arming switches and selected the first and last six stations, the incendiaries, and station eight, the Cookie. Now, when the bomb doors opened, power would be applied to the clamps and the fusing links would be firmly attached to the aircraft. He checked the interval selector below the arming panel to make sure the incendiaries would fall a quarter of a second after the Cookie, igniting fires in the wake of its blast.

The zigzag course continued and Bob started to feel queasy. He climbed back into the front turret to see if he would feel better there. He didn't use the turret seat but stood behind the guns. He would have to make trips to the window chute every two minutes so there was no point in getting too comfortable. He did feel less airsick in the turret while they were weaving and he realised that, with night fighters around, it was probably best that he stayed there anyway. They were about to cross the coast over the Zuider Zee. Then they would turn southeast. Bob watched the coastline approach. When they were overhead he called Ron and they swung on to a weaving course 20 degrees either side of their new base course of southeast. This leg would be 80 miles long and it would probably take them twenty-five minutes to reach their next turning point.

It was time to drop the next bundle of window. He squeezed out of the turret and crawled to the back of the compartment again, dropped the window then squirmed back into the turret. Having to do that every two minutes was going to be a real pain in the arse, he thought, but if it was going to help keep them safe he was going to make sure he was very conscientious about doing it.

The cold was intense, minus 40 degrees outside and little more inside. It had worked its way through Bob's heavy trousers and thermals and his legs were cold. He rubbed his gloved hands up and down his thighs to try to warm them but it didn't seem to make much difference. The blacked out countryside below them slipped passed unseen in the darkness. There were no signs of life, no breaks in the blackout, no landmarks to call to the navigator. Time went slowly and he had to force himself to concentrate on looking out and scanning the ground. He spotted the Rhine to their right, a line slightly less dark than the rest of the countryside and he reported it to Ron. Normally the huge river would have stood out as a wide silver ribbon, but now a thin layer of altostratus cloud had moved slowly up from the southwest, high above them, cutting out all light from above and making the night as dark as a night was ever likely to get.

"Rear gunner to navigator. Bomber going down in flames 7 o'clock."

"Roger."

Another seven men were now fighting to survive. There were untold hazards out there. Bob was very keyed up, his nerves tight, ready to react instantly, but, with nothing to look at, he found himself getting bored and his mind wandering. This in itself surprised him because he had expected to be excited or maybe even scared but he had never dreamed he would feel bored.

More time passed. The cold reached Bob's fingers and he flexed them to try and improve the circulation. His feet were two blocks of ice and no amount of toe wiggling could warm them. He suddenly remembered his oxygen tube. The condensation from his breath as he breathed out would collect on the inside of the tube and, at this temperature, freeze, eventually blocking the tube. Feeling in the dark he located the tube and started to squeeze it up and down its length. This would break off any ice on the inside of the tube and as he breathed in he felt small fragments of ice hitting his cheeks and upper lip.

A solitary searchlight snapped on ahead of them but it was a long way off. The faint blue white beam swept from left to right and back again as they approached it. Suddenly within the space of a few seconds another twenty searchlights lit up. These beams were whiter in colour and carried out their own searches.

"Navigator to crew. Five minutes to turn."

The searchlights must be at Essen, thought Bob. They would turn northeast before they got to them and they should be seeing the yellow turn markers any time. As if ordered a yellow splash of fire erupted on the ground ahead of them.

"Bomb aimer to navigator. Turn marker in sight."

"Roger."

Lights started to twinkle in the sky ahead of them. The same sort of lights that he had seen at the coast but these seemed closer and looked more yellow than white. Bob realised it was a flak barrage. He kicked himself for being so naïve. More searchlights snapped on and started their weaving search patterns.

"Bomb aimer to navigator. Overhead turn markers."

"Roger, navigator to pilot. New course zero nine zero compass and we're one minute ahead of time."

"New course zero nine zero."

F for Freddy's next weave to the left was held for fifteen seconds to bring them through their new course and then back again so that their new mean heading was zero nine zero.

The wind must be from the south, thought Bob, this leg was supposed to be north of east so if we're heading east now the wind must be pushing us north.

He climbed out of his turret, grateful for something other than staring into the darkness and dropping window to occupy him, anything to take his mind off the cold. Looking through his bombsight, he tried to see if he could pick up any ground features. He could then use the bombsight's graduated scale to work out the Lancaster's drift and, from this, Ron could work out the wind speed and direction. But the ground was in complete darkness. Ron would have to rely on GEE which was probably being heavily jammed by now or H2S ground mapping radar, which could only see certain things.

In the cockpit Nigel leaned close to Doug's ear and shouted, "It's not wise to fly directly over turn markers. If we can see them so can the Jerries and their Wild Boars will fly straight to them and wait to visually pick up the next bomber that comes along. This time it didn't matter because we were over them almost as soon as they lit up but if you ever see them in the distance, give them a wide berth."

"Wild Boars?" asked Doug.

"Jerry day fighters sent up at night to search for us visually. They look for route markers or burning bombers to guide them into our stream. Then they try to silhouette us against the stars or clouds. Rumour has it Jerry sometimes sends up some of his bombers to fly above us and drop flares along our route to help their day fighters find us. By the way, you've got either a very good or very lucky nav there, Doug. I used to wander around Germany for hours in 1939 and hardly ever knew where I was for sure. I think he might be Pathfinder material. You want to hang on to him, bad navigation will get you killed as quickly as bad flying. Anyone wandering out of the bomber stream will soon get picked off as easy meat or he might lose your way home altogether."

Flak twinkled and searchlights danced in the sky to their left as they passed Munster but again it was in the distance. 95 miles to their next turn, twenty-six and a half minutes. Hopefully the turn northeast would have confused the German fighter controllers who might have expected them to head for the industrial Ruhr valley and might have sent their fighters there.

"Bomber going down in flames in our 5 o'clock," called Alex. If the German controllers had been fooled they had soon recovered.

This leg of the route took them close to the south of the town of Bielefeld which had good flak defences. They should pass safely to the south of the known flak area. Southwest of Bielefeld was the town of Gutersloh, which was not a known flak area and so they would pass over it. However, what the raid planners did not know was that a mobile flak detachment with the latest in Wurzburg radar guided 88mm flak guns had recently been stationed in Gutersloh. As the bombers approached, the Wurzburg was switched on and started to search for its victim. The narrow radar beam swept back and forth across the path of the bomber stream like an invisible searchlight until it detected a bomber. At first the radar was confused by the cloud of tinfoil strips surrounding the bombers but with some coaxing from the radar operators who from experience could tell the difference between a bomber and window, the Wurzburg locked itself to its target and tracked its every movement. Inside the bomber none of the crew had any idea what was happening. The Wurzburg passed the details of the target's course, height and speed to the batteries "Predictor", a crude mechanical computer that took into account the target's details then predicted where the target would be when the 88mm shells arrived. It would take seventeen seconds for a shell to reach 20,000 feet and, in that time, the target would move about a mile. Other information was also fed into the Predictor, wind speed and direction, air temperature; allowance was made for the position of the guns in relation to the Wurzburg. All these factors would affect the flight of the shells from the six-gun battery. The gunners were adjusting the shells' fuses so that they would explode as the shells reached 20,000 feet. The guns were loaded following the training and elevation instructions from the Predictor. The target was almost overhead.

"FIRE!" The six guns fired as one, recoiling viciously, their muzzle flashes lighting up the surrounding area, like a brilliant flash of lightning. The gunners leapt forward, new fused shells at the ready; breechblocks slammed open, hot empty shell cases clattered to the ground amid wisps of acrid-smelling cordite. Shells were pushed home and breeches clanked shut, the gunners jumping aside, as the second volley was sent skyward. The gunners would be firing their third volley as the first one arrived.

The Lancaster flew onward, the guns' muzzle flashes unseen almost directly below them. The crew were all tired. This was their fifteenth Op and their third in three nights, all of them to Berlin. The pilot knew that he should be making more of an effort to weave but he had started to feel airsick and he knew they were close to the front of the bomber stream. The fighters would be after bombers further behind them and there was no flak to worry about. Then the first six shells exploded.

Rarely were the first shells of a barrage as accurate. Lots of factors combined to lower their accuracy but the main one was always the behaviour of the target. While the Predictor could produce the aim-off angle for the guns, it was only valid at the time the guns fired. Once the shells were in the air, if the target changed its course, height or speed during the seventeen seconds before the shells arrived, the aeroplane would be somewhere else. But in this case the Lancaster's lazy weave, no more than 10 degrees about its base course in slow regular curves, didn't even register on the Wurzburg The only effect was that the shells arrived slightly ahead of the bomber. The first two shells were far enough ahead to be harmless. They exploded directly ahead and slightly above the Lancaster, the bright yellow flash with its red heart blinding the pilot flight engineer and bomb aimer. The second pair of shells was slightly spread left and right and exploded below the bomber's nose. Shrapnel tore upwards into the belly of the aircraft. Several small fragments slammed into the starboard inner engine, one hitting the propeller pitch control jamming it into fully fine pitch and causing the engine to start to speed up, like a speeding car suddenly forced into first gear. This would quickly lead to the engine over-revving and having to be shut down or tearing itself apart. Other fragments hit the engine block, one cutting a fuel pipe where it entered the side of the engine. Fuel squirted out under pressure onto the hot engine, the vapour ignited instantly and flames flared out from behind the engine cowlings. To the left of the bomber, shell number four sent three large jagged fragments into the port main fuel tank, causing fuel to flood out into the inside of the wing. The bomb aimer was lying looking through his nose blister and trying to blink away the blue haze left by the flash of the first explosions when a piece of shrapnel the size of a saucer came through the floor. It cut through the padded cushion he was lying on and sliced, edge on, straight through him at waist level, severing his backbone and eventually coming to rest embedded in the traversing ring of the front gun turret. He felt like he had been kicked. He was winded and couldn't breathe. He had no time to discover the full extent of his injuries before the final two shells arrived. One exploded abreast of and at the same level as the mid-upper turret. Shrapnel shattered the turret's Perspex, several pieces hitting the gunner in the chest. Any one of them would have been fatal but it was one the size and shape of half a tennis ball striking him in the side of the head that killed him. The sixth and final shell destroyed the Lancaster. It whistled into the bomb bay and scored a direct hit on a Cookie. The shell's altitude fuse didn't get a chance to operate as the nose of the shell hit the thin cased 4,000-pound high explosive bomb and detonated on impact. The resulting flash disintegrated the bomber and all of its crew and lit up the sky for miles.

"What the hell was that?" asked Doug.

"Scarecrow," replied Nigel.

"What?"

"Don't they teach you chaps anything during training?" Nigel teased. "When we first started to carry out big concentrated raids, we used to see flashes like that occasionally and we used to say that it was a direct hit on a bomber. But recently they've become more common and the official word is that the Jerries have a new shell. Large calibre and filled with phosphorous or magnesium or something which explodes with a gigantic flash to make us all think one of our bombers has just exploded and scare us. Of course it could be our chaps who are fibbing to keep up our morale."

"What do you think?"

Nigel stared back at Doug with raised eyebrows, which expressed exactly what he thought of the official British story.

"Navigator to pilot. We've got a 20 mph tail wind at the moment and we're already a minute ahead of schedule. Can you bring the speed back to 140 mph indicated?"

"Yes, we can do that but I wouldn't want to slow it down any further."

"20 mph will be fine for this leg. We should have less of a tail wind next leg."

"There's an old fighter pilot proverb," Nigel shouted in Doug's ear. "Speed is life." Doug looked at him. "Without speed you can't run away or manoeuvre."

"But if we arrive at the target early we'll have to orbit and waste fuel." The thing that really bothered Doug was the flying in circles. 500 Lancasters all flying in the same direction in the dark was bad enough but flying in circles the chances of a collision was massively increased. "This way we'll save fuel."

"You're the captain, old boy, and saving fuel is always good. You never know when you may need more than you thought. But we always lose more aircraft to fighters than to running out of fuel."

The next turn was to the east, just short of Hanover. Again they gave the city's defences a wide berth. 152 miles to go, more bombers went down and were reported to Ron, who logged the positions. They were still on track and now they were also on time. They had a 10 mph tail wind so they adjusted their speed to 150 mph indicated. But now they had company.

The shark like curves of the aircraft's nose was spoilt by the mass of wires projecting from it. The wires were the antennas for the Lichtenstein radar and the four sets of aerials that formed the H-shaped arrays were commonly known to the German crews as "Stag's Antlers." Behind the long thin nose was a longer canopy, made up of angular squares of Perspex. Either side of the canopy protruded the straight-sided square-tipped wings, each one sporting a 1,475hp Daimler-Benz DB 605B engine. Behind the canopy the thin fuselage ended in a twin tail with small fins and rudders. This was a Messerschmitt Bf 110G, one of the best night fighters of the war. Slowly the fighter closed in on its target. The radar operator was having difficulty with the interference caused by the window. But most of the window being dropped was intended to jam the Ground Control Intercept Giant Wurzburg radars along with the ordinary Wurzburg searchlight and gun control radars. His airborne set on a different frequency was less affected. The target was weaving. At first this didn't affect the fighter's approach and the radar operator ignored it. Once he had estimated the target's mean course he treated it as if it was flying straight and level. When they got closer however, the weaving took the target outside the edges of the radar's narrow 25-degree beam. If the fighter didn't follow the manoeuvres and keep its nose pointed at the target there was a chance that he might lose it. The night was so dark they would have to get much closer than normal before they would be able to see the bomber visually. Even now they were very close to the radar's minimum range and if they got much closer they would lose contact, but still they couldn't see it. Straining his eyes the German pilot searched the sky above and ahead of him until he noticed a dull blue light. Then he saw a row of similar blue lights and an area darker than the rest of the sky, his target. He could only see the faintest of silhouettes, highlighted by exhaust flames. He knew it was an enemy bomber but he could not be sure of the type and he knew from experience that if he could not tell the type, he could not see well enough to make an accurate attack. Patiently he sat behind the target and waited, hoping for a better background to highlight the bomber against.

Aboard F for Freddy, Harry was having his usual difficulty working with Ron. Every time he listened to the WT for the HF Morse transmissions from England containing the latest wind speeds and directions, he had to stop listening to the aircraft's intercom, which made him feel very isolated. If anything vital happened while he was on WT Ron was supposed to let him know but Harry didn't trust him to do it. Worse still, when he was operating the radio he could not watch the "Fishpond" tail warning radar. He handed a sheet of paper with the latest winds on it to Ron. Ron didn't even acknowledge him and Harry returned to the Fishpond. When he adjusted the set the screen started to settle down. As he had expected there were a lot of contacts. It had been the same over the North Sea. They were all the other bombers in the stream, stretching out behind them and off to both sides. One was very close, directly behind and just below. At first Harry thought there was a risk of collision but the contact was not closing, in fact it looked like it was flying in formation. Some of the other bombers he had seen when they were crossing the North Sea had looked the same but none were this close. Then he thought about the last time he had looked at Fishpond, halfway to Essen. They had been weaving then and the other contacts had all been weaving as well, independently of each other. This one was stuck to them like glue. OH SHIT!

"Fishpond contact! 100 yards! Port quarter down!"

They were in a weave to port at the time and both gunners were able to look down into the port quarter, their turrets swinging around to the area their eyes were searching. The earth was black and even at 100 yards it would be difficult to spot anything against it. Then they flew over a small lake. The slight change of background contrast made the difference and Alex caught the shape in the corner of his eye. Two engines and twin tail, a Messerschmitt 110.

"Corkscrew port!"

Doug instantly threw the control column to port, his past lessons learnt. The 45 degree angle of bank turn to port quickly became 90 degrees and Doug allowed the nose to drop, as he pushed the throttles through the gate into full emergency boost, spurred on by the long rattle of Alex's guns. With the nose 20 degrees below the horizon and the engines screaming at a much higher than normal pitch, Doug reversed the control column and started to pull back, so that the sharp descending turn to the left bottomed out and became a climbing turn to the right.

The Messerschmitt had been flying formation in F for Freddy's low 7 o'clock, following it through its turn and was caught by surprise at the sudden and violent diving turn. This put the fighter in the bomber's level 7 o'clock with the bomber now tilted at 90 degrees to the horizon. The poor visibility made it difficult for the Messerschmitt pilot to tell that F for Freddy had started to corkscrew until the mid-upper gunner fired at him. Red tracer whipped past very close over his head, getting closer all the time. He instinctively ducked. The bomber was in his high 12 o'clock entering a tight turn and very close. He was well out of position in full view of the bomber and to bring his own guns to bear would mean a collision. Normally he would have dropped back and used his superior firepower to bring the bomber down from long range. But the night was too dark for that. It would be easier to break clear and stalk someone else. He quickly reversed his turn and shot very close past the bomber's tail. A parting burst of tracer from the rear gunner passed behind his wing speeding him on his way and he vanished into the night.

Harry and Ron clung to their tables as Doug threw F for Freddy into the corkscrew. Bob, in the front turret, could not see anything and while both Jimmy and Nigel almost climbed out of the cockpit to try and see the fighter, neither saw a thing. Doug was far too busy flying the aircraft to look, so only Alex and George ever saw the fighter, and then only as the briefest of fleeting shadows in the night. F for Freddy came out of its first real corkscrew and went straight into its standard weave.

"I've lost him!" shouted Alex, straining in his turret to try and spot the fighter.

"So have I," said George.

"I can't see him on Fishpond," Harry said. "The only contacts look like other bombers."

"Is everyone alright?" Doug asked. "Check in front to back."

They all checked in. "Can anyone see any damage?"

"I don't think he had time to shoot, skipper," replied George. "He was too busy trying to avoid colliding with us."

"Alright, check for damage and report it in and, for God's sake, keep your eyes peeled. He may still be out there." The only damage was that the HF radio was no longer working, although there was no damage to the set. "The Jerry went right past our tail," offered George. "He probably took our trailing aerial off."

"Thieving bastard!" said Harry. "I hope it pranged one of his engines!"

Eight miles away the Messerschmitt was busy setting itself up to stalk another Lancaster; around its starboard wing root hung F for Freddy's HF trailing aerial. F for Freddy on the other hand, like a newt that had been attacked and shed its tail continued on its way.

Their choice of targets was now being drastically whittled down and most of the German controllers had long since decided that the target was again Berlin. Magdeburg approached and slipped by to the north. They crossed the river Elbe and turned northeast, 67 miles to the target. After six minutes Bob spotted the series of lakes to the southwest of Berlin. The southern tip of the first lake was where they would start dropping window at the maximum rate. The holding point for any bombers arriving early was to the west of the last lake. It would be an easy feature to recognise either visually or on H2S. They were nearly at the lake now, the massive city lying before them in the dark. Searchlights weaved to and fro and flak twinkled over the whole of its breadth and depth. They were to be one of the first Squadrons to bomb after the Pathfinders but, as yet, there were no

TIs and without them they would have to wait. Doug didn't want to have to circle the holding point wasting fuel but without the TIs he would have to. The thought of all those bombers flying round in circles at night in such a small area with all the risks of collision that entailed scared him more than anything the Germans could do.

Three yellow sky marker flares lit up the sky dictating the starting point for maximum rate window dropping to confuse the city's radar-guided searchlights. The markers seemed to hang stationary in the sky, visible for miles and lighting up the lake surface below them. Over the centre of the city more yellow flares suddenly appeared and Doug breathed a sigh of relief because he would not need to hold after all. He headed for the flares. Jimmy was in the rear of the bomb aimer's compartment now, tearing open paper bundles of window ready to drop through the chute. The Lancaster descended to 19,000 feet as it passed over the flares and Jimmy started to drop the bundles of window out of the aircraft for all he was worth. They were soon passing over the holding point and Doug continued to head straight for the yellow flares in the target area, about 12 miles away. More yellow flares lit up in the same area but as yet he couldn't see any red or green TIs. Illuminating blind marker Pathfinders, using H2S, had dropped these flares and now, unseen in the darkness above the flares, more Pathfinders should be moving in on the illuminated aiming point to mark the target with red TIs. He had hoped to see a TI by now so that he could steady on his bomb run. He wondered if something had gone wrong with the marking. There was nothing he could do about it now. With his heart in his mouth, he would continue his run in to the target.

A green TI was illuminated under the distant yellow flares. Damn it! thought Doug. The Pathfinders can't see the target visually and they've had to mark using H2S. The attack was now a Paramatta and because Doug was concentrating on lining up on the TI he didn't even notice the flak barrage as they entered the area.

106 Squadron were in the first wave of the main force bombers and they were now 10 miles from the aiming point. Bob squeezed behind Jimmy to double check the settings on the bombing computer. Target elevation 120 feet, terminal velocity of bombs 300 feet per second.

"Bomb aimer to navigator. What's the current wind speed and direction?"

"Two one zero degrees at twenty mph, three minutes to target."

The computer set, Bob moved forward to the bombsight to get his first close up look at Berlin.

5

F for Freddy was now level at 18,000 feet on the bombing run. Bob, lying prone on the padded cushion, pushed his intercom leads to one side and instructed, "Bomb doors open, master switch on, bombs fused and selected, skipper."

"Bomb doors open, master switch on, bombs fused and selected," repeated Doug.

Bob noticed a change in the noise of the airflow as Doug opened the bomb doors and the air entered the bomb bay on the other side of the bulkhead behind him. Once again he checked that the sixteen arming switches on the wall to his right were all set correctly. Then he looked through his bombsight and adjusted it for brightness. He was ready and now he took his first real close look at the target. The view was awesome. To the right a blue tinted searchlight swept back and forth while behind it a dozen more, with whiter looking beams carried out their own search. In the distance many more searchlights swept the sky, too many to count. White bursts of flak seemed to fill his view while the closer bursts looked more yellow, and the very close once had a centre of fiery red. Dead ahead yellow markers hung in the air low over the aiming point. They burned brilliantly and a cascade of yellow sparks showered down from them like a golden waterfall of fire. They lit a large area of the city and in the centre of these markers two green TIs marked the aiming point. He looked back through the sight into the darkness; a bump shook the aircraft and rattled the internal fittings. Pushing the spring-loaded lever forward the bombsight's sword moved ahead of the Lancaster and appeared to the right of the green TIs.

"Two minutes to target," called Ron.

"Bomb doors fully open," said Harry who had checked visually through one of the inspection hatches.

"Roger, I've got the markers," replied Bob. The glow from the yellow markers now provided enough light to make out the shapes of buildings on the ground ahead of them. Bob took hold of the bomb release in his right hand. It was a small cylindrical piece of Bakelite about the diameter of a marker pen but not as long. It had a single button at the end which, when pressed, would send an electric current to the various bomb stations in a preset order and at preset intervals, releasing the bombs. From the other end of the bomb release came a flex connecting it to the aircraft and Bob made sure it wouldn't snag on anything. Staring through the sight Bob tried to visualise the target from the maps and photographs at the briefing but he didn't recognise anything and a haze of smoke or mist was obscuring the details of the ground. The first green TI was still to the left of the sword, moving slowly down towards the hilt. He still didn't recognise anything. He started to worry. It was all up to him now and nobody could help him. Looking down he could make out the faint shapes of buildings below him but, in the haze, they all looked the same. He looked up. The green TI was still slightly to the left and still burning brightly, giving him confidence. If all else failed he would bomb the marker. He turned the rotary switch on his oxygen mask to "on" and left it there.

"Left, left." The left commands were always repeated whereas the right commands weren't, so the pilot would know which way to turn even if he didn't hear what the words were. He felt the Lancaster respond as Doug followed his instructions and the nose slowly moved left.

"Steady!" The green TI was now dead on the blade of the sword and the steady command was long and drawn out to make it distinctive. The Lancaster steadied on its new course straight towards the TI. A large white flash went off under the marker, followed immediately by a yellow flash and a ripple of small yellow and red flashes. Bob released the spring-loaded handle to see how far they had to go to the release point. He could still not see the green marker through the sight and he looked up again. Another white flash was followed by yellow and reds. Other aircraft were bombing. The yellow flash was the exploding Cookie, the ripple of small yellows and reds being the incendiaries.

Bob still didn't recognise anything and the green TI was now entering the top of his sight. He would have to bomb the marker, after all that was what it was there for. If it was in the wrong place that wasn't his fault. It had been dropped by someone with far more experience than him. He was disappointed because he had never had difficulty identifying a target before and he had hoped to ensure that his bombs hit the factory fair and square. The green marker was again slightly to the left of the trace and midway to the cross bar.

"Left, left…Steady!" brought it back to the centre. The smoke from the city's factories and the previous explosions drifted across his field of view, obscuring it further. There was another white flash and a split second later a yellow flash. This time the blast wave from the exploding Cookie sent ripples out through the smoke in concentric circles, like the ripples from a stone thrown into a pond. The green marker was now almost at the hilt crosspiece and now slightly right of the sword blade.

"Right….Steady!" He could hear his breathing through his earphones, magnified by his open microphone and he sounded like he had just run a race. He still didn't recognise anything. The green marker reached the hilt of the sword.

"Bombs away!" he shouted as he jabbed his thumb hard down on the button. "Hold her steady for the photoflash." F for Freddy reared upwards as it was freed of the 10,360-pound weight of the bombs and Doug felt he was now fighting to hold the aircraft down.

The photoflash was a small bomb shaped object designed to fall with the same ballistics as the bombs and explode with a brilliant white flash 4,000 feet above the target. At the same time as the bombs were dropped a timer was automatically started in the aircraft and when the photoflash was due to go off a camera pointing vertically downwards took eight photographs in quick succession and, hopefully, the photoflash would register in one of them. Using these photographs Intelligence Officers could assess where every bomb load fell. It was supposed to help in assessing the damage to the target and give an insight into how concentrated the raid had been. Cynics said it was to ensure the crews didn't just drop their bombs anywhere and head for home.

They had been flying straight and level now for some time on their bomb run and the seconds waiting for the photoflash seemed like hours. The bombs were falling at about 180 mph or 3 miles a minute towards their target 18,000 feet below. They could expect to see their photoflash about forty-seven seconds after bomb release. It was the longest forty-seven seconds of Bob's life.

18,000 feet below F for Freddy twenty people were huddled together in the cellar of their tenement building, listening to the bombs whistling as they hurtled down. It was becoming a regular occurrence, sitting close together in the cold damp basement, not knowing if the shivering was caused by the cold or the fear. The children had not been scared during the first few raids and it had been an adventure for them. Now the novelty had worn off and after a few bombs had landed close by on previous raids, they had seen at first hand the flattened buildings and the empty desks at school the next day. Now they were as scared as the adults. They sat quietly, ears straining, trying to assess how close the next bomb would be by its scream. Looking up at the cellar ceiling, as if it was possible to see through it, looking for the destruction from above that they could not escape even if they could see it coming.

One group of four, sitting in the corner of the cellar huddled under a blanket, consisted of a mother, her two children and their grandfather. They sat on some old tea chests covered with sacking. The father was away in the army. The grandfather, a farmer, normally lived in the country on the German French border near Strasburg. He had come to Berlin to try to persuade his daughter to leave the city and come to live with him where it was safe. But while she hated the bombing and was scared for the safety of her children, this was her home and she had a good job in the factory across the road.

The whistling of the first bomb had been incredibly loud and the explosion, when it came, was louder than anything they had heard before. The lights went out and people screamed. The children were crying and the mothers were trying to comfort them through their own tears. The only men present were too old for the military. They struggled with their medley of emotions, ranging from fear, to rage, to frustrated impotence. Eventually someone lit a hurricane lamp and the yellow glow spread round the cellar. More bombs had dropped, all very close and the hurricane lamp swung to and fro as the cellar shook. Dust fell from the ceiling with every impact and the young mother and her children flinched with every shock wave. The grandfather had seen it all before in the trenches of the First World War, but he never thought he would see it again, not in Berlin. When he was a soldier he had been scared but he had been with his comrades. Now it was women and children in the front line and that made him angry. He knew that the waiting for the barrage to end had been the worst part. Once the barrage had lifted and they ran from their bunker to the trench fire step it was their turn to hit back. But this time there would be no hitting back and the frustration was killing him.

His little granddaughter beside him was shivering uncontrollably and he decided to get her another blanket. His daughter tried to stop him going but he couldn't sit there any longer. He made his way to the top of the cellar steps and opened the door. The windows either side of the door to the building were shattered and the door had been blown open. His daughter's apartment was on the floor above. He was fifty-five years old, but a life on a farm made him as lean, fit and strong as men half his age. He coiled his six-foot frame like a sprinter on the blocks ready to make a dash for it. His grey hair was now a distant memory. He was back in France about to run to his Maxim gun and mow down some lines of Tommies. Then he heard it, a faint whistle, hardly audible over the other explosions. This one was going to be very close. For a second he froze, unsure what to do. Then he slammed the cellar door shut in front of him and turned to shout a warning to the people in the cellar.

F for Freddy's Cookie landed in the road outside the building and exploded on impact. The blast first blew out the last remaining fragments of glass from the windows, then the front door was torn from its hinges and hurled up the hall. Next the front wall of the building buckled inwards, bricks flying at hundreds of miles per hour punched through interior walls and the whole front of the building crumbled. The weight of the upper floors crashed down like a house of cards, flattening everything underneath.

One of the first pieces of glass to be blown into the building was a large razor edged shard which flew straight through the cellar door and neatly severed the grandfather's left hand at the wrist. A split second later half a dozen bricks beat down the cellar door knocking him backwards down the stairs. The floor above collapsed and the staircase above the one he was on crashed down pinning him, immobile and trapped, but still conscious.

In the cellar, the floor joists gave way under the impact of the falling building. The beam above the mother dropped vertically hitting her square on the head and killing her instantly. The children were missed by the beams and scooped off the tea chests onto the floor by the falling debris. Joists fell onto the tea chests crushing them to half their original height, but leaving enough space for the two terrified children to cower trapped beneath. The hurricane lamp had fallen to the floor and smashed. The wick ignited the oil which ran over the cellar floor.

Amid the choking clouds of brick and cement dust the burning oil found its way to where the two children lay setting fire to the tea chests, blankets and sacking. The grandfather listened helplessly to their screams as they burnt to death.

Aboard F for Freddy Bob heard the shutter of the F24 camera click, from its position behind the mark 14 bombing computer in the rear of his compartment.

"Photoflash fired, skipper."

"Roger, let's get out of here."

F for Freddy banked sharply to port.

"New course three one zero compass," said Ron, from behind his curtain. As they turned through 140 degrees to head out of the target area they looked back at the aiming point. More green target indicators were hanging low over the target and there were flashes from large bombs going off every few seconds. Large areas were burning. These were scattered around the green target indicators and more incendiaries sparkled on the ground.

A bomber was running into the target, coned by a dozen searchlight beams. It was more than three miles away and looked like a small silver moth held in a torch beam. The bomber was weaving around trying to escape, but the weaving was having no effect and the searchlights held it solidly. Flak sparkled all over the city, but around the coned bomber it was intense. Bob stared at the unfortunate aircraft and urged it to do something to break free of the lights but in the back of his mind he was thinking, thank God it's not us. While the lights were busy with that bomber, they wouldn't be looking for F for Freddy. The coned aircraft was now on fire and in a dive. The flames weren't visible in the glare of the lights, but the dark smoke coming from the bomber was. Yet another bomber would not be making it home. As its dive steepened some lights failed to hold on to it, but most were stuck like glue and held on until the Lancaster was in a vertical dive, low over the city with no chance of recovering. Then one by one they snapped out to reposition before switching back on again and starting another search. As the last light went out Bob caught a glimpse of the flames from the bomber before they disappeared in a flash as the aircraft hit the ground.

Bob dragged his eyes back out to the front and looking ahead was surprised to see how far they still had to go to get out of the flak. Berlin was a massive city and they would be over it for a long time. Now his job was done he noticed for the first time the sound of shrapnel rattling like hail on the skin of their aircraft and how the close bursts of flak left white clouds hanging in the air after their flash had disappeared. The flak did seem less intense now and they were obviously leaving the worst of it behind, but there was still the occasional jolt, which was very unnerving and stopped him from relaxing at all. Doug was still weaving them from side to side, but now it was less regular and involved an up and down movement as well. It was to make them a more difficult target for any radar guided guns and it would certainly have made it impossible for them to predict ahead, but it was also very nausea-inducing. They seemed to be gradually climbing and Bob guessed that Doug was trying to get them back to 20,000 feet.

Jimmy was still pushing out bundles of window as fast as he could and Bob started to help him open the packets. The large pile of window parcels was much smaller. Jimmy had obviously been working overtime to get rid of them so quickly.

By the time they reached the outskirts of Berlin F for Freddy, free of its bombs, had made it up to 23,000 feet and the flak fell away behind them. They only had twenty or so parcels of window left when they reached the yellow markers telling them to stop dropping at maximum rate. This should be enough to get them to the coast and once again Bob's mind allowed him to think of the cold and he climbed back into the front turret.

"Radio operator to pilot and bomb aimer, bomb doors fully closed, no hang ups and from what I can see all the fusing links are still aboard." Harry had again moved from his compartment to one of the inspection hatches to look into the bomb bay and visually inspect it with his torch. Sometimes the bomb bay doors would not close properly due to ice forming on them, or bombs would hang up inside the aircraft. This could also be due to ice forming on the dropping gear or electrical failure or even the bomb being attached to its carrier too tightly. Whatever the reason a hung up bomb was a problem that was best got rid of. Bob was particularly glad to hear that the fusing links were still aboard as these were the first things the armourers checked when the aircraft got back. If any were missing and there were no electrical problems on the aircraft, it meant the bomb aimer had dropped an unarmed bomb and he could expect a one-way interview with the Bombing Leader.

Ten minutes after they left Berlin behind Nigel leaned close to Doug's ear and shouted, "If I remember correctly, if you lower the nose to get an indicated airspeed of 200 mph you'll have a rate of descent of about 500 feet per minute and our true airspeed in the descent will average about 240 mph. So we'll reach the coast in thirty-six minutes at 5,000 feet and well ahead of anyone else!"

"Why would we want to race ahead of the rest of the bomber stream?"

"To get back before the Station Commander and the Wingco, old boy. Unless you want to be court-martialled of course?"

"Oh God, yes," exclaimed Doug, having quite forgotten that Nigel was a stowaway. He lowered the nose and without bringing the throttles back the speed soon built up to 200 mph in a shallow dive.

"Better tell your navigator the plan, old boy, or you'll screw up all his ETAs and I get the feeling he's not a tolerant sort of person!"

Doug told Ron the plan. Damn! thought Ron from behind his curtain. He had noticed the increase in speed, from the sound of the slipstream passing the outside of the fuselage and checked it on his own airspeed indicator. While the indicated airspeed would stay constant at 200 mph, the true airspeed would change constantly as they descended and the pressure changed. At high level they would be doing 280 mph true airspeed, while at 5,000 feet they would be doing 210 mph. How the hell was he supposed to work out ETAs at any ground features or even the coast with a constantly changing speed? Damn it! he thought again. We have a plan and we should stick to it. Well, damn the ETA at the coast. I'll pick up a fix at the coast and start navigating again from there. GEE will start working again as we get closer to England anyway.

Racing ahead of the bomber stream was not a particularly wise thing to do but it didn't increase the risk by much and if it meant they avoided the wrath of the Wingco it would be worth it. They reached the coast thirty-six minutes later at 5,000 feet as Nigel had said they would, well ahead of the next bombers and headed west. Now they were below 10,000 feet they came off oxygen and rubbed their faces where the masks had made red lines on their cheeks. The night was still very dark and no light reflected from the water below them. Jimmy opened a thermos flask of coffee and offered a cup to Doug who sipped it quickly, soon emptying the cup and giving his full attention back to flying the aircraft. Nigel also drank his quickly. Jimmy on the other hand had a mouthful, then took a good look around before taking another drink, only to find it was already cold, emphasizing to him just how cold it was inside the aircraft.

They started to relax. They were nearly home, out of range of any flak and any night fighters would surely be in among the bomber stream not stooging around over the North Sea looking for solitary bombers. However, George and Alex still swept the black skies. They were the coldest people aboard; it was always colder in the turrets than in the fuselage. They had no coffee. There was no room in their confined spaces and yet they were still the most alert people on board.

Eventually Ron reported GEE working again, and in a couple of minutes, he had fixed their position and worked out an ETA of twenty minutes to the coast.

"Pilot to radio operator, make sure we have the correct colours of the day ready," said Doug as he switched on the IFF which would identify them to British radars.

"Roger." Harry had already sorted the coloured flares but he checked them again anyway.

"English coast ahead," called Bob.

They crossed the coast south of the Humber estuary and headed two two zero degrees straight for Metheringham. The cloud was lower and denser now but, at 5,000 feet, they were still well below it and should have no trouble finding their way home. Soon Bob saw the flashing identification beacon of an airfield, its red light repeating two Morse letters over and over, BK, BK, BK, Binbrook. He had memorised most of the station identification beacon signals. He also carried a crib sheet in case he needed it. He called the station beacons by their station names as he spotted them. Kelstern, Ludford Magna. They were both Lancaster bases. Then he saw the beacon of Metheringham's sister airfield at

Woodhall Spa and, as they crossed the River Witham, he spotted the flashing MN of Metheringham.

Doug selected RT. "Coffee Stall, Coffee Stall, this is Hadnone F for Freddy, Hadnone F for Freddy. We have the airfield in sight and request permission to land."

"Hadnone F for Freddy, Hadnone F for Freddy, Coffee Stall answering. You are clear to land. Runway two zero left hand, QFE nine nine six. The circuit is clear."

"Hadnone F for Freddy, clear to land runway two zero left hand QFE nine nine six."

They had been in a slow descent from when they passed Ludford Magna and were now at 2,000 feet but they were still too high to make a straight in approach. Doug flew them through Metheringham's overhead and did a wide circuit of the airfield as they let down. During this time Bob left the nose and squeezed through the cockpit to his usual landing position behind the main spar. Without a bomb load and with little fuel remaining if they did crash on landing, there was a fair chance of surviving it, especially if you were behind the main spar, not in the nose. On his way through the cockpit, he was surprised to see the Squadron Adjutant standing behind Doug's seat. Bob and the two gunners had no idea that Nigel was on board because he hadn't spoken on the intercom.

No other aircraft had yet called in asking for permission to land so they were still probably well ahead of the rest of the returning Squadron. Doug had switched on the navigation lights and was making a wide left hand approach. All the pre-landing checks were complete. The approach looked perfect. They were again cleared to land by the green Aldis lamp from the runway caravan. The two rows of white runway lights slowly moved down the windscreen and as they flew low over the threshold he cut the throttles. Bob, Harry and Ron were now good at judging the stage of the approach by the noise of the engines. They were at a constant low speed in the early stages of the approach with the occasional small adjustment as the aircraft went slightly high or low. As they got closer to touchdown, the throttle adjustments became more frequent and the worse the approach, the more adjustments. This sounded like a good approach. Then the relative quiet as the throttles were cut just before touchdown, the aircraft floating, losing speed, until it no longer had the speed to fly and it started to sink. The object of the exercise was for the aircraft to lose flying speed with the wheels just above the ground and sink the last few feet until the wheels touched. With no flying speed left the aircraft couldn't bounce back into the air and all that remained to be done was keep it straight and stop it, which was a feat in itself on some aircraft types. Bob heard the engines cut and felt them float, then start to sink, followed by a bump and a short screech of tyres. Probably the best landing Doug's ever done at night, he thought.

"Oh bloody well done, old boy!" shouted Nigel. "I wish the Wingco could do that. Some of his landings will have your teeth out!"

Doug let F for Freddy run on down the runway and only needed the slightest of touches on the brakes to bring down the speed before entering the taxiway. The blue taxiway lights moved past slowly. Doug suddenly felt very tired. Bob came back to the cockpit and squeezed in behind Jimmy, beside Nigel. As they approached their dispersal they saw two dim torchlights held by the marshaller who guided them in. The engines were shut down, the wheels chocked and the brakes released. Bob retrieved his parachute and flight bag from the nose and made his way back past Jimmy and Doug who were still shutting down the aircraft. His head spun and his ears buzzed in the silence. He felt cold and stiff. Every move was an effort and he was dizzy and clumsy as he negotiated the obstacle course on the way to the rear entrance.

Emerging into the cold night air he could see the dark silhouettes of Harry, Alex and George and the red glow of their cigarettes lighting their hands and faces.

"Well?" asked George. "After all that, did we hit anything?"

"Yes! We hit the bull's-eye, you cheeky Pommie bastard!" replied Bob, pulling his flying helmet and gloves off as if there could have ever been any doubt.

"By that I suppose you mean Berlin. A city about 10 miles across." He smiled as he offered Bob a cigarette.

"By that I mean the bloody factory. Anyway did you hit that fighter?"

"He wasn't 10 miles across," countered George evasively.

"And he was nae 3 miles away either!" chipped in Alex.

"Alright!" George acknowledged, knowing he was on a loser, "but you didn't hit him either!"

"Christ!" exclaimed Bob, after his first draw of the cigarette. "What the hell is that?"

"Capstan, extra strong," replied George. "They clear your tubes."

"They'll rip your bloody lungs out!"

He choked as they all laughed.

Doug and Jimmy joined them and Doug noticed Ron standing by himself at the tail with his pipe. George offered them both a cigarette. Doug refused and Jimmy said he would smoke his own having been caught out by George's cigarettes before.

"It's the only reason he buys them," said Harry. "So nobody else will smoke them. The tight northern git."

"Is it my fault you Jessies can't take a man's cigarette?"

"Where's the Adj?" asked Doug.

"He took off in his car as if his arse was on fire as soon as we stopped," said Harry.

Doug knew Nigel was racing to get out of his flying kit and back into his uniform before the Wingco and the Station Commander got back.

"Look, chaps, if anyone asks, the Adj wasn't with us, alright?" They all agreed.

Sergeant Green walked up. "Any problems, sir?"

"None from our point of view, was there Jimmy?" answered Doug.

"No, sir."

Doug turned to the rest of the crew. "What about you chaps?"

They all shook their heads, except Harry. "We lost the HF trailing aerial."

"Forgot to wind it in before landing, did you?" asked the engineer.

"No! I think it was stolen by a Jerry fighter."

"If you say so," said the tired sergeant sceptically.

"Did you have any problems with the aircraft, Ron?" Doug called to the navigator trying to include him in with the rest of the crew.

"No, it was all fine," Ron replied coming a few steps closer but still standing apart from the rest. Ron was not at all sure of himself at the moment. His hands and knees were shaking. He was very glad to be back. He had been scared over enemy territory. Every time the gunners reported another bomber going down, he felt the fear increase. But the thing that had scared him most had been that he would get lost and not be able to find the way back to Metheringham. Now they were safe, warm waves of relief washed over him and he felt drained. His stomach was turning over and he thought he might be sick. While he would have liked to be closer to the crew, he was afraid they would see him shaking and he was determined not to show any weakness in front of the sergeants.

"Excellent, that's what we like to hear. The fewer the faults, the earlier to bed and there's only the one bit of damage that I can see. We'll check her over properly in daylight tomorrow."

"Damage, sarge?" asked Doug in surprise.

"Yes, sir. A lump of flak most probably, in the fuselage between the mid-upper and tail turrets."

They all walked around the tail and Sergeant Green shone his torch on the jagged-edged fist-sized hole, high up on the side of the fuselage. "It went in at an upward angle and came out through the roof," he explained. "But it didn't hit anything vital and it won't take us long to fix."

"Thanks, sarge, we'll see you tomorrow then," said Doug noticing the silhouette of Sally's truck waiting by the edge of the dispersal, not wanting to prolong the moment as all his crew were staring at the flak hole, the reality of their night's work having been brought much closer. He was also aware that it was after one in the morning and the sergeant and his ground crew could not go to bed until they had completed the aircraft's after flight checks. They would then be up again first thing in the morning to repair the damage and get it ready for its next flight.

Sally stood by the rear of her truck and saluted as the crew walked up. "Good trip, sir?" Her teeth showed in the dark as she smiled broadly.

"Yes, thanks, Sally," Doug said.

"Here you are, sarge." She handed an envelope to George as the crew climbed aboard. Then Doug helped her raise the tailboard. She had found out long ago that some members of a tired crew could not climb over the raised tailboard after a trip. So she always lowered it after an Op to save anyone from embarrassment.

Once they were on their way back to the crew room Sally started her own post flight analysis.

"Anything exciting happen, sir?" she asked without taking her eyes off the blue lights on the edge of the taxiway.

"Well," Doug paused. Should he say anything and if so what? He was still so keyed up he was bursting to talk to someone about it and Ron would be no good when they got back to their accommodation. Besides, Sally knew everything anyway but he would play it calmly. He didn't want to be thought of as a lineshooter. "We got attacked by a fighter on our way to the target."

"Oh, what sort?" asked Sally with great interest.

Doug felt slightly embarrassed. "Err I'm not sure, I didn't see it." He realised how little he knew about the incident that had nearly killed him but Sally soon restored his confidence.

"That's usually the case, sir. The pilot's too busy flying the aircraft to look for the fighter."

"Yes and the night was very dark." Doug heard a Lancaster making its approach to land.

"He must have got pretty close then?" The dark shape and red and green navigation lights sank towards the runway where the tyres screeched.

"Yes."

Doug knew the fighter had been close, but he had no idea how close and he was starting to dread the official interrogation ahead of them. After many more questions, few of which Doug could answer with any certainty, they arrived at the crew room and got rid of their flying kit, parachutes, harnesses, life jackets and empty thermos flasks. Outside the sound of a procession of returning Lancasters filled the air. Then, considerably lighter, they went to the interrogation room.

As they entered the hut a group of officers at the far end stopped talking and stared at them before splitting up and going to separate trestle tables. Each table had a folding wooden chair on one side of it where the officer sat and seven folding chairs the other side for the Lancaster crew. On each table was a pile of paper and a couple of ashtrays.

"Coffee?" a woman's voice asked from behind a line of three trestle tables to Doug's immediate right. The tables held three urns, 150 or so white half pint mugs and trays of sandwiches.

"Yes please," replied Doug automatically. The voice belonged to a lady in her late twenties or early thirties, wearing a tweed skirt and cream coloured cardigan. She was heavily pregnant and along with two other women of a similar age she was handing out coffee and sandwiches. The mug was hot in Doug's still cold hands and he wrapped them around it, feeling them tingle as the circulation returned. Moving into the room he was handed a large corned beef sandwich and with the sandwich in one hand and the steaming mug of coffee in the other he made his way to the first interrogation table.

As Doug and his crew sat down he took a sip of the hot coffee and was surprised to find it heavily laced with whiskey.

"Aircraft?" asked the young and pretty Section Officer WAAF.

"F for Freddy," replied Doug.

"Are all your crew present?"

"Yes."

"Did you bomb the target?"

"Yes."

"Was it clearly marked?"

Doug looked at Bob. "Yes, but it was a Paramatta with only green TIs," said Bob.

"Could you identify the target yourselves?"

"No," replied Bob truthfully, a little embarrassed. "There was a lot of smoke in the area."

"So you bombed one of the target indicators?"

"Yes." Bob was now feeling slightly defensive.

"Were there any fires in the target area?"

"I saw some explosions and there were some fires starting as we ran in to the target. But we were one of the first to bomb so there wasn't much damage to the target when we bombed."

Doug listened to all the detail Bob passed on. The aircraft's nose had hidden the target from him and he had no idea about where they had bombed. All the while the WAAF scribbled notes on one of the interrogation forms.

"What was the flak like on the way to the target?"

"Light," replied Doug. "None of it came close to us."

"There was some pretty close behind us just after we passed Munster, skipper," said George. "There wasn't much of it but it was right on our route."

"Was that when we saw that flash?" asked Doug.

"Yeah, it was right behind us. I couldn't see a thing for ages."

"Sounds like a mobile flak battery," said the WAAF. "Did you log its position?"

Ron pulled his log sheet from his flight bag and handed it to her pointing out the position.

"Good. What about the flak over the target?"

"Heavy," said Doug, aware that he had nothing to compare it with.

"And on the route home?"

"Light and none came close."

"Did you see any aircraft shot down?"

"Yes," said Doug, Bob, Alex and George simultaneously.

92

"Do you have their positions?"

"There in the log," replied Ron, sounding very tired and a little impatient.

"Did you see any fighters?"

"Bloody right we did!" exclaimed Alex.

"What type?"

"Messerschmitt 110."

"Did he attack you?"

"He damn well tried!" Alex was reliving the moment in his mind and his body was as keyed up as it had been during the actual attack.

"How did he make his approach?"

"We spotted him on Fishpond, low in our port quarter at about 100 yards," interrupted Harry sounding slightly excited.

"Then Ah spotted him as we weaved to port and Ah called for a corkscrew port!"

"Did you fire at him?"

"Bloody right Ah did!" Alex remembered himself as George elbowed him in the ribs. "Sorry, ma'am."

"Did you hit him?" she smiled.

"Ah might have done."

"If you did I'm a Dutchman," said George.

"Well if Ah didn't, Ah certainly got closer to him than you did."

"You fired as well?" asked the WAAF looking at George.

"Yeah, when we broke towards him he was thrown out of position in our 7 o'clock and too close to bring his guns to bear. So he broke away to his right, close past our tail."

"And that's when you fired?"

"Yeah and missed by miles," laughed Alex.

"How close was he?"

George felt his face start to colour and made a conscious effort to try and stop it.

"About 10 yards," he said looking down. The rest of the crew exploded with laughter. "Look!" he said glaring at them, "he was so bloody close I didn't know whether to shoot or shake hands! I thought he was going to chop the sodding turret off!"

"Never mind, George," said Doug, realizing the terror the gunner must have felt as the fighter nearly hit him. "It would have been a hell of a shot to hit anything with us in that corkscrew."

"Was that the only attack?"

"Yes."

"Did you see anyone else attacked?"

"The aircraft shot down at the Dutch coast was shot down by a fighter. He fired two or three bursts from below and behind, hitting the bomber in the port wing," said Doug.

"And he dropped flares as he went down and spread target indicators on the ground when he crashed," added Bob. The WAAF wrote it all down then thanked them and turned them over to the next table, the RDF or Radio Direction Finding specialist.

The RDF specialist was a middle-aged flight lieutenant in the Volunteer Reserve and he would ask them about all aspects of the electronic equipment aboard the aircraft. By now they had all finished their sandwiches and most of their coffee and, with the exception of Doug, they were all smoking.

"Aircraft?"

"F for Freddy," said Doug, again.

"Did you have any problems with any of the electronic equipment?"

"We lost the HF trailing aerial to some thieving Jerry," said Harry.

The humourless RDF man stared at him blankly.

"We think it was pulled off by a night fighter," explained Doug.

"Oh, and how did the WT and RT behave until you lost the HF aerial?"

"No problems," replied Harry. They were all tired and Harry had thought some humour would help, but the RDF man was not interested so it was best to get the debrief over as soon as possible and get to bed.

"Did H2S give good returns?"

"Yes," replied Ron succinctly.

"Could you navigate by them?"

"We got back, didn't we?" Ron's hands and knees had stopped shaking but he still felt sick and wanted to get out into the fresh air again as soon as possible.

The RDF man looked at Ron like a teacher would look at an unruly child that was trying his patience.

"What about in the target area?"

"As usual the built-up area stood out and so did rivers and lakes."

"Was this a help?"

"No."

"Why not?"

"Because the target was in the middle of a built up area 10 miles across," Ron said sarcastically.

The RDF man sighed. "What about GEE then? At what range did it stop being effective?"

"I saw jamming on it before we got to the Dutch coast and by the time we were fifty miles over the coast it was completely unusable."

"Did Fishpond work?"

"Yes," said Harry, retelling the story of the night fighter.

The RDF man seemed pleased with that. "Was the window effective?"

"How would we know?" asked Doug.

"Did any searchlights come close to you or cone you?"

"No."

"Then it was probably effective," replied the RDF man handing them over to the next table.

Between tables they were intercepted by the station padre, a slim six-foot middle-aged flight lieutenant with grey hair and a slight stoop. He wore a dog collar under his number one uniform and held the biggest teapot Doug had ever seen.

"Top up, gentlemen?" he asked. They all accepted and Doug was amazed that this too was heavily laced with whiskey.

"Aircraft?"

"F for Freddy," said Doug for the third time.

This was the Engineering Officer's table and the engineer was again a middle-aged flight lieutenant but this one was a regular and had probably worked his way up through the ranks.

"Did you have any problems with the aircraft?"

"No," replied Doug.

"Flight instruments alright?"

"Yes."

"Engines?"

"Fine."

"Fuel?"

"No problems."

"Do you have your fuel log?"

Jimmy handed it over.

"Any damage?"

"One piece of flak damage between the mid-upper turret and the tail but it caused no problems. Our ground crew say it won't take long to fix."

"Any other problems at all, from anyone?" he said looking around all of the crew.

"I've always wanted to be taller," said Harry.

The Engineering Officer smiled, "Alright, off you go then."

As they got up to leave they became aware that the room was now full of other crews following them around the room from table to table. All the tables were in use and there were other crews standing by the doorway waiting their turn to be questioned. The Station Commander was one of them and he stood talking to the pregnant woman who had given Doug his coffee. This turned out to be his wife; she always gave out drinks and sandwiches to the returning crews, often waiting well into the early hours, until there was no more hope of a crew returning.

Wing Commander Baxter also stood near the door talking to Nigel, who was now in his number one blue uniform with his greatcoat and scarf over the top. As Doug and his crew moved past them to leave, he turned to Doug.

"Well then, young Jackson, you got back early."

"Yes, sir."

"Didn't have any problems, did you?"

"No, sir." Doug felt more nervous talking to the Wing Commander than flying over Germany. He felt that Baxter could see straight through him and he deliberately kept his answers short, which only made him seem more guilty.

"Did you find the target alright?"

"Yes, sir."

"Excellent! Found the target and found their way back, what more do you want. You see, Nigel, you old woman, I knew they could do it."

"Ah, Jackson! Pleased to meet you at last," boomed the Station Commander. "Well done on completing your first Op. It's a pity you were thrown in at the deep end but you don't seem to have suffered from it." McKechnie's brown eyes seemed to penetrate straight through Doug, but his face was smiling warmly, his moustache flattened where it had been trapped under his oxygen mask. "Normally we would have flown you with another crew and then Wing Commander Baxter or myself would have flown with you on your first Op as a crew. But losing the aircraft last night and being two pilots short because of the flu bug that's going around at the moment, we were a bit strapped." He grinned. "But you probably wouldn't have wanted us along with you anyway." Doug wasn't sure what to say and mumbled something about always being interested in any advice. "Well, Jackson, the Wing Commander's and my doors are always open if you need us. Now off you go and get a good night's sleep and well done, chaps."

"Thank you, and goodnight, sir," said Doug, grateful that they had got away without the Wing Commander discovering their unauthorised passenger. He hurried off into the night as the Station Commander returned to his wife and the Wing Commander turned back to Nigel.

"So how did they really get on, Adj?" asked Baxter, staring Nigel straight in the eye.

"Sir?" asked Nigel innocently.

"Don't give me that, Forrester, you old rogue! I can still see the marks from your oxygen mask on your cheeks! I knew you didn't agree with them being sent on Ops so soon but I didn't expect you to go swanning off around Germany nursemaiding them!"

Nigel knew the game was up, but what the hell. He was a damn good Adj and he had been around long enough to know that so long as he held his head a little and made remorseful noises he would get away with no more than a slap on the wrist.

"Well, actually, sir, they weren't bad. They're still as green as grass of course but I would say they're slightly better than average. Jackson's not at all a bad pilot and his navigator's pretty hot too. In fact individually they're all fine but I think they still need more time to develop as a team."

"I doubt very much that they'll get the time to develop. I think we'll probably have at least another two maximum efforts this week before the moon gets too full and you are not! repeat not! to go with them, is that clear?"

"Yes, sir," replied Nigel, looking suitably chastised. He had no intention of flying with them again anyway, but hopefully he had given them the one or two vital pointers that Doug would have normally picked up on his familiarisation trip with an experienced crew. "And for the record, sir, Jackson had no idea I was aboard until after we were airborne."

"I thought as much which is why I didn't say anything to him. But you really pushed your luck this time, Nigel, and you'd better not do it again."

"No, sir," said Nigel giving his best guilty look and deciding to keep his head down for a while.

Back in their respective Nissen huts the sergeants were all soon fast asleep and didn't even stir when Digger and his crew came in. Doug and Ron were about to turn off the lights when Charlie and Taffy came in.

"You made it back then?" said Charlie cheerfully as he got ready for bed.

"No problem," answered Doug.

"Well the first one's the worst, so congratulations. Did you have a good trip?"

"Yes, we think we hit the target and we only got a small hole in the fuselage near the tail."

"Good show. We nearly got shot down by another Lanc before we got anywhere near the enemy coast!"

"What?" asked Doug incredulously.

"Oh yes!" exclaimed Charlie. "Some idiot put a dozen tracer rounds over our nose just north of Cromer. It quite spoilt my night I can tell you. It's about the closest we've come to getting shot down."

"Did you see who did it?"

"If I had we'd have damn well fired back. It's dangerous enough out there with the Jerries about without our own chaps taking pot shots at us! Good night, chaps," and with that he turned out the lights.

6

Jimmy was suddenly aware that he was cold. His feet were like two lumps of ice and the cold air entering his lungs was damp and stale. He became aware of noises behind him as people moved around and opened his eyes. All he could see in the gloom was the magnolia painted brick wall six inches in front of him. He had the end bed in the billet and, as the door was by his feet, this was probably why they were so cold. He had no idea what time it was but light was shining down the wall from behind the blackout curtain so it must be after reveille. Rolling over he noticed that his greatcoat had fallen off his bed onto the floor. George, in the next bed, was reaching onto a chair next to the bed for his cigarettes and lighter. Sitting up George lit his lethally strong cigarette and took a long draw, holding the smoke deep in his lungs. His face slowly went deep purple before exploding in a fit of coughing. Opening his watery eyes he blinked away the tears, while his face started to return to its normal colour. He looked over at Jimmy and smiled.

"That's better."

"I'm surprised you don't lose your teeth doing that."

"Just clearing the tubes, it's good for the lungs."

Jimmy noticed a corporal moving up the row of beds on the other side of the billet, shaking each occupant and realised that he too must have been shaken awake but he couldn't remember it.

"What time is it?"

George looked at his watch, tilting it to catch the light from under the blackout curtain. "Just after ten."

The corporal shook Harry in the bed opposite Jimmy's. Harry sat up with a start and looked around with a puzzled expression on his face until realization dawned and he relaxed.

"Report to the Squadron Office for eleven thirty," said the corporal in a monotone voice before opening the hut door and leaving.

"Aw shit!" said an Australian voice from the far end of the hut.

"What?" asked George, looking down the hut towards the owner of the voice.

"That, me little green mate, means Ops are on again tonight and we're all flying," replied Digger. "Right you lot! UP!" He scanned his crew, got out of bed and started to get dressed.

"I suppose we should move as well," said George, throwing off his blankets and swinging his feet, still in his heavy aircrew socks, over the side of the bed. He took another draw of his cigarette, coughed and started to dress. Jimmy and the rest of the crew followed suit.

The concrete floor was so cold it hurt to stand on in bare feet, so Jimmy stood on his fallen greatcoat.

"Good idea," said George nodding at the coat.

When he'd finished putting on his working blue battledress, Jimmy picked up his wash kit and followed the stream of people filing out to the ablutions. It was a dull and overcast day. While it didn't look like rain, the wind had picked up making it very cold. The cloud cover had prevented a hard frost and the ground, which had been frozen when they went to bed, was now thawing and starting to give under foot. By midday they would be living in a sea of mud and movement would be confined to tarmac roads and duckboards.

At the ablution block a small crowd of men stood in the doorway.

"What's up?" Jimmy asked George who had arrived just before him.

"Pipes are all frozen."

"I don't believe this bloody place!" said Digger, emerging from the doorway. "This is the fourth time in a week!"

While washing was out of the question, most of them visited the block to relieve their bursting bladders before returning to the billet to collect their greatcoats and cycle to the sergeants' mess for breakfast.

Outside the mess a mass of bicycles leaned against the side of the building while inside the queue for breakfast stretched around two walls.

"This is going to take ages," complained Harry.

"This whole bloody place is a dump! We freeze in the air. We freeze on the ground. We can't get washed, we can't get fed and we spend more time cycling than doing anything else," said Bob.

"Bet yer glad ya travelled halfway round the world to help them, aren't ya, mate?" said an Australian voice from behind them.

"Well, we're very grateful," replied Harry.

"We need to beat the rush," said George. "Tomorrow we'll come straight here and sort out washing later."

Although the queue was long it moved quickly and they soon got served. One rasher of cremated bacon, one spoonful of something yellow, which was probably powdered egg mix, one spoonful of beans and a dry slice of bread. All served by miserable and surly looking cooks. George dipped his bread in the bacon fat in the bottom of the tray, which held the rashers.

"Get out of it!" yelled the sergeant chef, swinging at George's hand with a serving spoon, but missing.

"Do they train you lot to be this miserable or do you practise?" asked George.

They sat in their group of five to eat the meagre breakfast and they all agreed that the best part of it was the mug of tea. This they savoured and warmed their hands on while Alex took delight in telling them that it was laced with bromide to "Curb your natural urges."

"If there was enough bromide in it to curb your natural urges it would be solid," said Harry.

"I have a normal appetite for my race. It's you Sassenachs that can't keep up."

"Bollocks!" said George. "You've taken it upon yerself to repopulate the Highlands."

Outside, they extracted their bikes from the others and cycled to the Squadron Office. Other crews were waiting outside while their captains reported in. Standing just outside the door, to shelter from the wind, Jimmy could hear Digger complaining to the Squadron Adjutant about the frozen pipes and Flight Lieutenant Forrester saying he would sort it out. Jimmy didn't know how he intended to do this, other than to let nature take its course. Five minutes later Doug and Ron arrived. Doug said his good mornings while Ron was, as usual, silent. They both went inside. Wagons started to arrive and park on the side of the road opposite the Squadron Office. One of them was Sally's and she waved at them. Captains started to emerge from the office and, collecting their crews, climb aboard their crew buses to go and check their aircraft. Eventually Doug and Ron came out.

"Well, as I'm sure you guessed, we're on Ops tonight. Main brief is at 15.00, specialist briefs at 14.00. The weather's not so good and it will be dark early so they want to get us on our way while there's still some light left. There won't be time to check the aircraft between the briefs so we'll do that now. Do we have transport?"

"Sally's just arrived, skipper," replied George.

Collecting their flight bags from their crew room lockers, they climbed aboard Sally's truck. Jimmy was the last in and sat, like the others, on the wooden floor with his back against the side. The wind whipped at the canvas top and a draught went down the neck of his greatcoat. Opposite him Ron stared out of the back of the wagon, avoiding eye contact. As the truck made its way around the perimeter track, they all sat in silence. Nobody ever relaxed around Ron and whenever he was there the atmosphere was always strained. When they arrived at the dispersal, they all got out quickly, more to escape Ron than to get on with their aircraft checks.

Sergeant Green stood in the dispersal shack doorway, cradling a large mug of tea in both his oil stained hands.

"Morning, sir," he called to Doug.

"Morning, sarge, any problems?"

"No, sir, like I said, this ones a good un. We patched up the flak damage this morning and refitted a trailing aerial. All the daily checks have been done and the 700's all ready." He stood to one side to allow them inside. The rest of F for Freddy's ground crew sat on the collection of chairs in the hut, nursing their mugs of tea while the primus stove roared under a tin kettle on the packing crate table.

"Morning, chaps," said Doug cheerily making his way to the 700. The ground crew all looked tired and half frozen. They had been up since six and working on the aircraft since seven in the freezing cold. Jimmy knew what it was like to work on cold machinery in the middle of winter in the open. He had done it often enough and these men would have been lucky to have had four hours' sleep, in a freezing cold Nissen hut. But still they all smiled and nodded at him.

The repair to the flak damage had been carried out by Leading Aircraftsman Powell, who was the airframe fitter, and checked by Sergeant Green. Both signatures were in the 700 and after a quick check that the daily inspections had also been completed and signed for Doug asked,

"It hasn't been refuelled yet?"

"No, sir," said Sergeant Green. "The bowsers haven't got to us yet but you'll have more than enough for your checks and then you'll have full tanks for the Op."

"Full tanks?"

"Yes, sir, full tanks, I got the word off the Chief earlier."

"The big city again then." Doug looked across at Jimmy, who looked a little nervous.

"Probably, sir," replied Sergeant Green.

Walking outside, Jimmy saw that the rest of the crew had quickly finished any outside checks they had to carry out and vanished inside the Lancaster out of the wind. Doug and Jimmy walked quickly to the bomber and started their external checks while Sergeant Green watched from the hut doorway. The ground crew would come out when Doug and Jimmy were aboard. There was no point in standing out in the cold wind any longer than necessary. They started the checks from the rear of the crew entry door on the starboard side near the tail. This was because that was also where they would finish the external checks, having walked right around the aircraft and they could then get straight aboard. After a quick glance at the side of the fuselage to check for signs of stress, they looked at the starboard tailplane and fin, checking leading edges and elevator and rudder hinges. Walking around the rear of the aircraft George waved at them through the Perspex from inside his turret, as they checked the tailwheel. They checked the port tail and fin the same way as the starboard then moved up the port side. The flak-damaged hole had been patched with a new sheet of metal, pop riveted into place, and although it had been painted it wasn't quite the same shade as the rest of the aircraft. Moving up to the wing root they stood directly under the trailing edge of the wing and inspected the flaps. Jimmy paid special attention to the port main wheel, looking at the tread and making sure the white line on the tyre and the line on the wheel hub lined up, showing there had been no tyre creep. Walking out under the wing to the wing tip, they checked that the engine cowlings were secure and the wing and ailerons were in good condition. Then walking back to the fuselage, below the cockpit, they checked that the protective Pitot tube cover and static vent plugs had been removed. The covers were to keep dirt out but if they were left in place none of the pressure instruments would work and flying a Lancaster without an air speed indicator or altimeter would be an experience any pilot would rather live without. They gave the empty bomb bay a quick inspection, knowing that Bob would have also checked it, then checked the starboard side in the same way they had checked the port. Back at the rear door the external checks were complete. Dumping his flight bag through the hatch Jimmy followed Doug up the short ladder into the fuselage.

The first thing Doug checked was the repair to the flak hole. Again it had been painted, this time the same light green as the rest of the inside of the aircraft, but it still showed up as a repair. Doug pushed on it to make sure it was secure, only to discover the paint was still wet and would take a lot longer to dry in the cold damp interior.

"Looks a good job to me, Jimmy," he said, wiping the green paint off his thumb onto his bag and moving forward. The smell of fresh paint lingered in Jimmy's nostrils, overpowering the normal aircraft smells of oil and fuel as he followed Doug forward, ducking under the mid-upper turret with Alex invisible above them in his sling seat. Jimmy stepped up onto the bomb bay immediately forward of the turret and, reaching up, rotated the release handle on the rear ground or ditching emergency exit, checking it opened freely. A wire running down the roof of the fuselage forward was the manual release for the crew dinghy, stowed in the starboard wing. He checked that it couldn't be accidentally pulled. Stepping over the rear spar, his huge body nearly bent double and filling the narrow fuselage, he put his bag on the rest bunk and checked the forward ditching escape hatch in the roof and, again, it clicked open. This area also held one of the emergency axes and a spare fire extinguisher. He checked both and made sure they were secure. Looking on the left of the fuselage at the bottom of the rest bunk, the emergency air bottle showed between 1,100 and 1,200 pounds per square inch as it should and the hydraulic accumulator pressure was above the 220 pounds per square inch minimum. Under the bunk were the oxygen bottles. Jimmy turned them on and rotated the ground flight switch on the starboard wall by the main spar to the flight position. Scrambling over the spar he stood beside Harry, who was sitting in his seat checking his oxygen mask. Harry's grinning eyes winked down at him above the mask as Jimmy knelt to check that the fuel cross feed cock in the floor by the main spar was turned off.

"I know you worship me but there's no need to kneel," Harry said as he pulled off his oxygen mask. Jimmy gave him a reversed victory salute with his free hand as he moved forward, past the radio equipment and the rear of Ron's seat, into the cockpit. There he took out his flying helmet, stowed his bag behind Doug's seat and, pulling on his helmet, took up his position standing beside his pilot.

With his intercom lead plugged in static buzzed quietly in his ears. Then Doug's voice cut in.

"Check in front to back ready for engine start."

Bob replied ready, Jimmy rotated his transmitter switch.

"Flight engineer ready," he said, as he checked his oxygen mask and turned on the fuel gauge contents switch. This was on his panel on the starboard wall of the cockpit. He checked the contents and made sure that Doug had closed the four master engine fuel cocks, two either side of the throttle pedestal. Then he checked the six Pulsometer electric fuel booster pumps, one in each of the Lancaster's fuel tanks. As he knelt on the floor facing the right side of the aircraft, he switched each of the booster pump switches on his flight engineer's panel to the test position. The ammeter at the top of the panel flicked round to show six amps.

"Perfect."

George, as the last crewman, checked in ready for engine start and Doug confirmed they would use trolley acc power for the start. (A trolley accumulator or trolley acc was a mobile battery trolley used to provide external power to the aircraft.) Looking out of the starboard side cockpit blister, Jimmy could see that the ground crew had already rolled the two-wheeled trolley acc cart into position and Jimmy signalled for them to plug it in. As they did so he moved back to the main spar, squeezing past a surly looking Ron to change the ground flight switch back to ground. Now the Lancaster would use the batteries in the cart, instead of the internal batteries, to start its engines, saving the aircraft's batteries for emergencies.

Back in the cockpit he checked that the two green lights on the undercarriage position indicator were still lit, showing that the trolley acc was definitely connected. The four slow-running cut-off switches on the top right of the instrument panel were at idle cut-off and the pneumatic pressure was above 130 pounds per square inch. Below this pressure the radiator shutters, superchargers and idle cut-off rams would not work. At the moment the pressure was being supplied from a compressed air bottle but, once the starboard inner engine was started, a Haywood compressor attached to that engine would increase the pressure to 300 pounds per square inch, and that was why the starboard inner was always started first.

Doug gave him a thumbs up to show he was ready for the start up checks.

"Master engine cocks," said Jimmy.

"Off," replied Doug, checking as he spoke.

"Throttles."

"Half inch open," said Doug pushing the four throttles slightly forward.

"Propeller controls."

"Fully up." Doug reached below the throttles and checked the four pitch control levers were in the fully up, fine, position.

"Slow running cut-off switches."

"Idle cut-off." A guard wire protected the four switches on Jimmy's side of the cockpit because when they were in the idle cut-off position they would stop the engines. Doug checked they were set.

"Supercharger control."

"M ratio." In this position the superchargers would work in low gear, which was best for lower level flying.

"Air intake heat control."

"Cold."

"Radiator shutters."

"Override switches at automatic."

Jimmy raised his head until it was touching the cockpit roof, to check the position of the ground crew. At six foot four that meant he was still slightly stooped. Sergeant Green was to the left of the nose where Doug could see him. Two others were standing by with a large fire extinguisher opposite the starboard inner engine. A third airman, invisible to him, was in the starboard wheel bay pumping fuel into the starboard inner engine, priming it ready to start. Jimmy turned to his side panel and rotated the two fuel tank selector knobs to the number two fuel tank positions. Then on the main instrument panel he selected the number three engine master engine fuel cock lever to the on position and switched on the booster pump for the starboard number two fuel tank on his side panel.

"Ground crew in position, number two starboard tank selected, booster pump on, number three master engine cock on. Ready to start three."

Doug leaned out of the cockpit side window and yelled down to Sergeant Green, "Clear start three?"

Sergeant Green looked across at the airman in the wheel bay to see if he had finished the priming and got a thumbs up. He in turn raised his thumb to Doug and repeated, "Clear start three!"

"Contact!" yelled Doug as he switched on the two ignition switches for the number three engine, in the centre of the instrument panel, and the booster coil switch, to the right of the ignition switches. Then he reached across to the right side of the instrument panel and, lifting the spring-loaded flap that covered the engine starter buttons, pushed the number three starter. The starter whirred and whined, then the propeller turned jerkily over again and again. The engine fired, then spluttered, missed, and then fired again. All the while, out of sight, the airman in the wheel bay pumped fuel through to the cylinders and suddenly the engine sprang into life. Doug released the starter button and, when the engine ran smoothly, switched the number three idle cut-off switch up to the engine running position. The engine settled down to a gentle tick over and Doug made some fine adjustments to the throttle until it was steady at 1,200 rpm. Then, reaching out of the window, he held up four fingers. Sergeant Green looked at the number four starboard outer engine and gave the thumbs up. The start up procedure was the same for number four, then number two, then number one and soon, after an initial reluctance, all the Merlins were roaring away contentedly. Doug switched off the booster coil switch while the ground crew secured the priming pumps. Jimmy turned the ground flight switch back to flight and the ground crew disconnected the trolley acc.

Now, with the start up complete and the engines running smoothly Jimmy scanned the instruments on his side panel. The four strip oil pressure gauges, at the top of his panel, showed the oil pressure stabilising at around 60 pounds per square inch, which was slightly low but within limits; it would increase as the engines warmed up. Below these the four conventional circular oil temperature gauges showed that the engines were slowly bringing the oil up to its normal running temperature and the four gauges below them showed the coolant temperature in the radiators doing the same.

Behind him, Doug was checking the operation of the flaps and bomb doors while Sergeant Green signalled to him the results of each selection. This would ensure the hydraulic system was working correctly. Finally, on the flight engineer's side panel, Jimmy turned off the fuel tank booster pumps to check that the engine driven fuel pumps would maintain the fuel pressure at the engines. No low fuel pressure warning lights showed so Jimmy turned back to face forward and reported, "Engines warmed up, fuel system fully serviceable."

"Roger, radiator shutter override switches to open."

Jimmy selected the switches. Now the automatic thermostatically controlled radiator shutters were overridden and they would stay open, so that the engines would not overheat during the ground run. Doug increased the propeller rpm to 1,500 and switched off and on again each of the eight engine ignition switches, two for each engine, to check they were all serviceable. Then he opened the throttles to plus four pounds per square inch of boost and 2,500 rpm and the engine noise increased as the Lancaster shook against its chocked wheels. He engaged the S ratio of the two-speed supercharger and the rpm on all the engines dropped, as it should. The S ratio, high gear, of the supercharger took more power from the engines to operate, so at low level it made the engines less powerful. But at high level this was more than compensated for by the fact that the supercharger forced more of the thinner air into the engines, increasing their power, when otherwise they would have been starved of oxygen. When the supercharger was returned to M ratio the rpm returned to 2,500. Doug moved the propeller speed levers to the fully down position and the rpm fell to 1,800. Then he brought the rpm controls back to the up, fine pitch position, and throttled back. The noise of the blades and engines faded to a low whine and rumble. Slowly he moved the left throttle forward, the noise increasing again to a powerful roar, until he felt a resistance. This was known as the gate and he checked that the engine was producing 9 pounds per square inch of boost. The Lancaster shook and vibrated as Doug pushed harder until he overcame the resistance on the throttle and it moved forward again to the stop. With the throttle through the gate to maximum boost the engine produced 14 pounds per square inch of boost, with a propeller rpm of 3,000. Outside the engine roar increased to a low-pitched scream, the aircraft pushing against its brakes and chocks in protest. The ground crew all covered their ears against the noise. Then Doug throttled back to the gate, checking the rpm fell back below 3,000 and, one at a time, deselected one of the engines magnetos. The rpm didn't drop more than 100 rpm. Finally, he throttled right back before going through the same routine again with the next engine until they had all been checked.

The check complete Doug turned to Jimmy and, holding his oxygen mask over his face with his right hand, he spoke over the deep contented rumble of the four Merlins.

"Looks good to me."

"Me too, skipper."

"Crew, check in front to back with any unserviceable equipment."

Once again there was no unserviceable equipment so Doug and Jimmy started to shut down the engines. With the engines throttled right back Jimmy checked the pneumatic pressure was above 130 pounds per square inch and one by one turned the slow-running cut-off switches to idle cut-off, until all the engines had stopped. Then he turned off the ignition switches and master engine fuel cocks and checked the fuel booster pumps were all off and the fuel tank selectors were at off. Finally he switched the slow-running cut-off switches back to the engine running position so that, if the ground engineers had to apply power to the aircraft during their checks, they would not continuously operate the idle cut-off rams.

When Jimmy emerged from the aircraft with Bob behind him Doug was already telling Sergeant Green how well the check had gone. Behind them a bomb train, consisting of a tractor and three bomb trolleys, was just arriving. It did a complete circuit of the aircraft to line up the trolleys with the front of the bomb bay. The first trolley had a 4,000-pound Cookie on it and three armourers were sitting astride it. As soon as the train stopped they jumped off and disconnecting the tractor they started to manocuvre the trolleys back under the bomber. The WAAF tractor driver drove off back around the perimeter track towards the bomb dump to pick up her next load and a fuel bowser pulled up to the front of the starboard wing.

"So you're happy with her then, sir?" asked Sergeant Green.

"Well I am, sarge. What about the rest of you?"

"Our guns haven't been cleaned yet," said Alex.

"Yes, I know, the Squadron had a lively night last night and a lot more than usual fired their guns. So the armourers are really busy but they have promised they'll get to us early this afternoon."

"We can do them ourselves," said George, looking over at Alex, who nodded.

"I only test fired mine," said Bob, "but I'll stay and give them a quick pull through if you've got the gear."

"Alright," said Sergeant Green. "The cleaning kit's in the hut and one of my lads can give you a hand dismounting them but you'll need transport to get them to and from the gun room."

"We'll send Sally back with the truck," said Doug. "Any other problems?"

The rest of the crew shook their heads. Jimmy looked at his watch. It was 12.15. The ground crew were now lying on the starboard wing starting to refuel F for Freddy. He guessed that it would take just over 1,600 gallons to fill the tanks right up. That wouldn't take too long to do. Bob could clean the light fouling off his guns in a few minutes but the bombing up would take longer and George and Alex would be longer still. They would be lucky to get finished in time for their crew meal and make it to the specialist briefing. He on the other hand was lucky. Because there were no faults he was now free until his specialist briefing at 14.00. So while Bob, Alex and George started to lift their guns one by one from their turrets, Jimmy went back to the Squadron Office with the rest of the crew.

Doug quickly checked in with the Squadron Adj to see if anything had changed while they were at the aircraft and then cleared them all off to do any "personal admin", which basically meant they were left to their own devices until the specialist briefings. As they were about to leave Sally returned with Bob in the truck and he, Jimmy and Harry cycled back to their billet to try and get washed and shaved, although they had little hope that the pipes would have thawed out yet. However, they had not reckoned on the resourcefulness of the Squadron Adj. Outside the ablution block was a hot air blower, mounted on the back of a truck, and an eighteen-inch diameter pipe running from the blower through the door of the block. Normally these were used when it was very cold to thaw out the insides of the aircraft but this one had been hijacked and was going from ablution block to ablution block thawing the pipes.

"Bugger me!" exclaimed Jimmy.

"You're not my type," replied Harry automatically.

"You've got to hand it to the old bugger," said Bob, referring to the Adj. "That's a bloody good idea."

"What the hell are we waiting for?" asked Harry. "Our ablution block is the warmest place on the station, let's not waste it!"

He ran into the billet, grabbed his wash kit and came running back out again with Jimmy and Bob close on his heels.

The ablution block was warm, almost too warm, but after the unrelenting cold everywhere else on the unit, they were prepared to put up with it. Stripping to the waist they filled three sinks with water to wash and shave in.

"Jesus Christ!" yelled Bob, after splashing water on his face. "This water's like ice!"

"That's because a few minutes ago it was," replied Harry.

"I'm not bloody shaving in that!" stormed Bob indignantly.

"You don't have much choice mate," said Harry, splashing the ice water on his own face and trying not to flinch.

Bob turned to Jimmy. "Do I look like I haven't shaved?"

Jimmy looked. Although Bob's hair was fair the short stubble caught the light and stood out against his tanned skin. "Yes," he said.

"Damn it! If you didn't look closely can you still tell?"

Jimmy reconsidered. "Well…"

"That will do for me. Sod the shave," and he made do with a quick thirty-second wash.

Jimmy considered not shaving but his conscience would not let him and Harry had already started to lather his face, so he followed suit.

"You bloody Pommies are all mad," said Bob.

Back in their billet Jimmy checked his watch, 12.45. He had always been paranoid about being late and now, as his mind turned to the night's Op, he started to get nervous and his paranoia increased. He estimated that they would have to leave the billet at 13.00 to get to the mess, eat their pre-flight meal, and then get to their specialist briefings. Fifteen minutes to spare. What would he do? Write a letter? He had done that yesterday and that had been very difficult. What would he say today that was different? He might as well lie on his bed and relax. He lay on his back looking at the ceiling while Harry and Bob rummaged around sorting out the kit that they would wear or take with them tonight. Jimmy, on the other hand, had always been very organised and orderly and all his kit was to hand. He looked at his watch, it hadn't moved, he held it to his ear and listened, it was still ticking. He would have a cigarette; he sat up and reached into his greatcoat pocket that was hung on the back of the chair by his bed. He pulled out his cigarette case and lighter. The cigarette case had been a present from his mum and dad and the lighter was from his girlfriend, Mary. It was an expensive Ronson wind-proof lighter and he was very fond of it. Mary had saved up to buy it for his twenty-first birthday which was next month but she had given it to him early, the last time he had managed to get a forty-eight-hour pass and ride his motorbike over to Norfolk. He lit the cigarette and inhaled the smoke deeply. He missed Mary a lot and, as he looked at the lighter he missed her more. Staring at the lighter he could see her face clearly and a warm glow washed over him. However, one thing kept bothering him. Why had she given him the lighter early? Did she think he wouldn't make it to twenty-one? The thought had become a nightmare to him and no matter how he tried he could not banish it from his mind.

He looked at his watch; two minutes had passed since the last time he checked. Harry was teasing Bob about not having a shave and being afraid of a little cold water. He closed his cigarette case and glanced at it before putting it in the left breast pocket of his battle dress. He always carried it there when he flew and although he had never actually thought of it before he realised that it was a sort of lucky charm to him. It was a highly polished stainless steel, with a minimum of decoration on it. His name on the nameplate near the bottom edge J.T. WILSON gave it a sort of permanence that he liked. He slipped the lighter into his left breast pocket with the cigarette case and fastened the button. He thought about his mum and dad. Right now his mum would be serving behind the counter of the little baker's in the market place in North Walsham. She had worked there as long as he could remember. He used to call in on her on his way home from school and sometimes the baker, Mr Harvey, would give him a mince pie or some other little treat. Now lying on his bed staring up at the curved white corrugated iron ceiling he could smell the fresh bread and he started to feel hungry. It must be nearly time to go and eat.

He looked at his watch; a minute had passed since he last looked. His dad worked on a local farm, just like most of the other men in the area, but Jimmy had never wanted to follow in his father's footsteps. He had always loved machines and it had to be fate when an apprenticeship became available in the local garage just as he left school. He got the job and worked there until he joined the Air Force. Somewhere near North Walsham his dad would be out in the fields, probably mending fences or taking feed to cattle or sheep. Whatever he was doing it would be cold in the flat Norfolk countryside. Jimmy realised that just lying on his bed in his battledress he was cold. He finished his cigarette, stubbing it out in a small tin he had acquired to use as an ashtray.

His watch now said 12.50, and he took off his battledress blouse and put on his heavy white woollen sweater, then pulled his battledress back on. Harry and Bob were in the middle of a good-natured argument about the qualities of British and Australian beer. He lay back and stared at the ceiling. He had always been a quiet person and although he didn't like being alone he was always content to be on the fringe of any group. Sometimes he was ribbed by the others for being so quiet but when he had to he could give as good as he got, so it never bothered him.

He looked at his watch; 12.52, Christ, time was dragging. His mind turned to the Op. Full fuel tanks! A long trip, probably Berlin again. He thought of the first time he had seen Berlin. Had it really only been last night? Flak bursting over a wide area, guns' muzzle flashes far below, searchlights by the hundred sweeping back and forth as they slowly approached. His stomach turned and butterflies whirled inside him at the thought of it. The whole scene had filled him with horror. It was so immense, so threatening. He had just stood and stared at it. When he went down into the nose to drop the window, he thought he would be able to escape from the terrible panorama but, while he had felt safer in the dark interior of the nose, this had instantly vanished when the first flak exploded close to the Lancaster, causing it to jump and buck, while shrapnel rattled on the thin fuselage skin. From then on the bombing run and the exit from the target had been the worst time of his life. Unable to see anything, his active mind filled in the gaps with its own terrible images. He had thrown himself into dropping the window. But tearing open the packets and pushing the hundreds of thin foot-long strips of metallic-coated paper down the chute had soon become automatic and his mind again began to torment him. Bombers in flames, bombers coned in a hundred searchlight beams, bombers blown apart by direct hits so the crew all fell to their deaths. Where was his parachute? Behind the pilot's seat; he would never be able to get to it in an emergency. It was too far away and the rest of the crew would all be coming the other way, fighting to get through the narrow gap under the instrument panel to reach the front hatch. He realised that every muscle in his body was tensed and his huge bulk had pushed his battle dress taut, so that it strained at the seams. His heart was racing and he was covered in sweat.

He looked at his watch; 12.55, he tried to slow down his breathing as his heart continued to race. For God's sake think of something else. His motorbike! It was still over at Syerston fifty miles away; if they were going to get some leave after the next Op he could hitch a lift over there and collect it. That would be great. His blue and silver Triumph 500 that tore up the miles of road so effortlessly, sailing round the curves of the country lanes with an easy grace. He loved his bike almost as much as he loved Mary; after all he spent more time with his bike than he did with his girlfriend. It was then that it suddenly struck him that he did indeed love Mary. He had never thought it before and certainly never told her he did but he was suddenly sure that he did. The butterflies in his stomach turned from ones of nervousness to ones of excitement at the discovery. They had been going out together now for two years. Most of that time he had been away in the Air Force, but they had known each other for far longer, right back to when they were at school. Then another thought struck him. Did she love him? The butterflies turned back to ones of nervousness. He thought she did but he wasn't sure. He would ask her when he went on leave. That would probably only be a few days away and the thought cheered him. But before that he would have to fly to Berlin again, possibly twice, and he started to despair. Even if he did get to see her again what were his chances of getting through a whole tour? He felt so frustrated he could have wept. He had just discovered he had a great reason to live at the same time that it had dawned on him that the impetuousness of his youth had made him volunteer for something extremely dangerous. He had to get out of the billet; the atmosphere was stifling him.

He looked at his watch: 13.00 Jesus! Time to go.

"13.00, we had better go."

"No, we'll be too early if we go now," Harry said and Jimmy nearly exploded with frustration. He could not lie there another second.

"But if we go now we beat the rush for our meal," smiled Bob.

"Yes," said Jimmy quickly.

"You and your bloody stomach. All you Aussies ever do is eat, drink and complain about the cold!" replied Harry.

"If you dozy Pomms had a decent country it wouldn't be a problem," said Bob, as he and Harry followed Jimmy out of the billet and cycled to the mess.

Chaining up their bikes outside the mess, they hurried inside out of the cold wind, which seemed to have increased from the west. The flat Lincolnshire countryside offered them no protection. Inside the mess it was warm from the heat of the kitchens and their hands and faces started to glow.

"That's more like it!" said Bob. "Now where's my egg?"

"Bloody food again!" said Harry.

They had indeed beaten the rush and were already sitting down before the next crews entered the dining room.

"I wonder how George and Alex are getting on with their guns," said Jimmy, trying to make conversation.

"They reckoned that if they did three guns each they could do it and still get back here for their meal," said Bob.

"No chance," replied Harry. "What do you reckon Jimmy?"

"It'll be close if they do make it." Jimmy didn't really want to be part of the conversation but he didn't want to sit in silence either. The strategy worked because Harry and Bob went on to argue over whether George and Alex would get their meal or not and it all ended with the usual bet: one pint of what Harry called good English beer.

By now it was after 13.30 and the dining room was full of aircrew, all sitting in their own crew groups.

"They're not going to make it, mate," smiled Harry, his confidence of getting a free pint increasing.

"Wait and see," replied Bob, sounding far more confident than he felt.

"We'll need to go soon," said Jimmy, worrying about being late.

"A couple of minutes yet," said Bob. They finished their tea and Bob was just about to reluctantly concede defeat when George and Alex came running in.

"Yes!" exclaimed Bob triumphantly.

"Not so fast," replied Harry. "They haven't got their meal yet." He was looking at George and Alex's hands which were covered in oil and he saw that the sergeant cook had also seen them.

As George and Alex got to the servery the sergeant cook stood opposite them on the other side of the counter armed with his weapon of choice, a heavy ladle.

"You're not eating in here with hands like that," he said in a voice loud enough to ensure that the whole dining room heard him.

"We've just come from the aircraft," explained George.

"I don't care, go and get washed!"

"We haven't time. We've got a briefing at 14.00," said Alex.

"That's not my problem, go and wash your hands."

"We've no time for this," said George picking up a plate and moving to the first tray of bacon to help himself. The sergeant cook was furious that his authority had been challenged and lashed out at George's hand with his ladle. George whipped his left hand with the plate in it back out of reach of the ladle and at the same time grabbed forward with his right hand, catching the cook by the front of the collar and pulling him close to his face. The cook was all of six inches taller than George, but years of digging coal had made George's arms as strong as a man twice his size. His cold blue eyes stared into the cook's with a hatred the cook could feel. The cook was transfixed, like a rat staring at a cobra. He offered no resistance as George spoke to him in a threateningly calm voice that no one more than a few feet away could hear. Then George let go and he and Alex helped themselves to their meal, while the cook looked on. A small cheer went up from the diners who had all watched the performance with interest.

"Bollocks!" said Harry. "I didn't count on that."

"Didn't count on what?" asked George as he and Alex sat down.

"Nothing, what did you say to the cook?"

"I just explained that we didn't have time to wash our hands, eat our meal and get to the briefing."

"And then he just let you eat?"

"No it was when he threatened to ram the ladle up his arse if he didn't let us eat that he changed his mind!" laughed Alex.

Jimmy took his seat with the other flight engineers in the Engineering Leader's office just before 14.00 and waited for the briefing to start. He had his flight bag with him and a notebook and pencil ready. Most of the other flight engineers chatted while others stared into space. Jimmy, as usual, sat quietly on the fringe of the activity and took everything in. The Engineering Leader, Don Small, a Warrant Officer, walked into the office on the dot of 14.00 and the room fell silent.

"I don't know the target for certain but its full fuel tanks all around so make your own guesses. Now, roll call." The roll was called and Jimmy counted the responses. It was to be another seventeen aircraft show by the Squadron. Next came the weather. "The Met man says the icing level is at 1,000 feet and in clouds icing should be moderate to light but I don't believe that myself, so if I were you I'd stay out of clouds if you can. The forecast wind is from the west and expected to increase through the night, so be careful to watch your fuel consumption, you're going to have a strong head wind all the way back. The only time you have too much fuel is when you're on fire! The total track distance for the round trip will be 1,351 miles, to be flown at 20,000 feet. Bomb loads." Don then went through each aircraft listing the total bomb loads; F for Freddy would be carrying 11,200 pounds of bombs. What that consisted of did not matter to Jimmy; only the total weight would affect his calculations, although he did realise that it was heavier than the bomb load they had carried the night before. "The engineers are working on the installation of the FIDO pipes by the runway, so be aware that there could be obstructions around when you taxi out and keep your eyes open. Here are your fuel logs. Are there any questions?"

He handed out the logs and no one asked any questions. "Right then, if you've no questions, have a good trip and for Christ's sake watch your fuel consumption!" The plea to watch your fuel consumption was echoed by half the other flight engineers, who had all heard Don end all his briefings that way and now that he had heard it twice Jimmy knew to echo it himself next time.

Jimmy walked the short distance to the main briefing room pushing his bike beside him.

"What bomb load are you carrying?" asked one of the other flight engineers.

"11,200 pounds."

"That's not too bad then. I've got 12,000 and they seem to be increasing them all the time. It's not good," he said sadly.

"According to the books we can go 1,660 miles with 14,000 pounds of bombs."

"According to the books we can," replied the other flight engineer, "but I wouldn't like to try it. And it's not the getting there and back that worries me, it's the getting airborne before the end of the runway. Plus have you done any fighter affiliation yet?"

"No."

"Well, you can throw an empty Lanc all over the sky like a big fighter but when you hang seven tons of bombs from it there's not a lot you can do in the way of evasive action."

They arrived at the main briefing room at the same time as the gunners.

"What did you find out?" Jimmy asked George and Alex.

"Not a lot," replied George. "Apparently we should look out for fighters, like we might have forgotten about that."

Doug arrived with the other pilots. They hadn't been told the target either. It wasn't long to the main briefing but they still had time to smoke a cigarette. George's extra strength Capstans brought on a coughing fit, which finished with George spitting a huge lump of phlegm out of sight round the corner of the hut.

"They're not doing you any good," said Harry as he walked up.

"Bollocks!" croaked George.

"Thank you for that comment from our cultural attaché," answered Harry. Doug looked embarrassed by the behaviour and stood a little to one side unsure of what an officer should do in these situations.

"Let's go in," said Jimmy as the armed policeman guarding the door stepped to one side, indicating that the briefing room was set up for the briefing. They were the first crew into the room and they sat four rows from the front on the left, the same as during yesterday's briefing. Bob and Ron were the last to arrive, not long before the 15.00 start time. They sat down and got out their maps, pencils, logs, rulers and any other tools they would need. As soon as they were ready there was a call of "Attention!" The Station Commander, Wing Commander Baxter and the Squadron Adj entered.

"Sit down, chaps," boomed the Station Commander jumping on to the stage. "Roll call." The captains' names were called and they all answered, but all eyes were on the curtain across the end wall of the room. "Curtain!"

As the curtain was pulled back the target and route was revealed: Berlin again. Although it was no real surprise a general sigh went up. The route was different to the previous night, heading east across the North Sea from Spurn Head until it hit the German coast at Nordstrand, just south of the Danish border. This would give a good positional fix. Then the route turned slightly south of east, across the peninsula into the Baltic, to the southern tip of Falster Island, before turning south to cross the north German coast east of Rostock. Two more doglegs followed, but the mean course was still south, to a lake with an island in the middle of it. This would be the holding point for the run into Berlin 35 miles further south. The route home was southeast, south of Magdeburg for 110 miles, to a turning point at a lake, then west, crossing the Rhine North of Koblenz. From there the route ran direct to Charleroi in Belgium, crossing the English Channel to hit the English coast at Margate, then north back to Metheringham. The Station Commander gave a similar chat to the previous day's briefing then handed over to the Met man.

The only thing that worried Jimmy about the weather was the strong head wind coming home because it would eat into their fuel and not leave them much to spare.

Then came flying control and Jimmy noted the engine start and taxi times, 15.45 for 16.00. The Station Signals Officer followed and Jimmy listened with little interest, as this had no bearing on his job.

Finally the Intelligence Officer outlined the route, pointing out that it was hoped that delaying the entry into Germany would keep them clear of the night fighters for longer, but few people thought that likely. A diversionary raid would be made by Stirlings of Training Command heading to the Dutch coast, dropping window so that they would look like a larger force. 100 Group would be sending Mosquito and Beaufighter intruders to patrol the German night fighter bases, so hopefully there would be some confusion in the enemy camp. But before they crossed the German coast it would be pretty obvious what their target was. The general feeling of the crews around him seemed to be that this was not a good route.

The Specialist Leaders followed and Jimmy got a general feel for the Op from their briefings and made a note of when he had to start and stop dropping window. The Wing Commander and Station Commander gave their final summing up, the Navigator Leader called the time check and the briefing was over.

The crew planning after the briefing seemed to go more smoothly than the day before. Jimmy made sure Ron had finished his planning before asking him for ETAs and total times of flight so that he could work out his fuel figures. He was still smarting from the telling off Ron had given him the day before in front of everyone and he didn't want a repeat of it. Today they were not the last crew to finish but there was still a queue in the crew room for harnesses, parachutes, flasks, sandwiches and any specialist kit. After emptying his pockets into his locker, Jimmy pulled on his heavy fur-lined boots and Irving jacket, then squirmed into his Mae West and parachute harness. This was the moment yesterday when it had struck him that he was going to war and the hairs had stood up on his neck. Today, like yesterday, he pushed the thought to the back of his mind, though he could not forget it completely. As always he checked his safety equipment very carefully. Two personal items he had not emptied out of his pockets, as he should have, were his cigarette case and lighter. These were still in his left breast pocket and he lightly touched them to check they were still there. He helped Alex into his harness, which was doubly difficult for the gunners because of their bulky electrical suits. George was tying up the middle finger of his left flying glove with a rubber band and Jimmy was about to ask what he was doing when he realised that that was the finger George had lost and he was tying the glove out of the way.

Sally was waiting outside. They slung their kit aboard her truck and climbed in. As usual she was smiling and George handed her the envelope full of letters for her to keep.

"Same routine, bonny lass."

"Same routine, sarge," she replied.

During the drive around the perimeter track to the aircraft, the butterflies in Jimmy's stomach, which had never gone away, seemed to multiply. Conversation had stopped, which was probably because Ron was there, otherwise Harry would have been chattering away twenty to the dozen, making jokes and having friendly digs at the others. As it was Harry hated Ron so much he hardly ever spoke when Ron was around. The wind rattled the canvas on the back of the wagon, whistling through any gaps. The sky was completely clouded over but the clouds looked high and not very thick. Jimmy tried to guess their height. If they were below 20,000 feet they would have to climb through them and they might pick up some airframe icing. Worse still, moonlight or even bright starlight would silhouette them against the white cloud tops to anyone flying above them. It would be far better if the cloud was just above 20,000 feet.

The wagon stopped at the dispersal and Jimmy waved to Sally as he, Doug, Bob and George walked to the ground crew shack. Sergeant Green watched them approach from the doorway with his usual mug of tea in his hands.

"Yes, the armourers have topped up your ammo boxes!" he yelled to George, above the wind. George waved and turned back towards the aircraft. "Evening, sir," Sergeant Green said to Doug. "She's all ready for you, bombed and fuelled up and no problems."

"Thanks, sarge," replied Doug as he scanned down the 700. Jimmy looked over his shoulder to check the fuel figures and make sure the oil levels on the four engines' individual oil tanks had all been topped up to thirty-seven and a half gallons. Doug signed for the aeroplane and they left Bob to sign for his bombs.

Leaving their parachute packs and flight bags inside the aircraft entrance door they carried out the same external checks as they had that morning, the only difference being the loaded bomb bay, showing the round bulk of the single Cookie and the rows of small bomb containers. With the bombs on board the aircraft sat low on its suspension and the tyres looked flat. Dust blew up off the dispersal as they finished the check and climbed aboard.

"The wind's picking up," said Doug, sounding a little concerned.

"It's not gusting though," replied Jimmy, trying to be positive although he didn't feel it. The internal checks up the fuselage followed, until finally he emerged into the cockpit. With his full flying kit on the cockpit seemed to have shrunk since the morning and with his broad shoulders, Jimmy seemed to always be pushed against either the side of the cockpit or the pilot's seat. He carefully placed his parachute pack in its position behind the pilot's seat and slid his flight bag into the same space. Then he helped Doug with his parachute, which was of the seat type, the same as fighter pilots. Once that was secure he held the seat harness straps so that Doug could strap into his seat. Outside, the ground crew were moving into position to start the engines, a sure sign that engine start time was imminent, because they would not want to stand in the cold any longer than they had to. Jimmy pulled on his helmet, fastened the chinstrap, plugged in the intercom lead and quickly ran through the pre-engine start checks. Once he had found these so complicated, but now that they were familiar to him, they seemed so straightforward. The static in his earphones was interrupted by Doug's voice,

"Check in front to back ready for engine start."

7

With F for Freddy's four Merlins rumbling contentedly outside the cockpit window and all the internal systems functioning normally Doug prepared to taxi out of the dispersal. Unlike yesterday the sky, although overcast, was still a dull grey and night had not yet started to draw in. The wind was snatching at the Lancaster's control surfaces and Doug was forced to hold onto the control column tightly to stop it moving. Two bombers had already taxied slowly past and Doug decided to slot in after the next one.

"Before taxi checks Jimmy."

"Ground flight switch set to flight, navigation lights."

"On," replied Doug. It wasn't dark yet, but at this time of year once it started to get dark, night would set in quickly.

"Altimeter."

"Set to QFE."

"Instrument flying panel. Four and a half pounds per square inch vacuum on both pumps," said Jimmy, checking the suction gauge, as he changed over the pumps to check both were working. "Radiator shutters open and brake pressure 270 pounds per square inch. Ready to taxi."

"Roger, here we go." Doug waved away the chocks and the ground crewmen ran clear, pulling the wheel chocks behind them on long weather worn pieces of rope, while Sergeant Green, waving his arms up and down by his sides, marshalled them forward. After moving forward a few feet Doug tested the brakes, then proceeded onto the taxiway, slotting neatly in behind another Lancaster. Sergeant Green waved to them as they left the dispersal and Jimmy and Doug gave him a quick wave back, before concentrating on keeping on the taxiway and not getting too close to the other Lancaster. They had to do this without using the brakes too much or they would deplete the pneumatic pressure. Slowly they wound their way round the perimeter of the airfield, past the gate where the same two boys waved at them. Jimmy waved back and looking back along the top of the fuselage he could see Alex in his turret, waving and dipping his guns at them. Looking back inside, Jimmy saw the pneumatic pressure was down to 90 pounds per square inch; Doug must have been using a lot of brake.

"Brake pressure 90, skipper."

"Yes, I know, Jimmy. It's the wind, I'm having to use more brake than usual."

"I think we'd better stop and run the starboard inner up for a bit to build up the pressure." Once the pressure fell below 80 pounds per square inch the brakes would fail, so it was best to stop and run the starboard inner engine up to a fast tick over. The pneumatic pump was attached to this engine and revving it up would soon increase the pneumatic pressure to an acceptable level.

"Right," said Doug stopping. He felt a bit embarrassed at having to stop, as it was looked on as a failing if a pilot could not taxi without running down his brake pressure. It only took a minute to get the pressure back but in that time George reported that they were causing a traffic jam and Doug could feel his face starting to colour with embarrassment. Once on the move again things were easier, as there was no Lancaster immediately in front of them. But the first bomber had just taken off and now Doug was worried about getting to the end of the runway in time for their takeoff.

"Before takeoff checks."

"Auto controls."

"Clutch in, cock out." This disconnected the autopilot.

"DR compass."

"Normal."

"Pitot head heater."

"On." This would stop any water entering the tube from freezing at high level and blocking it.

"Trimming tabs."

"Elevator slightly forward, rudder neutral, aileron neutral."

"Propeller controls."

"Fully up." The fully fine position, which was the equivalent of a low gear for fast acceleration.

"Fuel contents sufficient, master cocks on, number two tanks selected, cross feed off and numbers one and two booster pumps on," said Jimmy confidently. "Superchargers."

"M ratio."

"Air intake."

"Cold." This was the air for the carburettors, which could be heated to prevent icing, but hot air was also less dense and so less efficient.

"Radiator shutters."

"Automatic." They were almost at the end of the runway and there was no chance of the engines overheating now.

"Flaps."

"Twenty degrees."

"Takeoff checks complete." They had caught up with the other Lancaster just as it started to taxi onto the runway. Jimmy took advantage of the few seconds they had before they had to taxi out to check the engine temperatures and oil pressures. Then he double-checked the flaps, pitch controls, engine boost and rpm. All was set, the other bomber started its run and Doug moved F for Freddy slowly onto the runway, lined them up on the centre line, ran forward slightly to ensure the tailwheel was straight and then stopped, waiting for the green light from the caravan.

Standing beside Doug, Jimmy watched the other Lancaster race down the runway. Then he looked over at the caravan and the group of well-wishers standing beside it. Sally's wagon was there and Sally was standing hanging on to the open driver's door with her left arm while she waved her hat over her head with her right. Jimmy waved back and at the same instance a green light flashed from the runway caravan.

Doug moved the throttles smoothly forward about an inch with his right hand and checked that all four engines reacted evenly. They all showed zero boost and sounded healthy. It never failed to impress him how well the four throttle levers had been designed. The two inner throttles were short and fitted neatly into the heal of his palm, while the two outer throttles were longer, with the tops bent inwards above the inners, so that he could manoeuvre them with his thumb and little finger, if he needed to adjust the power to either outer engine to correct a swing on takeoff. He was holding the Lancaster on its brakes and now he released them, while at the same time slowly but firmly pushing the throttles further forward. Immediately the bomber started to move forward and Jimmy took hold of the instrument coaming with his right hand to steady himself, as he stood beside Doug. Jimmy's left hand was palm up below Doug's on the throttles, with the shafts of the throttle levers between his fingers and he followed Doug's movements as he advanced the throttles. Jimmy could feel the Lancaster pulling to the left and knew that Doug was moving the port throttles forward slightly ahead of the starboard to counteract this. The throttles reached the gate and Jimmy snatched a glance out of the windscreen. They were very slightly left of the centreline but running straight down the runway. Pulling his eyes back to the instruments he saw the engines were stabilising at plus 9 pounds of boost and he felt Doug push the throttles through the gate into full boost.

"Your throttles!" yelled Doug, over the roar of the engines.

"My throttles!" replied Jimmy, holding the throttles hard against the stops, as Doug took his right hand away, so that he had both hands on the control column. The Merlins were now all showing plus 14 pounds of boost and 3,000 rpm, maximum power and Jimmy reported this to Doug.

"30," said Ron, reading off the speed from the airspeed indicator in the navigator's station. Jimmy felt the tail start to lift and glanced out again. They were back on the runway centreline and swinging slightly from side to side, as Doug struggled with the rudder pedals to keep the bomber straight.

"Tail up," reported George.

Looking back in he concentrated on the four red-rimmed boost gauges, which were still steady at 14 pounds of boost. If an engine was going to fail now was the most likely time for it to happen. If it did happen he would close all the throttles and they would try and stop before they ran out of runway.

"60!" yelled Ron. They could still possibly stop, but it would be a perilously close run thing.

"90!" Now there was no chance! They were in the dangerous gap where they were going too fast to stop and too slow to fly. Again Jimmy looked out and caught a glimpse of the flying control tower passing out of the corner of his eye but the thing his eyes were drawn to was the rapidly approaching end of the runway. The straining engines sent vibrations through his feet up his legs into his groin, making him feel numb. His big left hand pushed hard forward on the throttles, as if to squeeze extra power from them. He was vaguely aware of the aircraft bobbing up and down slowly but he dismissed this as impossible; they still had 10 mph to go before they could take off. He knew he should be checking the instruments but if anything went wrong now there was nothing he could do to save them and he allowed himself to become transfixed by the end of the runway.

"100!" Only another 5 mph, they would make it. This was a good aeroplane, he could feel it, and he had always felt it. He was an instinctive person and he had always known that F for Freddy would not let him down. But they were not going to clear the boundary fence by much.

"105!" The swinging stopped and almost imperceptibly the ground fell away. Doug's right hand selected the undercarriage lever to up, while he held the bomber level with his left. The end of the runway shot underneath them and Jimmy gritted his teeth as they cleared the boundary fence by what seemed like inches. Even now an engine failure would make a crash inevitable and they were not safe until 130 mph, after which a good pilot and flight engineer could save the day. With the wheels up the Lancaster accelerated better and at 140 mph Doug raised the nose slightly into a very slow climb to get some clearance between them and the ground. At 500 feet and 160 mph they raise the flaps slowly and in stages, and then started a slow climbing turn to the north, heading for Spurn Head. Jimmy relaxed as the ground fell away and the speed settled at the normal climbing speed of 160 mph. He took his hand off the throttles and looked at the deep grooves left in his flying glove, realising how hard he had been pressing the throttles forward. His other hand was still gripping the top of the instrument panel and he felt foolish and let go as he forced himself to relax.

When established in the climb Doug brought the throttles back to plus 7 pounds of boost and 2,650 rpm, which would give them a good rate of climb while maintaining a good fuel consumption. Jimmy checked the coolant temperature was stable at 100 degrees and the oil temperature was a steady 85. He turned off the fuel booster pumps as they climbed through 2,000 feet and entered the figures in his log. Now providing nothing went wrong he would not have very much to do until he had to change supercharger ratio and switch the fuel booster pumps back on to maintain the fuel pressure after they had climbed above 17,000 feet. After that the next thing to do would be halfway across the North Sea when he would have to change over fuel tanks and transfer the fuel from the number three tanks to the number two tanks. Until then he would monitor the engines and be an extra pair of eyes, looking out for other aircraft.

Taking a good look around Jimmy could see lots of other aircraft around them, none very close and all heading in the same direction. Most were just black shapes against the failing light of the sky; some he could recognise as Lancasters, others below the horizon he could not see at all. Their presence was only betrayed by their red and green navigation lights. In the west the last light of the day was fading and in the east darkness closed in. The briefing had said this was to be a mixed Lancaster and Halifax raid, but all the Halifax squadrons were now based in the north, so all these aircraft must be Lancasters. His heart swelled at the thought that he was a part of something this big. One day he would tell his children about this, he thought.

He had never thought about having children before; he was only twenty, why should he have thought of having a family? He was far too young for that yet. But, thinking of Mary, she would make a great mother and the thought of raising a family with her gave him a warm glow that momentarily stilled the butterflies in his stomach.

"Lancaster closing in, 7 o' clock high." From Alex, this brought Jimmy back to the present with a start that made his heart stop and instantly dissipated the warm glow. Jimmy's head shot round, looking over his left shoulder to see a Lancaster 400 yards away, slowly closing in on them diagonally. There was no risk of collision, but it would pass low over the top of them, so Alex had been right to warn them and Jimmy's heart started again. The dark undersides of the bomber showed up well against the clouds above them in the last light and the Perspex cockpit, nose and turrets stood out. Slowly it moved directly over them, appearing to crab sideways as all aircraft on divergent courses do. Looking straight up at its black belly less than 100 feet above them Doug and Jimmy watched the blue red exhaust flames coming out of the sides of the engines light up the undersides of the wings. They could hear its engines over the noise of their own and F for Freddy vibrated in the slipstream of the other aircraft, as it pulled ahead.

"I didn't realise how much light came from the engine exhausts," said Doug.

"It would be worse still without flame dampers," replied Jimmy.

They reached Spurn Head ten minutes after takeoff and turned east across the sea. Ron had got a good fix at the coast and felt happy that although the westerly wind was strong it was pretty much as forecast and it would mean a quick crossing. As they turned east they had seen navigation lights to the north that must have come from the Halifaxes and it was a good reminder to turn their own navigation lights off.

At 10,000 feet they went onto oxygen and the gunners tested their guns, sending red lines of tracer into the night, which was now completely dark.

"We're down to plus 6 on the boost, skipper. Shall we go to S ratio?" Jimmy asked. The boost had fallen from nine to six as the air thinned with height and the engines were slowly starved of oxygen.

"Yes, change over now, Jimmy."

Jimmy pulled back all four throttles to zero boost and selected S ratio on the superchargers. There was a thump, the engines coughed, then Jimmy eased the throttles back up to plus 9 pounds of boost. Now the higher gear on the supercharger would force more air into the engines to restore their power.

Jimmy checked the fuel consumption and logged the contents. They had used slightly less than he had anticipated and that was good because they would need a lot to fight the headwind on the way home. All through training the flight engineer instructors had hammered into their students the need to guard their fuel jealously and keep as big a reserve as operational needs permitted.

F for Freddy droned onward and upward and Jimmy kept up his lookout, but could only see the last light fading on the horizon behind them and the occasional line of tracer as bombers behind them tested their guns. At 17,000 feet he turned on the fuel booster pumps for the number two, in use, fuel tanks, because the engine driven fuel pumps could not maintain the desired fuel pressure above this height. Checking the contents, he found they had used about 230 gallons, which was about right for this stage of the flight, and it would be a while yet before the number two tanks were empty enough to transfer the contents of the number three tanks into them.

A Lancaster's fuel system was identical in each wing, the number one tanks, closest to the fuselage, each holding 580 gallons, the number two tanks, between the engines, each holding 383 gallons and the number three tanks, between the outer engine and the wing tip, each holding 114 gallons. At any time the two engines on each wing could be run off either the number one or number two tanks. The number three tanks on the other hand were only connected to the number two tanks and could not feed either engine directly. For this reason it was standard practice to use the fuel in the number two tanks first, until they were showing 200 gallons remaining, then run the engines on the number one tanks and transfer the fuel from the number three tanks to the number two tanks, filling them up again. After about a further two hours of flying on the number one tanks they would have about the same amount of fuel remaining as the number two tanks and after that the flight engineer would swap over between the number one and number two tanks every half hour. This way the fuel was spread evenly between four tanks, so that if a tank were holed no more than a quarter of the remaining fuel would be lost.

They reached 20,000 feet, Doug levelled off and brought the boost back to 7 pounds per square inch and eased the rpm back to maintain 160 mph. Looking around outside there was very little to see. It was another very dark night, just like the last one. The layer of altostratus cloud was just above them, covering them like a dark grey protective blanket and cutting out any moon or starlight and that suited Jimmy. He didn't care if they found the target, so long as no Germans found them. As for finding their way home, Ron might be a stuck up pain in the arse but he could navigate. At least he could navigate if he didn't panic, like he had on the flight to Metheringham. Jimmy had no idea what had happened to Ron on that flight and had no way of knowing that Ron's professional flaw was his pathological fear of making a mistake and being ridiculed for it.

He was cold now. He hadn't noticed it before and he had never been prone to the cold, working as he had done, before joining up, in cold unheated garages, or in the open. But now he was conscious of the cold in his fingers and toes and he started to flex them to restore the circulation. He moved up and down in the narrow space beside the pilot's seat and was surprised at how stiff his knees had become from standing in the confined space. After a while he knelt on the cockpit floor and inspected the fuel gauges carefully. The cold metal floor took the heat from his knees through his trousers and long johns as if he wasn't wearing any. He filled in the latest fuel figures in the log and decided he could now transfer the contents of the number three tanks into the now half empty number twos.

Telling Doug what he was going to do he turned on the fuel booster pumps for the two number one fuel tanks, then turned the two knurled fuel tank selector knobs, one for each wing, on his flight engineer's panel to number one tanks. After waiting a few seconds no low fuel pressure warning lights came on and the engines continued to run smoothly. So he switched off the number two fuel booster pumps and switched on the number three fuel tanks' booster pumps. The engines were now running on the number one fuel tanks and fuel was being transferred from the number three tanks into the number two tanks. Satisfied that all was well Jimmy logged the transfer time and standing up resumed his lookout.

Nobody had spoken for some time and Jimmy jumped when Ron suddenly reported that they should be crossing the coast in ten minutes. The 60 mph tailwind was pushing them along far more quickly than usual and hopefully their speed would take the German fighter controllers by surprise. Even with a 60 mph tailwind if they were only ten minutes from the coast they would now be visible to the German radars and the controllers would be trying to decide whether they or the Stirlings off the Dutch coast were the real raid. They had a 50/50 choice, would they choose the right one? If they got it wrong they would send their fighters the wrong way and leave Berlin open to the Lancasters and Halifaxes from the north. Fatalistically Jimmy believed they would get it right. Bomber Command had used this route before and while it had the advantages of keeping the bombers clear of flak and out of radar cover for as long as possible it also meant that the target was either Hamburg or Berlin.

"Enemy coast ahead," said Bob, over the intercom. Jimmy looked over the right side of the nose and couldn't see any sign of the coast. Then he saw a faint white line in the blackness below and realised that these were waves whipped up by the strong winds breaking on the shore. F for Freddy started to turn and Jimmy looked quickly over at Doug, but he was just starting the slow weave that he had used on the last Op. Normally objects on the ground seemed to approach slowly, but the dark night making things difficult to spot until they were close and the extra 60 mph meant they were over the coast very quickly. Germany slipped by below them in complete darkness. Over the sea at least the occasional wave could be seen as a splash of white in the darkness, but now there was nothing. Soon they were crossing the coast again, this time into the Baltic and suddenly twenty or more searchlights lit up to their right. Bob called them in to Ron, who calmly replied that they were at Kiel and well to the south of their route. Jimmy envied Ron his curtained off compartment. Ron could not see the threatening searchlights feeling for their victims in the dark, or the deadly flak that was now twinkling off to their right. It was no wonder Ron sounded so calm.

Jimmy had no way of knowing that Ron sounded calm because he now knew for certain where they were and they were bang on track and time. Ten minutes before they got to the German coast, with GEE jammed and no fix to be had over the sea, Ron had been in a complete panic. He had convinced himself that the strong winds had blown them miles off course and they were hopelessly lost. His announcement of ten minutes to the coast had almost been a plea for someone to spot something tangible that he could use to fix their position.

The Baltic must have been calmer than the North Sea because no waves could be seen from 20,000 feet and the bombers were whisked on unmolested. Soon they would turn south. The fact that no bombers had yet gone down showed that the German controllers must have been confused as to which had been the real raid, but now the game was up and there could only be one target, as Hamburg was now behind them.

"New course one six five compass," said Ron. Jimmy looked over the side of the Lancaster through the cockpit blister, but could still not see the southern tip of Falster Island, marking their turning point, and he concluded that Ron must have used H2S radar to spot the turn. Now they crossed the north German coast and continued their slow weave to the south, with Berlin about twenty-five minutes away.

Jimmy checked the engine instruments again. Boost, rpm, oil temperatures and pressures and coolant temperature were all well within limits. Number four engine, he had noticed, ran slightly hotter than the other three, but not enough to worry about. Doug had synchronized the Merlins well and their steady rhythmical drone rose and fell as one engine. Jimmy found the sound hypnotic and could easily have gone to sleep listening to it if he did not concentrate on his job. It seemed to numb his brain, as he once again checked his fuel figures. Kneeling down, looking sideways in the cockpit, the weaving motion started to make him feel queasy. His head reeled from the rhythmic vibration and his stomach started to turn. Better hurry he thought, knowing that he would feel fine again as soon as he could look outside.

"Rear gunner, bomber going down in flames 5 o'clock." It had started. Jimmy instantly forgot his stomach and stood up, looking towards their 5 o'clock, but he could see nothing. The first flaming bomber was soon followed by a second, then a third. Jimmy didn't see either, but he saw the fourth. It was closer than the other two, in their 8 o'clock and Jimmy watched it behind Doug's seat while the red flames turned yellow as they increased in intensity and spread. He had not seen the tracer from the German fighter and he could still not see the bomber itself, only the yellow flames suspended in the blackness. The flames sank lower and Jimmy had to move to the left side of the cockpit, behind Doug's seat, to keep them in sight as they descended. Although the bomber could obviously not maintain height, it seemed that the flames were going down under control and the crew had a good chance of baling out. All that is, except the pilot, who would have to stay at the controls to prevent the bomber turning over into a spiral dive, trapping the crew with the centrifugal force to the walls, floors or ceilings and holding them immobile until the ground brought them oblivion. Once the pilot was sure his crew had all gone, then he would try to make a quick dash for the hatch, but encumbered by bulky flying kit and wearing a large unwieldy seat-type parachute. The narrow gap under the right side of the instrument panel and the small forward hatch of the Lancaster often proved to be too much of an obstacle to be negotiated in the short time available. The flames fell away below and behind them and Jimmy, feeling a little sick, turned away. He looked at the back of Doug's head and knew if it ever came to it Doug would do all he could to get his crew out safely. The thought brought a lump to his throat. Doug, as an officer, didn't eat or sleep with his crew. He came from a completely different background to Jimmy, and they hadn't even known each other very long. But Jimmy had always liked Doug and he was certain that Doug would give his life for his crew, and the thought that he might one day have to tied his stomach in knots. He reached out the toe of his right boot and touched his parachute pack in the dark behind Doug's seat, checking it was still there. If they ever had to bale out he would not be the one holding Doug up, and until that day came he would do all he could to keep his pilot safe.

They had turned onto the next leg and were now ten minutes from the holding point. Searchlights were visible in the distance to the left, which could only be Berlin and as he watched it flak started to burst amongst the beams. They were flying into the wind at the moment and their progress over the ground was slow. But once they turned onto the bombing run the wind would once more be behind them and the time over the target should be blessedly short. Yellow markers suddenly erupted on the ground in front of them, marking where they would start to drop window at the maximum rate. The flak and searchlights got nearer and Jimmy stared in horror at it all. Soon they would be in the middle of it. Ron had said they were on time, so there should be no need to hold, and after a final check of the instruments he told Doug he was going into the nose to get ready to drop the window.

Sitting on the cockpit floor the cold almost took his breath away and he slid forwards under the instrument panel, curling his broad shoulders inwards as he did so to get through the narrow gap. Sliding down the two steps, he could see Bob silhouetted against the yellow glow from the ground markers, as he leaned over his bombsight in the extreme nose of the aircraft. Turning to his left he gathered together half a dozen packets of window and tore one open ready to drop. Each packet was about the size of a house brick and contained hundreds of strips of paper about a foot long by a quarter of an inch wide, with metal foil on one side. The length of the strips was critical. It needed to be half the wavelength of the radar they were trying to jam, in this case the Wurzburg radars used to control the master searchlights, as well as the radar predicted flak batteries. Although it would also confuse the Giant Wurzburg radars used by the German fighter controllers to talk their night fighters into positions from where they could detect the bombers with their own Lichtenstein radars. The Lichtenstein radars worked on a different frequency and were not affected by the type of window F for Freddy was carrying, but half of the aircraft on each squadron, and so half the aircraft spread throughout the bomber stream, carried window cut to half the wavelength of the Lichtenstein radar. Together the bomber stream provided each other with mutual support, which would confuse and hopefully overwhelm the enemy. Opening the window chute, Jimmy was greeted by a blast of cold air that stung his eyes above his oxygen mask.

"Start dropping window," said Bob.

This was it; they were on their way into the flak. The floor moved, as the Lancaster started its turn onto the bomb run. Jimmy pushed the first packet down the chute and reached for another. This was the bit he hated most, the run over the target, where all the dangers were so visible. Night fighters scared him, but as he couldn't see them he could pretend they weren't there. Flak and searchlights on the other hand could not be ignored. On the first raid he had been so terrified by the sight of the Berlin defences that he had nearly forgotten to go into the nose to drop the window. Had that really only been last night? He fumbled to open another bundle of window with his heavy gloves on. Looking forward, he saw Bob was moving around checking switches and making adjustments to the bombsight. Over Bob's head Jimmy could see the searchlights moving back and forth. He had been told the light blue ones were the radar controlled master searchlights, which had to be confused by the window. They were a different colour because they were two metre diameter lights and therefore brighter. At night this made them appear blue, compared with the smaller, one-and-a-half-metre-diameter manually-aimed lights. Once a master searchlight held you in its beam as many manual lights as possible would also latch onto you, holding you trapped in their fingers, while all the time the flak gunners hurled shells at you. Jimmy pictured the bomber he had seen last night coned by the lights and surrounded by flak. The Lancaster suddenly jumped and the fittings rattled. Doug had once told him that if they were ever coned he intended to dive at the lights and veer away at low level. One of his instructors had once told him this was the best way to get away from searchlights, but Jimmy was sceptical of that. There was a rattle, like someone had thrown a handful of gravel at the fuselage. Over Bob's head Jimmy could see red flashes, as flak burst around them. A searchlight flashed by close ahead and the intense light flooded the nose compartment, lighting up every recess of the black painted compartment, but it didn't latch onto them.

"Bomb doors open, master switch on, bombs fused and selected, skipper," said Bob.

"Bomb doors open, master switch on, bombs fused and selected," repeated Doug.

There was the sound of air rushing into the bomb bay the other side of the bulkhead to his right. Damn these gloves! He had only dropped three bundles of window and they must be near the aiming point. He pulled the gloves off and carefully put them to one side, where he would not lose them in the dark. Now he could drop the window much more efficiently, as long as he was careful not to touch any metal, which at this freezing temperature would stick to his skin. Now he went to work with a vengeance, dropping bundle after bundle in quick succession, convincing himself that every bundle was keeping them safe from the deadly lights. F for Freddy lurched and he heard a woofing sound over the noise of the engines and slipstream. Bracing himself as best he could against the bumps, he continued to shovel out the window and all the while the aircraft jumped, bucked and rattled through the barrage. In his own little dark world Jimmy was screaming to escape. His active mind, starved of visual references, invented its own and he fought to keep them out by bundling out the window as fast as he could. How he wished he could see what was going on. He knew the sight would terrify him, but left to its own devices his own mind scared him more. Maybe Ron wasn't so lucky after all.

"Left! Left…Steady!" Jesus Christ! Bob was only just starting to line them up on the markers! How much longer would this go on? How much more could he stand? He glanced to his right along the cockpit floor, past Doug's seat, looking for his parachute; it was a long way away. Get a grip of yourself! Concentrate on your job! Slow down your breathing! Take deep breaths! Jimmy's hands were shaking with fear and numb with cold. Just keep pushing out the window and you'll be alright. Just keep pushing out the window and you'll be alright. He repeated it to himself over and over. Somewhere in the background he could hear Bob talking on the intercom but he could not hear what he was saying, his mind was numb and all he could do was push out the window. Suddenly a huge lurch brought him to his senses. They'd been hit! No, it was the bombs dropping! Thank God! Let's get out of here. More window, that would keep them safe. Rate "G", five bundles a minute, one bundle every twelve seconds, sod that! He would throw it out as fast as he could. To his right he heard the bomb doors close, then the camera behind him clicked.

"Photo flash fired. Let's go home, skipper," said Bob.

At last they were on their way out of this hell. Bob came back to help him drop the window and was amazed to see that there were only a quarter of the packets left and they still had a long overland transit ahead of them.

"Christ! You've been busy!" he shouted over the top of his oxygen mask into Jimmy's ear. But Jimmy just nodded and carried on dropping the window as fast as he could. By the time Bob told Jimmy he could stop dropping window he felt totally drained and he slowly pulled on his gloves and returned to the cockpit. Once there he stood behind Doug, next to the curtain which separated the navigation compartment from the flight deck. Here he composed himself and tried to stop his hands shaking. Outside flak still burst in red and white flashes around them, but none of it seemed as close as before and most of the searchlights were now behind them. He took long slow breaths, his head was pounding and he felt sick. His skin was wet and clammy and now it was starting to freeze. He shivered and felt dizzy. Maybe I'm going to faint, he thought, as he hung onto the side of the cockpit, steadying himself. Damn it! I'm not going to bloody faint! Get angry! People are relying on you! Don't let them down! Now get to work! And he knelt down and started to check the engine instruments and fuel gauges.

Berlin fell away behind them as they climbed to just below the layer of cloud at 24,000 feet, but they could still see the glow from the numerous fires 50 miles away as they headed between Magdeburg and Leipzig.

142 miles southwest of Berlin they would come to a lake where they would turn west. Just before the lake was the town of Erfurt and both these features would show up well on the bomber's H2S. The town was not on any bomber command flak map and if it were defended at all it would be light and no significant threat to the bomber stream. As F for Freddy approached it was obvious that Erfurt did have some defences as two searchlights weaved back and forth and flak burst ahead of them. The barrage was very small and sporadic, probably no more than one or two six gun batteries. Jimmy watched as they approached the flak and decided to take his mind off it by doing a fuel check. The two number one tanks had 315 gallons left in them, while the two number two tanks still had the 314 gallons left after the fuel transfer over the North Sea. Jimmy decided to run on the number one tanks for another half hour, and then change to the number two tanks. Then he started to stand up.

The RAF intelligence had been right, Erfurt did only have one battery of flak guns, but the townspeople did not think this was enough and they had put pressure on the Burgermeister to increase their defences. The Burgermeister had not thought it was necessary but, bowing to public pressure, he had written letters asking for more guns. He was amazed when, for one week only, his town was allowed to host a mobile flak battery and its Wurzburg guidance radar. Now, while the old flak battery blazed away at random into the bomber stream overhead, the Wurzburg radar picked out its victim and tracked it. The six guns predicted ahead then, as one, fired.

Doug had kept up his slow steady weaving course until he was close to the flak. Then he decided that although the barrage was pitifully small he would make a detour around it and so on his next weave to the left, instead of rolling back to the right, he rolled out on his new heading, 30 degrees left of his base course. At that moment the six-gun box barrage arrived at 24,000 feet and their altitude fuses detonated. The first two shells detonated 100 yards away in F for Freddy's 2 o'clock, in the exact place the Lancaster would have been if it had continued on course. By themselves they would have been close enough to be frightening, but when they were followed almost instantaneously by two more fifty yards closer, the shock factor was huge. However, none of F for Freddy's crew even noticed these four shells, because the last two shells got all the attention. One of the shells exploded twenty feet from the right wingtip and lacerated the metal skin, while the blast threw the wing violently upwards. But it was shell six that was almost a bull's-eye. It exploded slightly below and in front of the starboard wing, ahead of the number three, starboard inner, engine. The blast caused the bomber to jump violently upwards and roll left. Numerous small pieces of shrapnel pierced the fuselage and wing, but four large pieces caused all the main damage. The first hit the starboard inner engine square on the bottom of the cast iron engine block, shattering it. Two more pieces punched through the starboard number one fuel tank from below and continued out through the top. The final piece was smaller and had less energy, but still managed to burst through the lower skin of the starboard number two fuel tank. Then, slowed by the fuel, it hit the top of the tank and stopped.

Inside the bomber, the horrendously loud bang, violent jump and roll felt like they had hit something solid and threw Jimmy onto his back behind Doug's seat. George, Alex and Bob, in their turrets, were shaken around but suffered no more than a shock, although the flash meant Bob was blinded for quite a few seconds. Ron and Harry were thrown across their desks, and maps and codebooks fell to the deck. Doug instinctively fought with the controls to bring the Lancaster back to straight and level flight, but while his ears still rang from the explosion, he could hear more bangs over the noise of the engines and a flickering yellow glow filled the cockpit.

Looking vertically up through the cockpit canopy from where he had fallen, Jimmy could also see the yellow glow and instantly knew they were on fire. Springing to his feet he looked out of the starboard side cockpit window to stare directly into the flaming yellow heart of the burning number three engine. The inner engine cowling was gone and he could hardly see the engine for brilliant yellow flames, which seemed to emanate from the engine exhausts, whipping downwards and back in the slipstream. Loud bangs erupted from within the engine and with each one there was an even larger gush of flame.

Flicking on his microphone he yelled, "Fire in number three!"

Doug knew from the yellow glow that they were on fire, but he hadn't had time to look and see the damage for himself. Glancing at the instrument panel he saw that the boost and revs for number three were falling fast. He leaned across and took hold of the number three engine master fuel cock.

"Confirm number three!" His voice was loud, but calm.

Jimmy looked to see Doug had hold of the right fuel cock. "Confirmed!"

Doug closed the fuel cock, then the throttle, and turned the number three engine idle cut-off switches to idle cut-off, while at the same time yelling to Jimmy, "Feather number three and hit the fire extinguisher!" Jimmy pushed the large number three propeller-feathering button on his side of the instrument panel, holding it in until it remained in on its own. Then he lifted the spring-loaded guard below it, which covered the number three engine fire extinguisher button and pushed that. Feathering the propeller would bring the blades edge on to the slipstream, so they would not windmill round. In this position they would produce as little drag as possible. The fire extinguisher was a one shot button. Once activated the fire extinguisher would discharge into the engine until it was empty and hopefully by this time the fire would be out. Jimmy stared at the flames as they whipped back around the leading edge of the wing, curling over the upper surface, almost to the trailing edge. Go out! Go out! he willed them, without much hope, as the engine was well alight. The paint on the wing was burnt black and starting to blister. Was it his imagination or were the flames getting smaller? The banging had stopped now and the flames were no longer pulsing out of the engine, but that did not mean they would go out. What Jimmy had not noticed was that Doug had gone to full power on all the other engines and was in a shallow dive to increase their speed, hoping that the increased slipstream would blow out the flames. F for Freddy started to buck and bounce as the speed increased. The lost height would not matter, a Lancaster could not maintain height above 10,000 feet on three engines. The flames were definitely smaller now and getting smaller with every second, but how much longer would the fire extinguisher last? It became an endurance contest between the extinguisher and the fire as to which would last the longest, but with the help of the slipstream the fire extinguisher won. Jimmy saw the flames disappear, then pulse out of the exhausts once, then disappear for good. They were replaced by white smoke from what was left of the fire extinguisher and hot glycol coolant evaporating on the hot engine. The smoke trailed out behind them in a long straight line as far as he could see.

"Any other damage?" asked Doug.

Jimmy hadn't checked because he had been mesmerised by the flames. Now he was galvanised into action. Kneeling down, he checked the other engines' temperatures and oil pressures; all were normal. Next the fuel. NO! NO! NO! All the fuel from the starboard number one tank was gone and the number two fuel tank gauge was slowly but surely unwinding.

"Fuel leak!" he yelled, turning the starboard fuel tank selector to the number two tank and switching on the tanks booster pump. Then he rushed aft, out of the cockpit, pulling his intercom lead and oxygen pipe out of their sockets as he went. Through the curtain, bent double, into Ron's compartment he went, pushing Ron out of the way over his map table as if he wasn't there. Then into the space beside Harry's seat and onto all fours, feeling in the dark for the fuel cross feed cock, not noticing the radio operator's worried eyes looking down at him. Turning the cock on, he ran back to the cockpit, bent forward so that he didn't bang his head and again he pushed Ron out of the way. Ron was ready this time and tried to fend Jimmy off but Jimmy's large powerful arms swept him aside knocking him off his chair onto the deck. On the flight deck he turned off the port number one fuel booster pump and then selected off on the port fuel tanks. All the engines were now being run from the leaking starboard number two tank. Reconnecting his intercom and oxygen he breathlessly reported to Doug,

"We've lost all the fuel in the number one starboard tank and we've got a bad leak in the number two starboard tank. All the engines are running on the damaged tank so we'd better use as much fuel as we can before it leaks away, but I don't know if there's enough left to get us home."

Doug's brain was still numbed by what had just happened and no sooner had he started to recover from the fire than he was hit with another problem. The vital fuel was draining away and every second counted. He had to make an immediate decision, but it also had to be the right one and he felt pressure like he had never felt it before.

"Ron, give me a course for the nearest English airfield." At the same time he turned onto a westerly heading and, still in a slight dive to 10,000 feet, checked that all the engines were at maximum power. Every gallon of fuel in the leaking tank that they used before it drained away would get them closer to home, so they entered the second race of the night, the number of gallons used by the three remaining thirsty Merlins, against the fuel draining away.

One thing that was in their favour was the fact that the Lancaster had self-sealing fuel tanks. Each fuel tank was double-skinned and between the inner and outer skins was a rubber substance which would expand when it came into contact with fuel. When a tank was holed the fuel would leak out coming into contact with the rubber material. This would expand and hopefully block the hole. With small holes it worked well but the hole in F for Freddy's tank was too big for the rubber to fill and the best it could do was slow the leak.

"Course for Manston, two eight five degrees compass," said Ron.

"How far is it?" asked Doug.

"360 miles."

"Can we make it?"

"How much fuel have we got left?"

Jimmy had just finished working this out. "About 630 gallons plus what we can use from the starboard number two before it leaks away."

"That's no use to me, sergeant!" snapped Ron, who was still annoyed that Jimmy had pushed him over. "I need to know our endurance!"

Blushing in the dark Jimmy sat on the cockpit floor and took out his torch and fuel consumption tables. Beneath him the Lancaster bounced along as fast as the three engines would pull it and his torch jumped around the pages of tables. He glanced at the boost and rpm settings and discounted the remaining fuel in the leaking tank, which was now almost empty, and decided that they could remain airborne for another 150 minutes. "Two and a half hours."

"I need it exactly, Sergeant Wilson!"

"That is exactly, sir!" snapped Jimmy angrily.

"Stay calm," said Doug. "We've done all we can. We're on a direct course for Manston and we're using as much leaking fuel as possible. Then we'll use the fuel in the port tanks as economically as we can. There's nothing else we can do except fly an accurate straight course. So let's all go through the figures and see if we can make it."

"And if we can't?" asked Ron.

"We'll make that decision if we have to," replied Doug.

They levelled off at 10,000 feet and, with the fuel in the leaking tank all but gone, Jimmy turned on the booster pump for the port number two tank and selected the port number two tank to on and the leaking tank off, as its gauge read zero. Now he would swap between the two port fuel tanks at half hourly intervals, until they landed at Manston, or ran out of fuel. With the frantic activity over he could now take stock of his actions and as he stared out of the side window at the white smoke from the dead engine he wished he had spotted the fuel leak sooner. Even a few seconds might make a difference to them getting back. Still, he thought, once he had seen it he had done all the right things and now it was up to Doug to fly a straight course, with the most efficient engine power settings, and Ron to keep them on track. Nothing else appeared to be damaged but he couldn't be sure of the condition of the starboard main wheel. The only way they would find out about that was when they lowered it to land and that was too far away to think of yet. Other things powered by the number three engine were the front turret, which was now out of action. All the other hydraulic systems could be powered by the pump in the number two engine, but the pneumatic system, that was another matter. Only the number three engine had an air compressor and now they only had what was left in the accumulator. When that fell to 130 pounds per square inch they would no longer have high gear superchargers, automatic radiator shutters or idle cut out rams. None of these really mattered as they would be flying at 10,000 feet or below now, but he wasn't sure how to stop the engines properly without the idle cut out rams. That, he decided, was the least of his worries and at least the system would maintain 130 pounds in reserve for the wheel brakes.

Behind his curtain Ron was working frantically. The wind at 20,000 feet had been remarkably accurate and constant and he was happy navigating by it. But now he had no idea what the wind was at 10,000 feet and without it he couldn't navigate a course straight to Manston. To make matters worse any error with the fuel this critical was likely to drop them in the sea short of the English coast. The track he wanted to follow over the ground was two eight five degrees compass, but the wind would be blowing them off to one side or the other of that heading and without knowing the wind speed and direction at 10,000 feet he had no idea how to allow for that. If he was wrong by 10 degrees over 360 miles that would put him 60 miles off course, with no spare fuel to put things right. Working on the wind speed and direction at 20,000 feet the headwind gave them a ground speed at 10,000 feet of 120 mph and at this speed it would take him three hours to reach Manston, or in this case, he would run out of fuel 60 miles short, over the English Channel. He would never make it. He would fall into the sea and in this wind the sea would be too rough to surviving a ditching. He would have to bale out over enemy territory. He thought of his wife and imagined her getting the telegram posting him as missing and his heart ached for her. Would he ever see her again? She had hated it when he had volunteered to go aircrew. She had said no good would come of it and she was right. Her letters to him were now distant and without feeling and he knew he was losing her. Now, if he was to be taken prisoner, he was sure she would find someone else. A black wave of despair descended over him and he was about to bury his head in his hands when a thought suddenly struck him. Wind speeds almost always increased with altitude, so now he was at 10,000 feet he should have less of a headwind than he had at 24,000 feet. He reached for his Dalton computer and made a guess at what the wind might be. Two six zero degrees at 50 mph, that would give a ground speed of 132 mph, so he could fly for 330 miles, still 30 short! But the headwind might be even less than 50 mph and that idiot Wilson probably under read the gauges, so he might just make it. Damn it, he had to make it! If he didn't he would lose his wife! The small spark of hope glowed inside him. This was not a problem of his making and nobody could blame him for their predicament. He felt more at ease knowing that this was not his fault, but he must get back to Janice.

"New course two eight zero degrees compass. And I think we can just make it to Manston, but it will be very close and I'll have a better idea as we reach the coast."

Now they were alone in the darkness and although they rarely saw any other bombers in the stream, it was always good to know that they were there, if for no other reason than to share the danger. Their course was arrow straight, with no weaves or jinks to add to the distance home. Jimmy, like everyone else in the crew, except Ron, was looking out of the aircraft into the darkness, trying to spot the night fighters that liked nothing better than to finish off lame ducks. Ron was checking his calculations and trying to fix his position using H2S. If he could do that he could take a better guess at the wind. The engine was still trailing white smoke, which Jimmy supposed must have been visible for miles, even on this dark night. But now, an hour after they were hit, no fighters had attacked.

"I think we might be over a town," said Bob, his eyes straining into the dark from his bomb aimer's position, below his useless turret. Instantaneously what seemed like every searchlight in Germany lit up around them and flak burst above them in a massive barrage.

"Jesus Christ! Where the hell are we?" asked Doug, using language that his father considered to be the ultimate in obscenity.

"The Ruhr," said Ron calmly.

"The fucking Ruhr!" repeated Harry. "That's the biggest fucking flak trap in Germany! What the hell are we doing over the Ruhr?"

"We don't have the fuel to go around," replied Ron remarkably calmly. "Unless you want to swim home."

Harry decided to shut up, but standing in the astrodome he wished that Ron could see the brilliant firework display that was being put on for their sole benefit. Let's see how calm the arrogant bastard would be then, he thought. While the searchlights were all around them, miraculously none of them found the lone Lancaster as it bounced along in the eddies of the hundreds of shells.

"They all seem to be bursting above us," remarked Doug.

"They probably can't believe we're stupid enough to fly across the Ruhr this bloody low!" exclaimed Bob above the noise of the engines and bursting shells, as he threw out all the window he had left as quickly as he could.

"Well, we're certainly safer down here than up there," said Doug.

"Unless they have a direct hit," said Alex, who felt particularly exposed, surrounded as he was with Perspex.

"You're always Mr Cheerful, aren't you?" goaded George. "Dour Scots! Miserable gits is what A call them!"

"Alright," cut in Doug. "Let's all keep our eyes peeled."

"Oh, come on, skipper!" said Bob. "What Jerry in his right mind would fly through this to take a pop at us!" And in the frustration and fear of the moment the whole crew burst out laughing at the absurdity of it all.

A mile to the east a Messerschmitt 110 turned sharply away from the barrage and left the target it had been stalking for the last ten miles to the tender mercies of the guns.

The barrage was not as intense as that over Berlin, but it went on for a full ten minutes with F for Freddy as the sole target. Doug knew that if he didn't use up precious fuel weaving it was only a matter of time before they were hit, so reluctantly he manoeuvred the damaged bomber around the sky. Knowing that they were the only target meant that by the time they left the Ruhr behind they were all shell-shocked and vital extra fuel had been used. The darkness was a massive relief to them all, except Ron. He had not been able to fix his position. The Ruhr was a big area and on H2S it all looked the same, but he did think he was ahead of schedule, so the wind must be less than his estimate. Now he had more chance of getting home, but he needed to fix his position before he got to the coast, about 130 miles away. As it was, Ron thought he was flying along the Dutch Belgian border, but he was wrong. His guess at the wind being two six zero degrees at 50 mph was not bad, but it was actually two four zero at 40.

While this meant less of a headwind, it also meant he was being blown slowly north of his intended track.

"Bomb aimer to navigator, I can see the coast."

"Rubbish! We won't see the coast for another half an hour yet."

"Well, come up here and see for yourself!"

Ron was so surprised he pushed the curtain aside and stood behind Doug's seat looking into the dark. But with his eyes unaccustomed to the darkness he couldn't see anything so he returned to his seat and checked on H2S. The orange screen did appear to be showing a coastline. It looked like two large estuaries, reaching far inland from the coast itself. This was not right, he had planned to hit the coast near Ostend and it shouldn't look anything like this. He looked at his map and searched the coastline for features that matched his radar screen and soon found them. He had to be over Holland instead of Belgium! The southern coast of Holland had four of these large estuaries and his radar was showing him two. If he was over the southern two estuaries he was 10 miles north of track and 110 miles from Manston. If he was over the northern two he was 30 miles north of track and 125 miles from Manston.

"Navigator to flight engineer, what's our endurance?"

"About forty-five minutes."

"I need it exactly!"

"That's as accurate as I can be."

Ron checked his computer. If the wind had been constant over the flight at 10,000 feet the wind was two four zero degrees at 40 mph and it would take him just over forty-five minutes to get to Manston, if he was 110 miles away. If he was 125 miles away it would take him over fifty-one minutes. What the hell was he going to do? If he was 10 miles off track he could just make it, but if he was 30 miles north of track he would run out of fuel and crash into the rough sea without any hope of survival. Or they could bale out now over Holland, then he was sure to survive. He would be a prisoner, but that would be better than dying. But then there was Janice. When would he see her again and would she wait for him? He didn't think she would, so he had to chance it.

"New course two seven five degrees compass for Manston." He had to be over the southern inlets. If he wasn't, he was going to die in the cold dark waters at the entrance to the Thames estuary and the thought of the icy waters closing over him made him shiver.

Out they headed over the dark sea, the surface of which was now covered in white splashes from the breaking waves. As they left Holland behind them the GEE set started to break through the jamming and Ron tried to take a fix, but it was still difficult to read and it would take time.

"Tell us when we're 50 miles out from Manston, Ron," said Doug, who wanted to know when to start their descent.

"Wilco," replied Ron, wishing he could guarantee ever getting within 50 miles of Manston.

"I could get an emergency homing," said Harry helpfully.

"We don't need it," snapped Ron, not wanting to admit he needed help. It wouldn't matter now anyway. If he was further north than he hoped he would not make it to Manston even if he could fly straight to it.

Shortly after crossing the coast Jimmy changed to the port number two fuel tank for the last time. It had enough fuel in it to last ten minutes, and then there were seventy-five gallons left in the port number one tank and that would last less than twenty minutes. Each minute seemed to drag by as he stared intently into the dark, looking for the English coast with Manston and its long east west runway just inland. The fuel gauge relentlessly unwound as their lives slowly drained away through the three Merlins.

Then after what seemed an age Ron got his GEE fix.

"Navigator to pilot, we're 60 miles out from Manston. Begin your descent in four minutes." As he said it the number two engine coughed and backfired. But Jimmy was ready for it and selected the number one fuel tank and booster pump. He didn't really need the pump but having run the tank to empty there would be air in the pipes and he wanted to get fuel back to the engines as quickly as possible. The engine continued to cough, then the number one engine coughed as well. The Lancaster wallowed and everyone held their breaths, except Jimmy, who had worked on engines all his short life and he knew what he was doing. After one last backfire the Merlins ran smoothly.

"We're on our last seventy-five gallons," he reported.

"How long will it last?" asked Doug.

"At our present rate of consumption, eighteen minutes."

"How long to Manston, Ron?"

"Twenty-five minutes," came the crestfallen reply.

"Roger..." Doug's heart sank and he felt a hollow pain in the pit of his stomach. They were so near, but they just weren't going to make it. "Harry, you'd better get ready to send an SOS. Give him our position, Ron."

Meanwhile Jimmy was juggling his fuel figures and searching through his consumption tables.

"Skipper, if we can stretch our descent we can throttle back to zero boost and cut our fuel consumption to 175 gallons per hour and we might just make Manston with maybe a gallon to spare."

The news brought Doug out of his thoughts of their impending deaths like a syringe full of adrenalin.

"When do we need to start our descent?"

"Aiming for a rate of descent of 500 feet per minute, twenty minutes from Manston."

"In three minutes," said Ron before he was asked.

Twenty minutes out Doug throttled back to zero boost at 2650 rpm and lowered the nose to maintain 160 mph.

Doug selected Manston's frequency on RT. Manston's flying control frequency was busy and it was obvious that a lot of bombers were trying to get down at this emergency-landing airfield.

"Manston, Manston, this is Hadnone F for Freddy, Hadnone F for Freddy. We are 40 miles out on three engines and nearly out of fuel. Request immediate permission to land, over."

"Roger, Hadnone F for Freddy, you are number six to land QFE nine nine zero, call airfield in sight, over."

"QFE nine nine zero, Wilco."

Down they went, the speckled surface of the sea below them getting ever closer. All the while they listened to the crackling RT as one by one the aircraft ahead of them made their approaches to land, each one carrying seven men to safety.

"I can see the coast," said Bob, as the dark line crept out of the darkness, slowly becoming clear. "I've got the lights!" exclaimed Bob excitedly. "1 o'clock!"

Doug turned towards the faint white lights and lined them up for the approach.

"Manston, this is Hadnone F for Freddy, airfield in sight, over."

"Roger, Hadnone F for Freddy, you are number three orbit at one thousand feet, over."

Doug looked across at Jimmy. "We haven't the fuel, skipper."

"Negative, Manston, we haven't the fuel to orbit, over."

"Roger, Hadnone F for Freddy, continue and call crossing the coast, over."

Jimmy willed the slowly approaching coast onward until it slid beneath them. Below, in the darkness, the people of Ramsgate listened to the returning bomber as it flew low overhead. Most of them were so used to the sound of damaged bombers they could tell how many engines a bomber had left and many said silent prayers for the crews that were so close to safety, but not quite home yet.

"Hadnone F for Freddy crossing the coast."

"Roger, F for Freddy, call finals."

Now at least they wouldn't drown. The flare path was getting closer and they were well placed for an approach as Bob came through the cockpit to sit behind the main spar.

"Landing checks."

"Auto pilot controls."

"Out."

"Superchargers are in M ratio," said Jimmy, knowing the pneumatic pressure had fallen below their operating limits. "Air intake."

"Cold."

"Brake pressure, 130 pounds per square inch. We have enough for two or three applications of brakes only."

"Roger."

"Flaps."

"20 degrees."

"Undercarriage."

"Down." Jimmy moved the lever and they both held their breath and crossed their fingers during the age it took for the wheels to come down. Would the starboard wheel, just behind the shattered number three engine come down? Finally two green lights showed both wheels locked down, but had the starboard tyre been damaged?

"Propellers."

"Fully fine."

"Fuel booster pump on. Ready to land skipper."

"Manston this is Hadnone F for Freddy finals to land over."

"Hadnone F for Freddy you are number two go around acknowledge."

Doug looked at Jimmy. "No chance skipper."

"How much fuel have we got left?"

Jimmy burst the bombshell that he had been keeping to himself, making a shiver shoot down Doug's spine.

"The gauges have been showing empty for two minutes, skipper."

"Manston, this is Hadnone F for Freddy, we are out of fuel, we are coming in, over."

"Roger," replied the exasperated but resigned voice of the controller. "Proceed with caution, and good luck."

The runway rose up towards them, they were going to make it.

"Halifax closing in 7 o'clock!" yelled George.

"We can't go around, George, warn him off!" replied Doug.

George swung his turret towards the Halifax, elevated his guns as far as they would go and sent a short burst of red tracer soaring almost straight up over the other bomber. The Halifax swung away and overshot into the airfield's circuit.

Despite only having three engines Doug pulled off a near perfect landing and gave one long smooth application of brake to bring the speed under control long before the end of the runway. Then he let the Lancaster run on and turned onto the taxiway towards the hangars, using as little brake as possible and keeping a close eye on the remaining pressure. Jimmy leaned close to his ear and shouted over the engines, off intercom so that nobody else could hear, "We don't have enough pneumatic pressure to work the idle cut off rams. Do you know the recommended way to stop the engines without the rams?" As he spoke the number one engine coughed and spluttered, then died, closely followed by the number two engine.

"I don't think that's going to be a problem Jimmy," replied Doug.

8

F for Freddy stood quietly on the taxiway, its engines silent except for the hissing and clicking as they cooled down. The white smoke still drifted up from the number three engine until, caught by the wind, it was whisked away into the night, leaving only the sickly sweet smell of glycol behind. Both physically and mentally exhausted, the crew dragged themselves from the fuselage. As he dropped out of the entrance door Bob patted the side of the Lancaster.

"You bloody beaut."

"We cut that a bit fine," said Harry, dropping to the ground.

By the time Jimmy and Doug got out everyone had lit up cigarettes and were smoking away their tension under the starboard wingtip and looking up at the damage. With a squeal of brakes a jeep pulled up and an irate officer shouted across to them.

"You can't stop there. You're blocking the taxiway and we've got other aircraft coming in!"

"We're out of fuel!" replied Doug.

"Damn it! Wait here, I'll get a tractor."

"Well, we can't bloody go anywhere, can we?" said Harry quietly, as the jeep sped off.

Jimmy shone his torch up at the aileron.

"Look at that," he said. "The hinge is hanging on by a thread." The aileron was very badly damaged and had only just held together, while the wing tip itself looked like a colander. Slowly they walked down the front of the wing and stared up at the fire-blackened engine in silence.

"You know, George," said Doug slowly to the small gunner in his ridiculously large heated suit. "When I asked you to warn off that Halifax, I meant you to flash the tail-light at him, not put a shot across his bows."

"Oh," said George, realising he might have been far too aggressive and now be in big trouble. "Sorry, skipper."

"He was nae puttin a shot across his bows, skipper. That's how he shoots when he's aiming at something," said Alex. George coloured slightly in the dark at the crew's laughter. He was starting to feel a bit touchy about comments made regarding his shooting since he had missed the night fighter.

"Look at that!" said Jimmy, pointing down the runway. Another bomber was coming in to land, both port engines on fire. The flames were mainly red with the occasional flare of yellow and the aircraft was wallowing around on the approach. They heard the engines cut and almost immediately the tyres screeched. It had landed a long way into the runway, but still had plenty of space to stop as it raced towards them. They could see it was a Halifax now that it was closer. A siren started to wail off to their right. The fire trucks raced over the grass towards it, their lights bouncing in the darkness.

"That's not the one you fired at, is it, George?" teased Bob.

"Nae, George could nae even hit something that big," laughed Alex.

"You'll get a right slappin if you're not careful," said George.

As he said it the Halifax, which was still doing about 60 mph, dropped its left wing to the runway, amid the screech of tortured metal, as the port undercarriage collapsed. Sparks flew from the wingtip and the bomber slewed sharply to the left out of control. The fuel tanks in the left wing ruptured and as the fuel gushed out the fire from the engines immediately ignited it in a massive sheet of yellow flame. The bomber left the runway and bounced over the grass in a wide left turn, shedding bits of debris as it went, until the sideways stress and uneven grass became too much for the remaining undercarriage and it too collapsed. Still the heavy aircraft slid forwards, now at 90 degrees to the watching group, with flames flaring out behind it. The nose looked crumpled as it dug a furrow through the grass, throwing up large sods of earth until it eventually ground to a halt 200 yards away. After the roar of engines and screeching of tearing metal the crackling of the distant flames seemed almost silent as they all stood transfixed and stared at the wreck. Lurid flames jetted skywards from the far left wing backlighting the rest of the wreck as a dark silhouette in the foreground. The red and yellow flames shone through the cockpit and fuselage windows as they ate their way forwards. Then something moved in the cockpit. The pilot or flight engineer had been stunned by the crash but had now recovered and was trying to free himself and get out before the flames arrived.

Doug and his crew had watched the drama unfold silently and without realising they had started to walk slowly towards the bomber, as if hypnotised by it. George recovered first.

"Come on!" he yelled, breaking into a run, closely followed by the rest of the crew. The fire truck was still off to the right making hard going of the wet grass and it looked like Doug, Jimmy, Harry and Bob would get there before it. Ron didn't appear to be in a great hurry and George and Alex were too heavily laden down with their heavy suits to run far at any speed. At 100 yards they could feel the heat and by fifty yards it was stinging their faces. The ditching hatch in the roof of the bomber, between the wing spars, was punched free and three men clambered out to fall from the fuselage onto the starboard wing root. Doug put his head down and charged the wall of heat, trying to shield himself from as much of it as possible behind the fuselage. Screams came from the bomber as he ran along the trailing edge of the wing to the wing root, arriving just as the first of the crew slid to the ground. He was a big man and as he landed his right leg gave way under him and Doug grabbed him, to stop him falling. Then Jimmy was there.

"Mine, skipper!" he yelled over the terrible screams and roar of the flames, as he threw the man over his shoulder like a sack of corn and ran away from the bomber, as if he were carrying nothing at all. The fire engine was now at the nose of the Halifax, spraying it with foam, while two firemen clambered up to the cockpit. Doug wondered how they stood the intense heat which even behind the fuselage was almost unbearable. The next man off the wing had a broken arm and the third man was concussed and confused. Bob and Harry led them away. Doug had a quick look around; the firemen were at the cockpit and the screaming had stopped. The mid-upper turret looked empty, what about the rear gunner? He ran down the side of the fuselage towards the tail and saw George standing by the rear turret. The little gunner looked almost ball-shaped in his bulky suit, lit by the flames. George looked across at him, shook his head and waved him away before running back the way he had come.

Doug's crew met up again at the two ambulances that had positioned themselves 100 yards upwind of the crash so that they would be out of the smoke, which now billowed black from the wreck into the night sky. They were all out of breath and sweating profusely. The three smoke blackened Halifax crewmen, who were all Canadian, were refusing to get into the ambulance until the firemen freed the pilot and flight engineer. Smoke was now starting to obscure the scene, but it looked like the firemen had got the two men out.

"What about the gunners?" asked Doug.

"They were both dead before we landed," replied the large navigator as he sat up on a stretcher where Jimmy had put him.

Two firemen ran towards them dragging something behind them. Then at 50 yards they stopped and helped the man they had been dragging to his feet and led him slowly to the ambulance. Behind them, sharp cracks went off inside the bomber as the ammunition reached a critical temperature and exploded. The last surviving Halifax crewman was literally smoking as he approached. He shrugged off the firemen's offers of help and walked unaided up to the ambulance. White smoke drifted up from his charred leather flying helmet and jacket. The white sheepskin collar was singed black and blobs of foam clung to his steaming trousers. His eyebrows were gone and his face was bright red. Already a large yellow blister was starting to form on his nose, while his smoke-blackened face was streaked with tears.

"Walt was trapped in his seat," he explained to the remainder of his crew, as his voice started to break, pointing back at the Halifax with a hand that was burnt black and already swelling to twice its normal size. "I couldn't get the harness free and as the flames came in he just screamed." He took a deep gurgling breath. "By the time they pulled me out he was burnt black!" He sobbed. "I could see his skull!" The last exclamation took all of his strength and his knees collapsed. Two ambulance men picked him up and led him into the ambulance, followed by the other Halifax men. Doug and his crew looked at each other then stared at the still burning Halifax, with its two mangled gunners and cremated pilot still inside it.

"You there! Is that your Lancaster?" yelled a voice behind them.

"Yes," replied Doug.

"We're ready to move it now."

"Right," said Doug, glad of something else to occupy his mind. "Come on."

With F for Freddy parked out of the way they carried their flight bags, harnesses and parachute packs to a waiting wagon, which deposited them at Manston's Operations Room. The room was full of other bomber crews, all of them checking in with their own airfields and waiting for further instructions. After a quick look around they established that there were no other Metheringham crews there, so the sergeants stood in a group and smoked while Doug went to phone Metheringham. Ron, as usual, stood to one side with his pipe. A WAAF offered them all a large mug of tea and they stood for a long while in silence, with a cigarette in one hand and the tea in the other, smoking and drinking, and staring into space.

"Did you smell that flight engineer?" asked Bob eventually. "I've never smelt anything like that before." They all shook their heads.

"I have," said Harry. "Roast pork... My mother's a bloody awful cook!"

"You're a cold bugger," smiled Bob.

"If you don't laugh you'll cry," replied Harry, his voice devoid of humour.

"Imagine how much that wid a hurt," said Alex. "That flight engineer was burnt black up tae his elbows and his face had started tae melt. Ah once burnt me sell on a hot range an it hurt like hell, but that was nothin' tae what he was like."

"How could he still walk? He must have been in agony," said Bob.

"Shock," said George, as he stripped off his electric suit and buoyancy oversuit. "He probably couldn't feel a thing then. But he'll be feeling it now alright."

Jimmy had gone white. In his mind he had already swapped himself and Doug for the Canadian crew and he could almost feel the man's agony. His hands started to shake and he had to put his tea down to stop himself from spilling it. He took a deep draw on his cigarette and tried to calm himself down.

"Well, we made it alright and that's the main thing," said Alex.

"Yeah, thanks to Jimmy," added Harry, slapping Jimmy on the back and jerking him back to reality.

"And you, Ron," said Bob, looking over at the navigator.

"Thank you, sergeant," replied Ron, with a nod. It was the first compliment the crew had given him and although they were only sergeants he was quite pleased by it. Unfortunately, Ron didn't realise that by using Bob's rank instead of his name he was making it look like he was looking down on him.

Arrogant twat, thought Bob, turning back to the other sergeants and raising his eyebrows in derision. To a man the sergeants had to admit they admired Ron as a navigator, but didn't think much of him as a person.

Doug came back into the crowded Ops room and looked around for his crew. Spotting them he walked over.

"We've got to go straight back to Metheringham," he said.

"How?" asked Ron, who was thinking they would get a few days off Ops as a result of their diversion and the damage to the aircraft. But now that idea was vanishing before his eyes.

"Train," replied Doug. "From here to London. Change at King's Cross then up to Grantham. They'll send a truck to get us from there."

"And I suppose they want us back on Ops tomorrow night."

"I have no idea, Ron, but I've got the rail warrants and there's a truck leaving for the station in half an hour, so you had better all be ready."

"What about Freddy?" asked Jimmy.

"The engineers here will assess the damage and let Metheringham know the score. After that it's up to them. Thanks," he said, taking a mug of tea from George.

"We don't want to lose it, skipper, it's a good aeroplane," said Jimmy.

"Yeah, skip, it's lucky," chipped in Bob.

"Well, it's not up to me, but I'll ask when we get back. They'll probably do any repairs necessary to get it airworthy, then fly it back to Metheringham for the other repairs." Doug had never realised how superstitious his crew were until now. The truth was, they didn't realise how superstitious they were until now either. The events of the night had changed them all to some extent and they were a lot more aware of their own mortality.

The cold draughty truck took them to the cold draughty railway station, where Doug exchanged the rail warrants for tickets. Thirty minutes later a train for London arrived and they rattled their way to the capital, through the blacked out countryside. It was the slow train and it stopped at every station between Manston and London, so it was after midnight when they arrived in London. George and Alex had never been to London before, but in the darkness there was nothing to see, and looking from the train window into the darkness even Harry, as the resident local, didn't recognise anything. Getting across London from Waterloo station to King's Cross wasn't straightforward because they were all carrying their parachutes, harnesses and flight bags. George and Alex were especially laden as they carried their bulky suits rolled up under their arms. At King's Cross they waited another half an hour for a train to Grantham. This train however was faster, but still dark and cold. Fortunately they were dressed for the cold and the train was almost full so although the atmosphere soon became smoke laden, body heat kept the cold at bay. Most of them took the opportunity to sleep, but Jimmy's mind was still too full of thoughts of burning bombers and although Ron was now in charge, as the senior officer, it was Doug who stayed awake to make sure they didn't miss their stop. Two hours later the train pulled into Grantham station and Doug roused the sleepers. As they stepped onto the dark windy platform the cold air after the warmth of the carriage made them shiver as they walked up the platform to the station entrance.

After waving all the bombers off Sally had driven to the NAAFI and had a hot mug of tea to warm up. She followed the same routine every night when Ops were on. After warming up she would go to the flying control tower, where two of her WAAF friends worked as flying control assistants. They would be the first people to hear if a bomber had returned early with a fault, and if it was her crew she wanted to be ready for them. The other drivers would go to the station cinema or play cards in the MT section hut. Others would go back to their billet and read or sleep until the bombers were due to return. Sally thought this was too far from the action, and although after talking to her friends for an hour or so she would go downstairs, push two armchairs together, and sleep until someone woke her with news that her crew were checking in, at least she was on the spot if she were needed. Tonight she felt that she had hardly closed her eyes when she was aware of Merlin engines overhead. Throwing off the blanket she had wrapped around her she climbed back to the little greenhouse like hut on the roof of the flying control building. Inside, low lighting lit the boards, with pins representing each bomber as it checked in, and then marked its height in the stack as they took their turn to land. Outside, dark shadowy bombers with red and green navigation lights on touched down on the dimly lit runway.

"Nothing yet, young Sally." The voice was calm and soft and Sally recognised it immediately as that of Flight Lieutenant William Fairclough, the Senior Flying Controller. In the darkness she could just make out the shape of the kind old pilot, who ran the flying control tower. He was such a popular and respected officer all the WAAFs looked on him as a father figure and he was generally referred to by them as Uncle Bill. Quietly and calmly Bill spoke to each bomber as it checked in and he directed it to its level orbiting the airfield, while his assistants moved the pins around the boards and reported each bomber safely landed to the station operations room. As Sally's eyes became more used to the dark she could see more of what was going on. She had seen it many times before, as she waited for her crew to return, but the calm efficiency of the glass room always impressed her. A phone rang and without breaking his concentration Bill answered it.

"Flying control…Yes…Yes." He looked straight across at Sally and she went cold. Some people said she was psychic, although she just thought she had good intuition. It was true that sometimes she would have a premonition about something, but more often than not she believed she just had very good instincts. Now her instinct knew that Bill was talking about her crew and she feared the worst. She had lost crews before and it always hurt her, but for some reason she was particularly fond of this one. They were all nice characters, except perhaps the navigator, but she just stayed away from him, and the pilot was very nice.

"It's alright," Bill said, putting down the phone and seeing the look on her face. "They diverted into Manston. Ops just got word from them."

"Are they all okay?"

"Yes, they're all fine, but they'll need picking up from Grantham station at about 04.00."

"Right, sir, thank you." It was now just after 22.00 and it would take the best part of two hours to get to Grantham, so she could get another four hours' sleep.

Sally was parked opposite the entrance to Grantham station and as the 04.00 train to Newcastle pulled out of the station she saw seven men carrying bulky bags from the station onto the pavement and looking around in the blackout. It could only be her crew and she flashed her lights at them and started the truck's engine. A chorus of greeting met her as the crew filed past her window to jump into the back and Doug climbed into the cab and slammed the door.

"Welcome back, sir."

"Thanks."

"Did you run into some trouble?"

"We lost an engine and half our fuel. We only just got into Manston with empty tanks."

"Was it a fighter?" Sally was driving through the blacked out town, staring intently through the windscreen, while listening to every detail of what Doug said.

"No, flak."

"Was it on your way back?"

"Yes," yawned Doug. "360 miles from Manston."

"Well, it's good to have you back," concluded Sally, who was dying to ask more but Doug was obviously very tired and it was best she let him sleep. Her instinct told her he would be flying again that night.

By the time they had got back to Metheringham, deposited their flying kit, completed interrogation and cycled back to their billet it was 07.00 and dawn was starting to break. Ron and Doug entered their hut quietly and went straight to bed without turning on the light. In the dark they could hear either Charlie or Taffy snoring, so they knew that they too had returned safely.

Ron had just closed his eyes when he was being shaken.

"What!" he said angrily, opening his eyes and surprised to find it was full daylight. Goddard was standing beside him with a cup of tea and not a bit shocked by Ron's angry reaction.

"It's 13.00, sir, and I'm afraid you're to report to the Squadron Office for 14.00, sir."

"Oh." Ron's heart sank. He had hoped against hope that they would get a few days off Ops after having to divert into Manston. That would have taken them into the bright phase of the moon when there would be no Ops and maybe he would have been able to get some leave and see his wife. Now there was no chance of that and he sat up in his bed to drink his tea. Only he and Doug were still in the hut; Charlie and Taffy would have left earlier to check their aircraft. The Squadron Adjutant had obviously let them sleep in. Or had they just found a serviceable aircraft for them? And that was another thing, what aircraft would they get? Probably an old clapped out wreck. It was sure to be Berlin again, he could feel it. Berlin on a light night in a wreck of an aircraft. It didn't get any worse than that. Maybe he should go sick? He could say his ears were blocked or he had sinusitis. He would get away with it. Let someone else make a maximum effort. Doug smiled across at him.

"Morning."

Ron grunted his reply. Why the hell was he so happy every morning? They were living in a dump and every night people tried to kill them. He was still tired and he missed his wife. He wrote to her every day but she had started to write less and less. He hadn't heard from her since he had arrived at Metheringham, but that was probably because the mail was still being forwarded on, he told himself. He needed to see her to reassure himself that she still loved him, because all the love seemed to have gone from her letters and he was convinced he was losing her.

"Well, we can't put it off any longer," said Doug cheerfully, springing out of bed and going to get dressed while Goddard brought in a bowl of hot water to wash and shave in.

"I don't feel very well," said Ron. But Doug had disappeared into the locker room.

"I'm sorry to hear that, sir," replied Goddard. "Maybe you'll feel better once you're up." Ron scowled at him as he slowly got out of bed. What Ron did not know was that Goddard might have been old and frail looking, but he had seen more years of service than he cared to remember and nothing shocked or surprised him anymore. He could spot a real officer from a jumped-up fake in a second. Not feeling very well? Feeling a bit twitched more like, he thought, using the RAF slang for scared. He had seen it many times before and in far better men than this stuck up so and so.

Ron and Doug cycled over to the Squadron office, arriving just before 14.00. The sergeants were waiting outside for them. The previous day's wind had blown itself out and the sky was a clear blue, with a few patches of white fair weather cumulus dotted around. Although the sun was shining, at this time of year it had no heat in it and it was still cold. The light breeze was from the north and cut through all but the thickest of clothes, but it was a big improvement on the wet and ice of the previous days. As they rode over Ron told Doug he didn't feel well and Doug said he would see the Squadron Adj about getting him to see the doc. But Doug wasn't happy about it. Although Ron wasn't popular with the rest of the crew and Doug himself found him hard work to be with, there was no denying he was a good navigator and if Ron wasn't fit to fly there was no telling what the replacement navigator would be like.

"Afternoon," he greeted his crew. "Everyone alright?" Jimmy looked pale and tired, but he smiled and nodded with all the others. They all went into the Squadron Office where Nigel was sitting behind his desk looking through some papers. As they trooped in he looked up.

"Good afternoon, all," he smiled. "Bit of an exciting night for you all last night I hear."

"Yes," replied Doug. "You could say that."

"Bit careless of you to lose the Squadron's only new Lancaster," he grinned.

"We didn't lose it," said Harry. "We know exactly where it is and we'd like it back. Wouldn't we, skipper?"

"Yes, if you could swing it, that is."

Nigel smiled; crews quite often developed an affinity with a particular aircraft and liked to consider it their own. If it made them feel any better who was he to argue with it and unofficially he tried to pair up crews to aircraft whenever possible.

"Well, actually Manston have been in touch and your kite needs a new number three engine, two new fuel tanks and a new aileron to get it airworthy. Then they want someone to go down there and fly it back here to have the other damage patched up. So I don't see any reason why you can't have it back."

"Great."

"But that won't be for a while yet and you're on Ops tonight, so you'll have to take V for Victor.

"But we didn't get to bed until 0800 and we won't have time to check the aircraft over before takeoff," complained Ron.

"Yes, I know it's not ideal. But it's a late takeoff so specialist briefings aren't until 17.00; main briefing 18.30, so you do have time to check the kite. Sally should be waiting outside for you, see you at the briefing." With that Nigel went back to his paperwork and the sergeants, who were nearest the door, turned to leave.

"Er, Ron thinks he needs to see the doc," said Doug.

"Oh," said Nigel, looking up. "What's the matter with you?" His eyes fixed Ron with a blank stare.

"I can't clear my ears," replied Ron, slightly unnerved by Nigel's gaze. A heavy cold often blocked the tube connecting a person's inner ear to the back of the throat. When this happened it was impossible to equalise the pressure between the inner and outer ear, so any rapid change in pressure like during a climb, or more often, in a dive, would exert pressure on the eardrum and cause excruciating pain and ultimately burst the eardrum. So anyone who couldn't clear his ears to equalise the pressure was grounded until he could.

"Right. If you all wait with Sally," he said to Doug and the sergeants who had all stopped to listen to Ron, "I'll see what I can do for you." He returned his stare to Ron.

Doug and the rest of the crew left, collected their flight bags from the crew room and went over to where Sally was waiting for them.

"You've got a problem with your ears then," said Nigel, still staring at Ron.

"Yes." Ron shifted nervously.

"No temperature or running nose or anything."

"No."

"Strange." Nigel paused but kept staring at Ron, knowing he was making him feel uncomfortable and knowing the reason for Ron's discomfort was guilt. It was amazing how many people couldn't clear their ears the day after a bad trip, when they found they were on Ops again. "Well, of course I can get you to see the doc now if you want me to, and if he thinks you're unfit to fly I'll have to find a replacement navigator for your crew. The only replacement I have is a bit of a dud though."

"Well, if I can't clear my ears it can't be helped, can it?"

So, thought Nigel, the selfish bastard didn't give a damn about his crew. Well, he would get him another way.

"Of course it means your crew will finish its tour before you and you'll have to do an extra trip with another crew and they will probably be new boys and not up to the standards you're used to." That had made him think a bit, but it would probably take a little more.

"I still want to see the doctor."

"Well, think about this." Nigel's voice was firm, but not raised. "Lots of people have ear trouble after a tough Op and the best way to get over it is to fly the next Op as soon as possible."

"What the hell are you suggesting?" asked Ron indignantly.

"I'm suggesting that you go out to V for Victor and check it out, and while you're there you think about this. This will probably be the last Op for a while because of the full moon. You had a hard time last night and if you don't fly tonight the trip that will stay in your mind will be last night's. The only way you'll be able to relax over the next couple of weeks, before the next Op, will be by flying tonight and having a good Op to chase the gremlins away. So go away and think about it and if you still want to see the doc when you get back I'll arrange it, but you won't be doing yourself any favours. You volunteered for aircrew and you can't un-volunteer, so you're in this for thirty trips and the only way through it is to grit your teeth and do it. Unless of course you want to go LMF?"

Nigel saw the look of horror on Ron's face. LMF, or Lack of Moral Fibre, was the ultimate disgrace, used ruthlessly by the RAF to stop aircrew from refusing to fly. Anyone refusing to fly was stripped of all rank, posted from his unit as soon as possible, usually within hours, and given the worst, dirtiest, coldest and most unpleasant jobs to do. Finally, their personal record had LMF stamped on it in large red letters so that they could never get away from it or redeem themselves. Nigel knew he had him.

"Think about it. Your crew are waiting."

He watched Ron leave. He had had to do the same thing many times before and he would probably have to do it many more times. Usually he felt sorry for them, they were ordinary people who were scared. Christ, who wouldn't be scared doing what they had to do? But they had to face their fears and carry on. The vast majority did, until they completed their tours, completely worn out, or they failed to return from an Op and were posted missing. One or two however, did break down completely and were sent LMF and these he felt really sorry for, because most of them were good men who had just been pushed too far. Ron though was different. He was selfish, he didn't care about the rest of his crew and although he was a good navigator Nigel was sorry that Doug had to fly with him.

Ron climbed into the back of the wagon and it set off around the perimeter track to V for Victor. He could feel all the sergeants looking at him, as if they knew what he had tried to do and he felt embarrassed. He was also angry that Nigel had embarrassed him in front of everyone. Eventually Bob spoke.

"Are you coming with us tonight?"

"I'm going to see what I feel like after we check the aircraft." An oppressive silence once again descended on the truck.

V for Victor was in the first dispersal on the south side of the airfield. It was the aircraft generally used as the Squadron spare and it didn't have a regular crew. The truck stopped and they got out. There was no sign of the ground crew, so Doug and Jimmy went in search of them in the hut at the edge of the dispersal, while the rest of the crew climbed aboard. Ron checked the Distant Reading or DR Master unit, just inside and to the right of the entrance door, then made his way through the cold dark fuselage to the navigator's station.

The DR master unit contained a gyroscope as well as a magnetic compass. In the air, ordinary compasses suffer from the acceleration forces in an aeroplane and tend to lag behind the actual heading of the aircraft in turns. This makes them very difficult to use to fly accurate headings. Gyrocompasses on the other hand don't suffer from lag but do wander slowly off heading over time. By marrying the two together the gyro stops the magnetic compass from lagging and the magnetic compass stops the gyro from wandering off heading. The master unit is then electrically connected to a number of repeater units in the aircraft from which accurate headings can be read. One in the cockpit for the pilot, one for the navigator and one for the bombing computer.

Everywhere was damp with condensation and Ron often wondered how the electronics stayed working with all the water around. Putting down his flight bag he took out his flying helmet and pulled it on. He sat facing the left side of the aircraft a couple of feet behind the pilot. His seat blocked the passageway up and down the aircraft, so if anyone needed to pass wearing bulky flying kit, he had to stand up and get out of their way, which really irritated him. In front of him was his navigation table, which was about three feet wide by two feet deep. On the fuselage wall in front of him was a black panel with an airspeed indicator and altimeter in the centre. To the left of this was an instrument called the Air Position Indicator or API. This was a useful piece of kit, which, as the name suggests, kept a track of the aircraft's air position. Basically you set the aircraft's latitude and longitude into the box, and then the API took the aircraft's speed from the airspeed indicator and the heading from the DR compass and constantly updated the aircraft's latitude and longitude on two dials. Unfortunately, it took no account of the wind affecting the aircraft, or any inaccuracies in the airspeed indicator due to height or pressure and it tended to wander with time, so it had to be constantly updated if it was to be of any use. Mounted on the API to the left of the latitude and longitude dials was the navigator's DR compass repeater. Next to the API was an Anglepoise lamp, which could be pointed in any direction and was a vital piece of equipment to the navigator.

To the left of this, mounted above the level of the navigation table on a swivelling bracket was the most commonly fitted electronic navigation aid of the period, the GEE box. GEE was a wonderful piece of equipment which had saved the lives of many a bomber crew. It was reliable, accurate, and easy to use and the navigators all loved it. Unfortunately it relied on signals transmitted from ground sites in England and the aircraft had to be in line of sight with these sites for it to work. This effectively limited the range of the system to about 350 miles. Worse still, it worked on a fixed frequency, which the Germans knew about and they had been jamming it for some time. By the time the bombers were any distance over enemy territory GEE was almost useless, but when returning to England and the enemy coast fell away behind them, so did the jamming and GEE got many a lost bomber safely home.

It worked by measuring the time difference between electronic pulses received from transmitting stations. A master station in England would transmit a pulse on a fixed frequency in all directions. Another station some distance away, known as a slave station, would receive this pulse then transmit its own pulse, again in all directions. The equipment in the aircraft would measure the time difference between receiving the pulse direct from the master station and the transmitted pulse from the slave. A specific time interval was unique to a specific hyperbolic shaped line on a specially prepared GEE map. The lines representing the time difference between the master and the first slave were drawn in red and by adding a second slave station at a different location another set of lines could be drawn in green. The GEE set measured the infinitesimal time difference between the pulses and displayed them on a circular green oscilloscope screen, similar to those used in hospitals to measure a patient's heart beat. The screen showed two green horizontal trace lines one above the other with the blip of the master pulse on both lines near the left of the screen. The first slave pulse was displayed on the upper line to the right of the master pulse and the second slave pulse was displayed on the lower line. The screen was divided from left to right by intervals of time called GEE units and by measuring the number of these on the upper trace the appropriate red line on the GEE map was found. Doing the same with the bottom trace gave the correct green line and where they crossed was the aircraft's position, accurate to within a couple of miles. While Ron liked GEE his favourite piece of electronic equipment was to the right of his table mounted on a similar swivelling bracket to the GEE box, the H2S set.

H2S was new and up until recently had only been available to Pathfinder squadrons. 106 Squadron was one of the first main force squadrons to receive it and the Squadron boasted that this was because of the high esteem Command had for the Squadron. Whatever the reason H2S was a very useful piece of equipment. It was basically a downward looking radar, made possible by the invention of the high-powered Magnetron radio valve and the discovery that radar echoes are returned to the transmitting radar in a slightly altered form. Because of the Magnetron a high frequency radar could be made small enough to fit into an aircraft. The high frequency gave far better resolution than had been possible before and as different surfaces returned different types of echo a rough map picture could be shown of the ground over which the aircraft was flying. This was shown on a green circular cathode ray tube. Flat land or sea gave poor returns, which showed up dark on the screen and angular buildings or sea cliffs gave distinctive echoes and showed up bright on the screen. It took some practice to attune the eye to recognise ground features from the green glow on the screen but Ron seemed to have a gift for it. What was more, as H2S was not reliant on ground stations there was no limit to its effective range from England and the Germans had not started to jam it. Even on the darkest night Ron could see prominent ground features like towns or rivers and use them to map read his way around in the blackness.

When he had settled himself into his seat and connected his intercom Doug and Jimmy came forward up the fuselage after finding the ground crew and carrying out their external checks. Ron had to stand up to let them through to the cockpit. Then sitting down again he took everything out of his flight bag, placing it on his chart table and checking it before putting it back in the bag. Two sharp pencils, sharpened at both ends. A pencil sharpener, just in case. Two rubbers, a square protractor, a set of dividers, a torch and a long ruler all fitted into special pockets in his flight bag. Time speed scales, the current Air Almanac, Astro Navigation Tables, a bubble sextant, issued to him and as with all other navigators, corrected by him to eliminate his "personal error." Message pads, log sheets, a GEE map and his own personally prepared flak map of occupied Europe went into the main part of the bag. Finally his Dalton computer went into the smaller of the sub divided sections of the bag. An astrocompass was stored in the aircraft and he checked this and restowed it. The intercom was buzzing now as Doug checked they were all ready for engine start and Ron checked over his Dalton computer as he waited for the engines to provide the electrical power he needed for his checks.

The Dalton computer was nothing like a modern electrical computer. It was a metal box about four inches by six inches by an inch thick. On the back was a circular slide rule with which the navigator could do various mathematical calculations. The main ones were how long it would take to travel a certain distance at a certain speed or how far they would travel in a certain time at a certain speed. But it was the other side of the computer that did the really clever calculations. How many degrees an aircraft travelling at a certain airspeed would be blown off course by a wind of a certain speed from a certain direction and what its new speed would be over the ground. In short everything a navigator needed to know to navigate accurately, providing the wind entered into the computer was correct. A circular piece of Perspex in the centre of the box with compass bearings around the edge could be rotated to read any heading off the lubbers line at the top of the box. Through the Perspex a continuous paper belt with a grid system on it could be wound to set the appropriate airspeed by using a knurled knob on the side of the box. First the true airspeed would be set under the black dot in the centre of the Perspex; for a Lancaster this was typically 210 mph. Then rotating the Perspex so the correct bearing showed against the lubbers line set the forecast wind direction, say north. Counting down the appropriate number of mph from the aircraft's airspeed on the grid paper and marking it on the Perspex with a pencil set the wind speed, say 30 mph. Then you simply rotated the Perspex to the course you wanted to take over the ground, say east. As the Perspex was rotated the pencil mark would move from below the dot to the right of the dot and in this example show 8 degrees of right drift on the grid paper under the Perspex. So with this wind if the aircraft wanted to go east it would have to steer zero eight two degrees to allow for the wind from the north and as the wind is on the beam it wouldn't affect the speed over the ground. Without this simple tool it would have been impossible to carry out the necessary calculations to navigate accurately in the time available.

The engines were now running and Ron checked his oxygen, while listening to Doug and Jimmy over the intercom discussing the engines' performance. They didn't seem very happy. In his compartment everything vibrated and the condensation on the side of the fuselage started to run. Ron set his altimeter to the QFE and checked it read zero. It didn't, it was 50 feet low and he made a note of it. Then he switched on the GEE and H2S sets and waited for them to warm up. After what seemed an age the GEE came on line and he adjusted it for brilliance and focus, then checked on his GEE map that it showed his correct location. It was accurate but the screen would not stay in focus and the trace lines were wavering around. There was a lot of internal electronic noise in the set and it was making it difficult to read the pulses. Obviously it hadn't been as well maintained as the set in F for Freddy. The H2S was also warmed up and appeared to be working but it couldn't be properly tested on the ground and they didn't have time to do an air test. Ron did not feel confident.

"Navigator to pilot, I'm not sure about the H2S, is there any chance of an air test?"

"Sorry, Ron, there isn't time and the ground crew need to bomb up. The bomb trolley's just arrived so they need the aircraft as soon as possible. But we can go without H2S anyway if we have to can't we?" Ron couldn't argue with that as most Lancasters hadn't been fitted with H2S yet and so always flew without it.

"We can but I'd rather it was working."

"So would I but we're not going to get the time to check it."

Ron scowled at the H2S screen; he didn't like the look of this at all. It struck him that this aircraft without a regular crew was not as well maintained as the others and he suspected that all the duff mechanics that nobody else wanted were on this Lancaster's ground crew.

Doug throttled back the engines.

"Check in front to back with any unserviceable equipment."

"Bomb aimer, there's a small hydraulic leak in the front turret."

"Roger, make a note, Jimmy. Anything other than the H2S, Ron?"

"My altimeter's reading 50 feet low."

"Roger, mine's reading 50 feet high. Harry?"

"The 1155 receiver keeps going off tune and I don't think the Fishpond is working."

"Alex?"

"The Perspex on this turret needs a bloody good clean and it's not traversing as smoothly as it should."

"George?"

"There's a hydraulic leak somewhere in this turret as well but it's not too bad at the moment."

Doug shut down the engines and they all climbed out and went to see the crew chief.

The crew chief was a sergeant of many years' standing and he reckoned he had seen it all before. Now he saw the crew advancing towards him he knew they were not happy, but he also knew that he didn't care. Whingeing aircrew were never happy, they were cosseted from when they got up to when they went to bed. Most of them were so young they didn't need to shave. It had taken him ten years to get to sergeant, now this lot hadn't been in ten minutes and they were sergeants already, and as for the officers, what the hell did they know? He wasn't going to take any shit from any of them.

"Everything alright, sir?" he smiled.

"I'm afraid not, sergeant," said Doug. "We've got a list of faults."

"Alright, sir, leave it with me and we'll see what we can do. But the old girl's feeling her age you see, and as soon as we fix one thing something else goes wrong somewhere else."

"Well, there's hydraulic leaks in the front and rear turrets. The mid-upper Perspex needs cleaning. The 1155 keeps going off tune and we think there's a problem with the H2S. But the worst thing is the boost is down on all the engines and there's an excessive Mag drop as well so I think the plugs need changing."

"Well, we'll have a look at the leaks, sir, and the RDF flight can check the 1155 and H2S but it's an all-day job to change the plugs, sir," said the sergeant with his best, well I'd like to help you but what can I do look on his face.

"Do what you can, sergeant," replied Doug and left it at that. He might not have been in the Air Force long but he knew he was not going to get anywhere with this sergeant and it was better not to start any fights he couldn't win.

Back at Sally's truck the crew voiced their dissatisfaction out of the ground crew's earshot.

"That plane's a wreck!" complained Ron. "You should have torn him off a strip."

"It's not that bad but it could be better," said Doug. "And do you think giving him a rocket would have made any difference to him?"

"How old is that Lanc anyway?" asked Harry.

"No older than some of the others on the squadron," replied Jimmy.

"Look," said Doug not wanting his crew to get carried away with the faults. "None of these faults is a show stopper, is it?" They all had to agree that none of the faults was serious enough to prevent them going on the Op, much to Ron's disappointment. "And I for one would much rather fly this crate than those Stirlings at the Heavy Conversion Unit." Again they all agreed – the Stirling was not as popular a bomber as the Lancaster was.

"What about the low boost on the engines?" asked Ron. "That sounds like a show stopper to me."

"They're not that low," replied Doug. "If they're the same tonight we'll go, if they're any worse we'll scrub." He glanced across at Jimmy, who said nothing.

George turned to Sally who was standing to one side listening. "What's that sergeant like?" He jerked his head towards the ground crew.

"Sergeant Allen? That's not for me to say, sarge."

"I think that says it all," said George climbing into the wagon.

The usual silence in the back of the wagon was only broken once on the ride back to the Squadron Office when Bob asked Jimmy what he thought of the low boost on the engines and whether they should go or not. Jimmy felt he had been put on the spot and glanced nervously at Ron before answering.

"It's up to the skipper," was all he said.

Damn it, thought Ron, why the hell didn't the stupid man have the courage of his convictions and tell Doug they shouldn't go. He would have done it, but he couldn't do it now because the Squadron Adj would know he was just trying to get out of the trip.

Back in the Squadron Office Doug told Nigel about the state of V for Victor.

"Well, it's your call, old boy. Give her a good check out tonight before takeoff and if you're not happy you'll have to scrub. But make sure you can justify it. "What about you?" asked Nigel, suddenly turning to Ron with an icy stare. "How are you feeling now?"

"I'll be alright," answered Ron, not attempting to hide the hatred in his eyes.

"Well, see you all at the main briefing then."

Walking into their hut Doug and Ron noticed the post had been delivered. One letter was lying on each of their beds and as they sat down to open them Goddard put his head around the door from the batting room and asked them if they would like some tea. Ron felt his spirits lift as he opened the letter; he recognised the handwriting. It was from his wife and the terrible day he had had so far vanished at the thought that he would have some news from home, from the only person that really meant anything to him.

Dear Ron, the letter began very formally. *I have just received your letter saying you are starting operations and I hope you will be careful. I will listen to the news on the wireless every day from now on and wonder if you were involved in the raids they are always talking about. We always seem to lose some aircraft and it seems you have chosen a very dangerous job. I wish you hadn't volunteered to fly. Do you realise that since you went to Canada to train I have only seen you for one week and that feels like it was ages ago. Things were so much better when you had that nice little administration job. I'm sure you agree that one week's leave in over a year isn't adequate and you should speak to somebody about it. There are lots of jobs to do around the house and I can't be expected to do them all myself. I know you got leave when you got back from Canada but surely you must be due some more soon. Jenny at the bank is going out with a sergeant in the Artillery and he seems to get every weekend off. Although I know she's jealous that you're an officer.*

I suppose you're having a very exciting time while I'm here on my own. Mr Bradley is still bullying everyone although I'm now quite good at keeping out of his way. The bank has taken on some new staff now to replace those who have been called up. They are all quite young and they are all terrified of Bradley. He chases them around like a fox in a chicken coop, especially one young chap called John Hart, who is really sweet and not at all as incompetent as Bradley says he is. We all feel very sorry for him. He reminds me of how you used to be before you went away.

I still feel very much alone since you left and I often wonder how I will carry on, going home to an empty house every night. I hardly ever see my mother and since Daddy got the job in London I've only seen him twice. But I've decided I've had enough of my lonely existence so I'm going out with the girls to the pictures tomorrow night. So while you're having an exciting time I'll be having some fun too. Let me know if you'll be getting any leave soon.   Janice.

Ron read the letter twice, took the tea off Goddard, drank a quick sip then lay back on the bed and read it again. He supposed that it was better than nothing and it was better than some of her letters, the ones she had written when she had been angry, while he had been away training in Canada. They had said some very hurtful things and had blamed him for everything from being away to starting the war. But apologetic letters, which had made up for the others had always followed. True the apologies had often not arrived for over a week after the angry letter and he would fret and worry all that time that his marriage was over. But in a way this letter was worse. This had not been written in a fit of anger. It was calm and simply told him how she felt. She was lonely and bored. But the worrying thing was it said she was lonely but it didn't say she missed him. In a subtle way this was the most worrying letter to date and he could not blame it on a moment's anger or frustration; it was cold, formal and unfeeling. She no longer loved him, he was losing her and there was nothing he could do about it.

Since he first met her everything he had done had been for her, but time and again something had come along to spoil things and they had never had any length of time where they had been happy. Now they were apart and she blamed him for it. He had only volunteered for aircrew to increase his status and make her proud of him and now it was forcing them apart. He felt he could do nothing right and everything was conspiring against him. Tears of sadness, helplessness and frustration pricked his eyes and he blinked them away.

"Is that from Janice?" asked Doug.

"Yes," replied Ron, swallowing hard and holding the letter in front of his face.

"How is she?"

"Fine."

I don't know why I bother trying to have a conversation with him, thought Doug.

9

Ron had dried his navigation table with an old cloth but now the vibrations of the engines, as they taxied towards the end of the runway, caused the condensation on the walls to run and drips fell from the roof. His compartment was dark and eerie. The black curtain to his right was drawn to prevent the dim Anglepoise lamp reflecting its dull yellow glow into the cockpit. The light, positioned low over the navigation table, cast long shadows around the compartment and the vibrations from the engines shook the lamp, making it appear to flicker. It always reminded Ron of an underground cavern, lit by flaming torches. As yet he hadn't taken any of his navigation equipment out of his bag and the only thing on the table was the Form 441 Navigation Log. He had filled in as much of this as he could during the specialist and main briefings. He had the forecast wind speeds and directions at 2,000, 5,000, 10,000, 15,000 and 20,000 feet for Metheringham, North Sea, Germany and France. He had planned a route using these winds and if they were accurate he would have very little to do except monitor their progress. But the wind over Europe was notoriously fickle and Ron knew he would spend much of the next six or more hours making allowances for the inaccuracies of the Met man's forecast winds.

He had plotted the briefed route on his map and measured the track angles with his square protractor. From Metheringham zero three zero degrees to Spurn Head then zero six zero degrees for 325 miles to a lake just inside the Danish coast. One one five degrees for 106 miles to a peninsular on the island of Sealand in the Baltic, then one six zero for 76 miles to the southern tip of Falster island. Hopefully this route would take them around the northern end of the German radar and night fighter defences. Finally one five zero for 116 miles to a point 21 miles northeast of Berlin. It was a very similar route to last night and that didn't make it popular with any of the crews. At least the route out was quick. Two seven five degrees for 130 miles to another lake north of Hanover, then three two five for 90 miles to an island off the north German coast and from there two nine zero out to sea and safety.

Using these bearings and the forecast winds he had used his Dalton computer to work out the drift angles and ground speeds that would result from the wind's effect on the aircraft. He would have to constantly allow for these variables to stay on course and time. It wasn't just a case of getting lost; to a large extent the safety of all the bombers depended on them being in the bomber stream. The hundreds of bombers crowded together in a small space and passing through an area quickly would overwhelm the defences of a given area, so that only one or two bombers could be attacked. But a bomber wandering out of the stream in the darkness, due to a navigation error, was a much easier target. Ron had calculated the headings he would have to take to allow for the winds so that he would stay in the stream, and all the information was meticulously written on the Form 441 navigation log in his neat and precise handwriting. Now it just remained for Ron to check their progress until, inevitably, the wind decided it was not going to behave as planned, then he would be locked into a six hour mental battle with the elements, making constant adjustments, move and counter move. Any mistake could leave them vulnerable to attack.

Ron felt sick. He always felt sick before takeoff, because it was usually the last time before landing when he had time to think of anything other than navigating. Now he felt so bad he thought he would actually vomit. But even while he felt so wretched all he could think of was Janice's letter and how she felt about him. Even while he had been working out the courses for the Op, thoughts of Janice had been in the back of his mind and he had struggled to concentrate. Now the thought that he might have made a mistake while he was distracted nagged at him. But he would have to look out for any mistakes as he went along; after all, the planned courses were always different to those they eventually ended up using as the winds changed. Janice filled his mind and numbed his brain. His neck muscles were tense and it made his head ache. He could see her face smiling at him, the way she used to. It had been a long time since she had smiled at him like that, he realised. Now it was as if she was from a different world and he had no idea how he could reach her. No matter how bad other things had been in his life Janice had always been there, and now the certainty he felt that she would not be with him forever was unbearable. He had to see her soon and try to get her back, make her love him again. He had no idea how he would do it but he couldn't live without her.

Ron had been vaguely aware of Doug and Jimmy discussing the state of the engines while they taxied and although all was not perfect he had resigned himself to the fact that they would be going on this Op. Outside his curtained world it was night. The sun had long since set and only the blue perimeter track and the aircrafts' red, green and white navigation lights glowed in the darkness. Ron realised takeoff was close because the bomber was stopping and starting as it queued up for takeoff.

"Prepare for takeoff," said Doug over the intercom, as the Lancaster started to move forward again. Ron felt them swing to the left lining up on the runway centreline. If he could get through this mission he would see Janice and sort everything out, and all would be well again.

The engine noise rose and the bomber lurched forward as Doug released the brakes, throwing Ron to his left, so that he had to hang on to the edge of his navigation table. Ron looked at the airspeed indicator in front of him as it started to move around the dial and turned on his microphone switch.

"30."

"Boost's low on all engines," said Jimmy.

"How low?" asked Doug.

"13 pounds on three and four. 13 and a half on one and two."

Abort, abort, abort thought Ron.

"We'll continue," said Doug.

"60," said Ron. Why the hell hadn't Doug aborted the takeoff? He had his excuse. Did he really want to go to Berlin and get shot at? The airspeed indicator slowly moved towards 90 and the Lancaster started to sway from side to side. They were going now no matter what because there would be no stopping before the end of the runway at this speed. Ron could feel a slight bouncing, which he dismissed as impossible, they were far too heavy and nowhere near takeoff speed.

"90." It seemed to have taken them a lot longer than usual to get to 90 – the last 15 mph to takeoff speed always seemed to take forever – but this seemed slower than before.

"100." Come on, you old bastard! There couldn't be much runway left, they should never have taken this old crate. Thoughts of Janice were suddenly gone, as Ron realised that in a few seconds he could be dead. Just how much runway was left?

"Oh Jesus Christ," said Jimmy slowly and quietly over his open intercom, and Ron knew they were at the end of the runway.

"105!" he yelled, as the pointer barely touched the number. The floor lurched upwards as Doug heaved the sluggish bomber violently into the air. Ron waited, his body tensed and head hunched low over his table, waiting for the crash and explosion. The engines continued to roar and they climbed slowly away and Ron let out his breath.

"That's the last bloody time I ever stay in the nose for takeoff!" said Bob emphatically, over the intercom.

"It was a bit close wasn't it?" replied Doug.

"A bit fucking close! If that truck on the road to Martin village hadn't stopped, we would have hit it."

"We weren't that close."

"We were close enough for me to see it was a fifteen-hundred-weight truck," said Bob, knowing that if he could identify the truck in the dark they had been very close.

"Course zero two five degrees compass for Spurn Head," said Ron, as he tried to slow down his breathing.

V for Victor's engines strained to drag the heavily laden bomber upwards, but they had done many hours at maximum boost and were feeling their age. A loaded Lancaster could never be described as a sprightly aircraft, but this one Doug decided was far more sluggish than most. Very slowly the altimeter rotated and the rate of climb and descent indicator showed a rate of climb of barely 250 feet per minute, which was half that of F for Freddy.

The night sky was cloudless and a half moon shone far too brightly for Doug's liking. Now that they had crossed the coast it reflected on the sea below them, showing that the winds of the previous night had blown themselves out, leaving the sea moving in long regular swells, with no waves or white tops visible. They would have certainly seen them if there had been any wind, because although they had crossed the coast at Spurn Head ten minutes earlier, they were still only at 5,000 feet. For the tenth time since takeoff, Doug checked the throttles were fully up against the gate and hadn't somehow slid back, but they were still in the correct position and the boost was now 2 pounds per square inch lower than it should have been. Jimmy saw him.

"It's no good, skipper, she's already giving us all she's got, we'll just have to take our time."

Occasionally Doug caught a glimpse of another aircraft against the light of the moon. They were all well above them and Doug wished he had aborted the takeoff or said the aircraft was not serviceable. At least with the long sea crossing they had plenty of time to gain height and the moon should have set before they reached Germany, but even so, he would have felt far happier in F for Freddy.

Behind his curtain Ron was taking a GEE fix. They had left the British coast, on track and on time, but Ron was not happy with the slow rate of climb. The sooner they got to their operational height, the sooner he would have a constant wind to work with. Until then the wind would change frequently as they climbed and Ron would have to make ongoing adjustments. The H2S was working, but the circular green screen was giving a very blurred picture. Spurn Head, which was as good an H2S fix as you were ever likely to get, could only just be made out and Ron didn't think it was going to be of much use over Germany. Ron read the two GEE unit measurements off the flickering GEE screen and plotted them on his map. They were about a mile right off track and a little ahead of schedule, but at this early stage he decided he would just make a note of it and leave any corrections until later.

"Skipper, we've lost Fishpond," said Harry. Ron glanced over to his right at the H2S screen, which used the same scanner as Fishpond, and it too was blank.

"H2S is down too."

"Roger, Jimmy, go and take a look."

"Right, skipper, I shouldn't be long."

"Skipper, it's Alex. Ah can smell burning back here!"

"Roger, Harry, go back with Jimmy and take a fire extinguisher with you."

"On my way, skipper."

The H2S scanner was below the floor, just forward of the mid-upper turret and the loss of Fishpond, H2S and the smell of burning in the mid section all pointed to an H2S fire. Harry's small stature meant he got to the circular H2S cover in the fuselage floor behind the bomb bay before Jimmy. Shining his torch at the cover, he saw smoke rising from around the edges. The acrid smoke stung his nostrils and, as an electrician, Harry immediately recognised the smell of burnt out cables.

Jimmy arrived and knelt down beside him.

"I've pulled the H2S fuses, so the power's off. I'll lift the cover, you get ready with the extinguisher!" he yelled, over the noise of the engines.

"Right! I'm ready," shouted Harry.

Jimmy moved to the other side of the floor panel, on his knees underneath the mid-upper turret, and steadied himself to lift the panel up in front of him. That way, if flames were to flare up, the floor panel would protect him. He glanced up at Harry, who nodded he was ready, and then heaved the panel up.

A cloud of smoke billowed upwards into the fuselage and Harry squinted as the smoke stung his eyes. At first all he could see was darkness, then a flash of red appeared, followed by small blue green flames springing upwards, and Harry fired the extinguisher. The white cloud from the fire extinguisher blocked Harry's view, so he stopped and let the cloud clear, saw more flames and fired again. After five bursts the fire had had enough and succumbed to Harry's onslaught. Waving his hand to clear the smoke and coughing, Harry checked the fire was out, while one quick look by torchlight from Jimmy told him that there would be no way of repairing the H2S in the air. Replacing the panel they went back forward.

"We had a fire in the H2S scanner, but it's out now, skipper," reported Jimmy. "There's no way we can fix it."

"Right. Did you hear that, Ron? We've got no H2S."

"I heard," replied Ron. Things just keep getting better, he thought sarcastically.

"Ten thousand feet, time to go onto oxygen," said Doug.

The long drawn out climb continued until at 17,000 feet V for Victor had given it's all and could not be persuaded to go any higher.

"That's as high as I can get her to go," said Doug, feeling a little dispirited, as if a better pilot could have got the Lancaster higher.

"17,000!" exclaimed Ron. "They took Stirlings off long range Ops because they couldn't get any higher than this! We're going to be a sitting duck down here!"

"We'll probably be able to get higher when we've used more fuel," replied Doug, without much hope. The engine's performance had got gradually worse as they had climbed higher and now he was sure that the superchargers weren't working properly.

"I don't think we should be expected to go to Berlin at this height," said Ron defiantly.

"Are we still on time?" asked Doug.

"Yes, but we're south of track and I'm not sure by how much because the GEE is playing up too now. One thing is for certain and that's the winds are wrong and if I adjust to make good our track before the next turn we will be late."

"Well, if we are south of track the next planned turn is to the right, so we can cut the corner if we have to make up time."

"But that will put us out of the bomber stream."

"Not for long and we're not in a major night fighter area."

Ron knew he couldn't push things any further and reluctantly accepted that he couldn't talk Doug into turning back. Flying outside the bomber stream increased the risks enormously as there would be no protection from the clouds of window and the bomber would stand out and attract attention to itself.

"Well, I'm still not happy about this," he countered sullenly and went back to his navigation.

As well as the problems with the aircraft Ron was struggling with problems of nature. The winds were wrong and before the GEE finally faded away he knew they were south of their route. Working with his Dalton computer, the Air Position Indicator and the last GEE fix, he calculated that the true wind was zero one zero degrees at 35 mph, not the forecast zero three zero degrees at 30 mph. He adjusted their course appropriately; they should cross the coast in about ten minutes.

"What's the visibility like?" he asked.

"Excellent," replied Doug.

"Too bloody good," said Bob, who had spotted lots of other aircraft and knew that they too would be easy to spot.

"The moon should set soon," countered Doug, who was beginning to feel that he was the only person on the aircraft who still felt positive about the Op. "Then it should be a nice dark night with a good view of the ground."

The minutes passed and Ron waited to hear the report that the Danish coast had been sighted so that he could positively fix their position. As he waited he thought about Janice. She was going out tonight to enjoy herself. What had she said? So while you're having an exciting time I'll be having some fun too. Ron was not sure if he would describe flying as exciting, but he certainly did not think of it as fun. He was cold, tired and scared. He had a splitting headache, his stomach felt tied in knots and he thought he might be sick. Janice would be going to the pictures or maybe a dance. She loved dancing, but with everyone called up there was a shortage of male partners and she drew the line at dancing with other women. Maybe she would find herself an American to partner her; they were around in ever-increasing numbers these days. Or perhaps young John Hart from the bank, who she was obviously so taken with, would go with her. Ron clenched his fist and his body shook in anger and frustration. Then his stomach heaved and he knew he was going to be sick. Quickly he reached into his navigation bag and pulled out a small bag he kept inside it just in case. He was sweating heavily as he struggled to hold down the vomit until he was ready. It was rising in his throat as he fumbled with the catch of his oxygen mask; he wasn't going to make it. Finally the mask came free and he got the bag over his mouth just in time, as his flying supper broke free and splattered warm and smelly into the bag. After two or three heaves he retched dryly, knowing that his stomach was now empty. His head spun, his face was flushed and his skin cold and clammy. He sucked in a deep breath of cold air and shivered. She had no idea what he was going through and he had volunteered for this just to make her proud of him; it just wasn't fair. He wiped his watery eyes, stared down at his maps in despair and breathed deeply. His hands were trembling and there were pins and needles in his fingers. He took another deep breath and tried to slow down his breathing. He wiped the saliva from his lips with the back of his gloved hand, his lips started to tingle and his head buzzed. It was not unpleasant, a bit like being slightly drunk. He caught sight of movement out of the corner of his eye to the left and turning could see the dark shape of Harry's head looking around the corner of his radio set. It was like being in a dream. He could see things happening but it was as if they weren't happening to him. The noise of the engine vibrated in his head and from somewhere a voice said, "Put your oxygen mask on."

But it was far away and nothing to do with him so he ignored it and decided he was very tired and would close his eyes, just for a second. Suddenly someone was holding him and roughly pushing something over his face. What the hell was going on! He started to struggle, and opening his eyes to the dimly lit navigation compartment turned to look into Harry's face, the hard eyes above the oxygen mask and the crackly voice in his ears.

"Are you alright?"

Ron's mind struggled back to reality, but he felt flushed and his hands shook more than ever. His mind whirled, it was oxygen starvation, he knew that now, and he struggled to reattach his mask. His fingers fumbled and Harry did up the catch for him, then stared at him for a few more seconds, until he was sure Ron was recovering before going back to his radio.

"What's going on back there?" asked Doug.

Ron was still groggy so after a couple of seconds Harry answered.

"Ron had a problem with his oxygen, but he's alright now."

"Well, we're just about to cross the coast."

"Roger," replied Ron, returning to normal.

"I think we're off track," said Bob. "There's a huge lake just inside the coast."

Ron's mind was still spinning a little. "Er, if we are off track it should be to the south."

"I think I know where we are and we're about 25 miles south of track."

"I doubt we're that far off track," replied Ron indignantly, returning to his old self.

"Well, come up and have a look," said Bob, who didn't give a damn about Ron or his rank.

Ron shakily stood and turning off the Anglepoise lamp pulled back the curtain. It was a crystal clear night with hundred of stars overhead and the half moon just about to set. Standing behind Doug's seat he looked over the side of the cockpit through the cockpit blister. Below them the sea met the land in a dark line, but after a narrow strip of land there was more water. It stood out like a massive mirror, reflecting the starlight from above. Thinking back to his map he knew there was a fjord south of their intended landfall and the large lake must be that fjord. Looking up the coast he could make out two or three other lakes reflecting the moonlight in the distance and he had to admit they were probably 25 miles south of track. He returned to his compartment and closing the curtain turned the light back on. Surveying his map he realised they where probably at the southern end of the fjord, exactly where Bob said they where. The Op couldn't have got off to a worse start. He wasn't sure where they were, they were off track, he had lost all his electronic navigation aids and the aircraft was playing up. There was no way they could fly up the coast to the first turn and join the bomber stream there, because that would put them too far behind schedule and in this aircraft they would never catch up. The only way they could get back in the stream was to cut the corner and try to get back on track where the planned route re crossed the Danish east coast. They would fly due east allowing for the last wind he had calculated and try to pick up a landmark to fix their position in the Baltic.

Desperately trying to fight down the increasing feeling that they were lost and knowing panic would soon follow, Ron plotted his position from the Air Position Indicator onto his map, then, as their true air speed was 210 mph or three and a half miles a minute, he measured 21 miles further down their current track and put a cross. He noted the time 21.12 and adding six minutes wrote 21.18 next to the cross; this would be their air position in six minutes' time. He now had slightly less than six minutes to work out how to get them back on track and in the bomber stream. First, he applied the wind he had just calculated to the cross, measuring the bearing with his protractor and measuring the speed down the vector with his long navigational ruler. That should give him his "dead reckoning" or estimated ground position for 21.18. Then he drew a line from the dead reckoning position to the point where the intended route re crossed the Danish coast into the Baltic and measured the angle with his protractor. Zero nine five degrees true north. Setting his found wind onto his Dalton computer he calculated the drift the wind would give them for a track of zero nine five degrees. Ten degrees right drift, so the course would be zero eight five degrees to allow for that. Now he measured the distance to the Baltic coast. 52 miles, at a ground speed of… he checked his Dalton computer again, 205 mph. Now turning the computer over to the side with the circular slide rule he set the inner, time scale, 60 mark against the outer, distance scale, between the 20 and 21. The slide rule would now calculate distance and times for 205 mph. Looking at the outer distance scale for 52 it showed one tenth of a minute before eighteen, so it would take them seventeen minutes and forty-eight seconds to reach the Danish east coast, if his calculated wind was correct. Checking against his route timings Ron saw that the planned time for the bomber stream to reach this point was 21.36 hours. It would be 21.18 hours when they turned onto their new course for the Danish east coast and it would be... he added seventeen minutes to eighteen... 21.35 and forty-eight seconds when they got there. Twelve seconds early, as near as any navigator could ever hope to get.

Just then he felt the Lancaster start to turn and his eyes shot to the compass to confirm it. He was about to ask Doug what was going on when it started to turn back and he realised that Doug had started to weave. Well, that would lose them some time but not much and they should finish back exactly where they should be in the bomber stream. He checked his watch, 21.16, two minutes to the turn, just enough time to recheck his figures. A minute later he was happy and at exactly 21.18.

"New course zero eight five degrees compass."

"Zero eight five degrees compass," echoed Doug. Lancasters had magnetic variation setting correctors so there was no need to allow for the earth's magnetic variation and compass courses were the same as true courses.

Fifteen minutes later Bob spotted the coast and three minutes after that they crossed it into the Baltic and turned back onto the intended route. The weaving had made Ron feel airsick, but he knew his stomach was empty so he wouldn't be sick. Still the waves of nausea swept over him, made worse by knowing that he had been well off track and now while he should be back where he belonged he had no way of knowing for certain if he was back in the stream or not. If he were at the planned height he would feel an occasional bump as his aircraft crossed the slipstream of another unseen aircraft in the dark. This always scared Doug because he thought of it as a near collision, but Ron thought of it as a reassurance that he was where he should be in the middle of the bomber stream. But at this level there would be no reassuring friendly bumps, only the rising doubt in Ron's mind. While he had been distracted and thinking of Janice had he made a terrible error? From Bob's reports of what he could see on this, thankfully, clear night, they were on track, but what if he had got the timings wrong and they were miles ahead or, worse still, behind the main bomber force? They could be a sitting duck for the fighters. At this very moment a German could be sealing his fate and he would never know. Damn this Lancaster, damn the Germans and damn the war, all he wanted to do was go home to his wife. He was trapped in this hell and as the Adjutant had said, the only way out was to do thirty Ops. But this was only number three; he would never get through it. If he did would Janice still be there and if she wasn't, what was the point of it all?

"Bomber going down in flames dead astern, about two miles," reported George.

Ron almost cheered as he noted the position. He was in the right place at the right time.

"Looks like we're back in the stream, Ron, well done," said Doug.

Ron was so pleased he almost forgot his airsickness. In his lonely world not many people praised him and he almost smiled.

A sharp course change to the south took them over Falster Island, then 22 miles of sea and they entered Germany. Now they were only 110 miles from Berlin. Ron was now working hard, buoyed up by the unaccustomed words of praise. He took any position fixes he could get, updated the Air Position Indicator, and re-calculated the current wind. Harry had passed him the Group wind every half hour but Ron never trusted it and only ever used it as a guide.

Each bomber Group would select some experienced crews on each raid to be wind finders. The navigators of these aircraft would calculate the wind speed and direction every half hour and give it to the radio operator, who would transmit it back to Group Headquarters on a HF wind finder's frequency. Group would then average all the aircrafts' findings and re transmit the average wind speed and direction on the Group HF frequency to all the Group aircraft. It was useful information but not 100 percent reliable.

At 22.30 Alex spotted searchlights to the south, which could only be Berlin, and at 22.38 Bob spotted the lake that he thought was the holding point. At 22.40 yellow ground markers burst open marking where they should start maximum rate window dropping and at one minute before they reached the holding point Doug saw yellow flares in the target area, as the Pathfinders made their attack. It was going like clockwork now, and the only additional worry in Ron's mind on top of the usual ones he had when flying over a hostile city, was that this time they might also be bombed from above by friendly aircraft. The aircraft was in Bob's hands now. Ron had got them there, it was up to the bomb aimer and pilot to hit the target, and then Ron would get them all home. It should be easier now; he had a fair idea what the winds were. They had been different to the forecast, but the big advantage would be that once they were clear of the German coast they should get GEE back and then it would be easy. The Lancaster was not weaving now so they must be on the bomb run. For most people this was the worst time of the flight, as they flew straight and level over the target getting shot at all the time. But Ron didn't really mind this. He was not scared of death, although he did desperately want to live; the thing that scared Ron the most was taking the blame and over the target everything was out of his hands so whatever happened he could not be blamed. Now Ron took a rest, casually checking the course out of the target area. There was a loud thump and a rattle on the fuselage.

"Left, left…. Steady," said Bob, over the intercom.

There was another lurch and the internal fittings rattled.

"Jesus!" said Bob, forgetting his microphone was still on.

"Right… Steady, steady… Bombs away!"

There was the usual jump that left his stomach behind and Ron prepared himself to start work again. F for Freddy would now be shooting upwards with the weight of the bombs gone but V for Victor was not so keen and only slowly lumbered upwards to 19,000 feet then refused to go any higher. Ron watched his altimeter and was not impressed.

"Course two seven five degrees compass," said Ron and he was on his way home. The next turn was 130 miles away but with the wind 090 at 20 mph he had a ground speed of 230 mph so it would only take him thirty-four minutes. Then a turn northwest to the coast, another twenty-five minutes, less than an hour to relative safety. The gunners had reported relatively few bombers going down, so perhaps they had fooled the Germans and tonight was going to be an easy Op after all. When he got back there was sure to be leave, they wouldn't do any more Ops with the moon as bright as it had been earlier that night. Over Denmark Ron had been amazed at how much he could see in the silvery moonlight and if the moon had still been up when they crossed the target it would have been a slaughter.

Then Ron's thoughts of an easy trip were invaded by Jimmy's soft Norfolk accent.

"We're losing the oil pressure on number four, skipper."

"How long do you think it will last?"

"Maybe fifteen minutes, it's hard to say."

"Roger, how long to the coast, Ron?"

"An hour," replied Ron immediately, feeling quite pleased with the quick response.

"We'll just carry on in the stream until we hit the coast, then we might cut the corner and head direct for home from there. Can you be ready for that, Ron?"

"Wilco."

"Jimmy, just keep an eye on number four's temperatures and pressure. We'll keep it going as long as we can then shut it down."

"Roger, skipper."

Why couldn't he just have a nice easy straightforward trip, thought Ron? Why was everything against him? His whole life seemed one long struggle in which he had felt out of control; all he wanted was a quiet, peaceful, ordinary, and comfortable life. Dispiritedly he turned back to his map. The planned route crossed the coast west of Cuxhaven, took a fix off an island five miles off the coast before heading out to sea and out of German radar coverage. They could follow the route to the island then turn west dropping to a lower level and head home direct, skirting just to the north of the East Frisian Islands. From the island to Metheringham was just over 320 miles, almost all of it over the sea; but Lancasters seemed to fly well enough on three engines, so it shouldn't be a problem.

"Oil pressure's down to the 45 pounds per square inch minimum on number four and the oil and coolant temperatures are starting to rise, skipper."

"Roger, Jimmy, let me know when you think it's about to seize up and we'll shut it down. How long to the coast, Ron?"

"Forty minutes."

"Ron, a dozen searchlights have just lit up directly ahead of us."

Ron was suddenly worried. There weren't supposed to be any defended areas here. Was he lost? Was he to blame?

"How far away are the lights?"

"Oh they're a long way away at the moment, about 50 miles."

Ron looked down the route 50 miles to near the turn northwest. Just south of the turn was the town of Celle, which had to be it.

"It's Celle, we pass clear to the north of there."

"Well, it looks to be on our route at the moment and they've just started a flak barrage."

Damn the wind. He had had a feeling they were drifting left of track. Still this time the Germans had helped out. Celle was 5 miles south of track so if he doubled the correction and turned 10 degrees right, they should still pass to the north of the town.

"New course two eight five degrees compass."

"Two eight five degrees compass," repeated Doug.

"Bomber going down over Celle," reported Jimmy. "And I think we'd better shut down number four, skipper, the temperatures are nearly off the scale. If we run her any longer I think she'll catch fire."

"Roger, confirm number four," said Doug, reaching for the number four throttle and he and Jimmy shut down the engine. The number four engine powered Alex's turret so when it was shut down his turret was all but useless and Doug told him he could leave the turret when they were safely across the coast. Until then he would be an extra lookout.

"Great," he replied. "I'll come up front to warm up."

"If you can find anywhere on this wreck that's warm let me know about it," said Bob.

Ron listened to the change in engine noise and watched his altimeter start to unwind as the Lancaster lost height towards its three engine ceiling of 10,000 feet. More bloody changing winds and airspeeds, he thought. Still Doug kept weaving and Ron felt he must be bright green with airsickness and his stomach cramped, making him wince. By now he was freezing cold, his airsickness had made him sweat and that had frozen on him so he had spasms of uncontrollable shivers. At least at 10,000 feet they could come off oxygen so Ron poured himself a cup of warm coffee from his thermos flask. They were steady on course for the coast now, but on three engines it would take them twenty-eight minutes not twenty-five and the long haul across the North Sea would seem like forever, thought Ron in the middle of a spasm. He wrapped his cold, gloved hands around the cup of coffee and rubbed it up and down his frozen thighs, but it didn't help. His teeth were chattering and he tried to stop them, but in the end he just let them get on with it. The coffee did seem to warm his insides but his limbs stayed frozen.

Bob reported the searchlights of Bremerhaven and Cuxhaven, which made Ron's job easy as all Doug had to do was fly between them and he should see the island just off the coast. They crossed the coast as planned, immediately spotted the island and turned onto two seven zero degrees compass, which allowing for Ron's new found wind was the direct course for Metheringham.

"I'm going to take us down to 2,000 feet to try and get us below the Jerries radar cover," said Doug.

Brilliant! thought Ron, who had just finished his calculations using the wind at 10,000 feet and would now have to start again. Sod it! This will be a close enough course until we get back into GEE range, then I'll correct it from there, he thought.

By ten minutes past midnight they were 20 miles north of the West Frisian Islands heading straight for Metheringham. Doug had stopped weaving, Bob had dropped the last of the window and most of the crew had started to relax a little. They had drunk some of their coffee, the German defences were behind them, and although they were on three engines and none of those was giving full power, they were more than happy that they could get back on what they had.

20 miles northeast another three men were less content.

Gunter Voss had been a night fighter pilot since the very first specialist German night fighter units had been formed and as such he was probably the most experienced pilot in his unit. His experience had brought with it success and he had a credible score of kills, all of them against British bombers. However, as he was only a sergeant, he sometimes thought that his success was something of a double-edged sword. His unit commander was an ambitious major and he suspected that the officer was jealous of his success because since the major had taken command a month ago Gunter had been getting all the difficult jobs. Tonight was a classic case. Instead of being sent into the bomber stream with the rest of his unit, where there were easy kills to be made, he had been given the unit's oldest Messerschmitt and sent to a fighter box over the Frisian Islands. There under the close control of a ground station he was to try to hunt down some mine laying aircraft working close to the Dutch coast. It was a difficult job, with the low flying mine layers making difficult and elusive targets for the ground radars to track. On top of this his Messerschmitt's own Lichtenstein radar was swamped by ground echoes at low level and his operator could only detect targets at a fraction of its usual range. But the worst thing was the targets were all over the sea and an intercept inevitably meant a long chase away from the shore and a long flight back, especially if a bomber damaged them.

They were just returning from one of these chases now. It had been the second of the night and like the first had ended with the target fading from the screen of the ground radar operator before they could get a contact on it with their own radar. It had been another fruitless night chasing shadows. They had been in the air a long time and they were too short of fuel to set up for another chase.

Flying southwest at 2,000 feet they homed in on their fighter beacon and from there it was only a short flight home.

"Target crossing left to right!" yelled Gunter's radar operator, who still had his head jammed to the visor of his radar screen.

Glancing up from his instruments, Gunter caught a fleeting glimpse of a dark shape against the grey blackness of a layer of stratus cloud that had formed over the Dutch coast and was reflecting the starlight. The aircraft had been close, or he would not have seen it, and it was crossing their path at about 90 degrees. It would have already flown out of the side of the narrow 25-degree beam of the Lichtenstein radar, which only looked forwards. Gunter threw the heavy fighter into a tight right turn looking back in at his instruments, checking his angle of bank and making sure he did not let the Messerschmitt's nose drop in the turn. After turning 90 degrees his operator called. "Contact! Stop turn! Target 1,000 metres slightly right."

Rolling out of the turn the operator talked Günter into a position directly behind and slightly below the radar contact.

"We'll have to be quick, Karl," said Gunter. "We don't have much fuel to spare."

"We're right on him, bring your speed back, he's a lot slower than the others."

Gunter adjusted the throttles, while his eyes flicked from the instruments to the dark sky, searching for the target. Suddenly a flicker of dull blue caught his eye. Searching with the corner of his eyes he saw more blue exhaust flames. Three pairs, that was odd. The dark shape was almost certainly a bomber, but he had better be sure. He pulled over to the left and accelerated until the bomber was in his 3 o'clock and slightly above him. Against the stars he could clearly make out the shape of a Lancaster, while he was invisible, hidden against the black background of the sea. Sliding slowly to the right, he manoeuvred directly under the bomber and confirmed what he had suspected all along: this was a lame duck returning home on three engines. With his curiosity satisfied and his target positively identified his low fuel level meant he would now have to act quickly.

"Everyone ready to attack?" he asked.

"Ready," replied his radar operator.

"All clear behind," replied his gunner.

Gunter closed his throttles slightly and descended to about 100 feet below the bomber, then levelled out and let his speed fall away until the bomber started to pull ahead of him. He would wait until he was just behind the bomber's tail, then pull up his nose and before his gun sight touched the bomber's nose he would open fire and let the bomber fly through his stream of fire, raking it from stem to stern. He was almost in position now, the dreaded rear turret just above him, but he was hidden against the black sea, while the bomber was silhouetted against the starry sky. Starlight caught the port side of the bomber's twin tail and he barely perceptibly increased the backpressure on the control column of the

Messerschmitt to bring the nose up. Slowly the bomber sank towards his sights until, with only a few degrees to go, Gunter saw a flash of reflected starlight on the side of the rear turret.

George was fighting to keep his eyes open. The three nights of Ops in a row had taken it out of him and despite the "Wakey Wakey" pills he was now resorting to chewing at his tongue in the hope that the pain would keep him awake. His legs had long since gone into cramp and even someone his size could not stretch them enough in the small turret to find any comfort. At least it was warmer now they were no longer at high level. But that was a relative term, he realized, because he was not actually warmer, just less cold. He rotated his turret to the left so that he could look over his right shoulder and down directly at the sea below and behind the tail. It was all a uniform blackness and the thought of the icy water made him shiver. He couldn't swim and had once nearly drowned when a pit fall had trapped him in a flooding coal mine. He had been scared of water ever since and hated flying over it. A small splash of light caught his eye and he thought it must be a lone wave on the sea below. Then there was a second flash in the same place and George was no longer tired.

Gunter knew it was a race to get the first shots off and pulled the Messerschmitt's nose up quickly so that the guns would bear. But he knew in his heart he would be beaten to the draw. The tail of the bomber was suddenly a mass of yellow flashes and streams of red tracer rocketed back towards him as he pulled his own trigger and heard the hammering of the cannons beneath his feet.

George's four streams of .303 bullets slammed into the Messerschmitt's starboard engine causing showers of yellow flashes, while Doug hurled V for Victor into the tight left hand corkscrew George had called for. A combination of George hitting the Messerschmitt in the starboard engine and the bomber's sharp turn to the left meant Gunter's fire first missed the Lancaster's nose then instead of slamming into the fuselage hit the starboard wing. Because Gunter was hurrying to get his guns on target before George, the fighter's nose rose more quickly than it should have and only two 20 mm cannon shells hit the bomber, before the rest of Gunter's burst was wasted in the air behind the wing. Unfortunately, one hit the starboard inner engine, shattering its fuel pipes and starting a fire. The other hit the starboard inner fuel tank, causing fuel to gush out and immediately igniting in the flames from the number three engine.

Gunter felt the bullets hammer into his fighter and he broke away to the left, rapidly increasing the deflection the gunner would have to allow to hit him and making himself a much more difficult target. The red tracer followed him, but it was passing behind and he would soon be out of range. The oil pressure of his starboard engine was dropping fast and the temperature was rising. He would have to shut it down and head for home quickly if he was not to end up in the sea.

"Emergency homing for base!" he yelled.

Inside V for Victor there was chaos.

"I've hit him!" yelled George.

"Fire in number three!" yelled Jimmy.

"Shut it down Jimmy! Where is he, George?" asked Doug

"7 o'clock low, turning away!"

"Number three shutdown and feathered, fire extinguisher discharged!" yelled Jimmy.

Ron was hanging onto the edge of his table, as the bomber lurched through its corkscrew. As he hung on he looked back at Harry, who was staring out of the small square side window of his compartment, which looked along the upper surface of the starboard wing leading edge. The radio operator's face was brilliant yellow in the reflected flames, his eyes wide as he stared into the inferno.

"Skipper, it's Harry. The fire's burnt the metal skin off the leading edge and I can see the main spar. It doesn't look to be going out!"

"Roger, we can't dive, we're low already."

"Harry's right, skipper!" called Jimmy. "It's not going out and if we don't put her down soon we'll lose the wing!"

Doug knew there was only one thing he could do. They were very low to bale and if they did make it they would not last long in the sea without a dinghy.

"Harry, send an SOS. Ron, give him our position. Crew, ditching stations! George, where's the fighter now?"

"I can't see him, skipper."

"Get to your ditching station then."

"I'd rather stay here if that's alright."

"If you think you'll be okay back there."

"I should be fine, unless you're intending to reverse into the water skipper."

"Well, it's not the recommended technique, but you never know. Off you go to your ditching station, Jimmy."

"I'll stay and give you a hand if that's alright, skipper."

"No, Jimmy, you get behind the main spar! I'll manage here!"

"I'm staying, skipper," said Jimmy quietly and unusually forcefully.

Doug was slightly shocked at Jimmy's defiance but didn't have time to argue.

"Okay, but get behind my seat before we hit the sea."

The shock that he was about to land in the water, after he had just convinced himself he was safely on his way home to his wife, stunned Ron into inactivity for a few seconds and he just stared into space.

"What's our position?" yelled Harry over the intercom into his ears, but it was like it came from another world. He was going to die tonight in the cold waters of the North Sea and tomorrow his wife would get a telegram telling her he was missing. He felt sorry for her and the hurt she would feel and he felt it was his fault because he hadn't needed to volunteer for flying duties. Her mother would be there to help her, and her friends. No doubt that bastard John Hart would be around too; Ron's eyes hardened.

Harry kicked him in the leg to get his attention.

"What's our position?" he repeated. "I need it now for our SOS!"

Ron snapped back to the present. He wasn't going to give in to John bloody Hart. He found himself staring into Harry's face as he peered around his radio set, his whole compartment lit by the flickering flames. Get a position, you don't have much time, he thought, but where the hell was he? He was relying on GEE to fix his position when he got back in range, now it was his only hope. Frantically he adjusted the focus and fine tune knobs, praying the set would work. Blips started to appear on the green trace lines and he took measurements on them. Quickly he plotted them on his map, wrote down the latitude and longitude and passed the paper to Harry. 5312N00154E about 26 miles northeast of Cromer, not too far off the coast. He would at least have a chance of being picked up, if he survived the ditching and got into the dinghy. Bob pushed past behind him making his way to the crew ditching station between the main spars and Ron suddenly realized that he should be going there too.

Moving aft he passed Harry who was still rattling away on his Morse key, while the flames outside turned his compartment into a hellish cavern. Alex was already sitting with his back to the main spar, his knees up and his head bowed onto them, as if he was praying. Bob stood against the rest bunk behind Harry's seat with his headset plugged into a spare intercom lead, so he could hear what was happening. Ron crawled awkwardly over the spar and squeezed in between Alex and Bob.

With the two right hand engines dead and the two left hand engines at full boost Doug was holding V for Victor straight with full left rudder and his leg was starting to ache with the pressure on it. If it hadn't been for the fire about to burn the wing off he knew he could have nursed the Lancaster at least as far as the English coast and his crew could have baled out over land. Now he looked out at the black water skimming past just below him and knew it was now or never. It was an almost flat calm with a long gentle swell, which he now flew parallel to. He tried to judge the height, but it was very deceptive and he knew it would be all too easy to fly straight into the sea in these conditions. There would be no second chance; he would just have to go for it. He lowered 30 degrees of flap, as recommended in the Lancaster's pilot's notes, paused for a second, took a deep breath and closed the throttles.

"Get behind the seat, Jimmy! Brace! Brace! Brace!"

Jimmy swung nimbly behind Doug's seat and sat with his back to the armour plate. Bob heard the engines cut, then Doug's yell and realizing that Harry intended to continue transmitting the SOS until they hit the sea, reached forward grabbing Harry under the arms, pulling him up and backwards over the main spar as if he was on a bungee chord.

"You dozy little Pommie, you'll smash your skull in against the radio up there!" he yelled, knowing full well that Harry already knew that.

After the roar of the engines there seemed to be an incredibly long silence. They glided on and on for what seemed like forever and when the impact finally came it was gentler than some of Doug's regular landings. However, that was just a glancing bounce that sent them back into the air. The second impact rattled their teeth and the third would have been a nose dive into the depths that would have killed them all, if the starboard wing had not entered the swell and swung them sharply right, spinning the Lancaster round and dousing the flames at the same time. The nose plunged into the swell and a wave of green sea engulfed the outside of the cockpit running back up the top of the fuselage to the mid upper turret, before subsiding. The rapid deceleration and sharp turn stunned the whole crew so that it was some seconds before they started to come to their senses and feel the gentle rocking of the aircraft in the water.

Alex got up first, disentangling himself from the pile of bodies between the spars and jettisoning the escape hatch in the roof. Ron was next, pushing at Alex's boots as the Scot clambered through the hatch. Harry was scrambling around in the darkness grabbing pieces of equipment.

"Come on, Harry!" yelled Bob. "She won't float forever!"

"You go first and I'll pass this out to you," he replied, holding up his flight bag, which he had been stuffing things into.

In the tail George had been pushed hard into the rear doors of the turret but was unhurt. Now he opened the doors and rolled out backwards into the fuselage. This put him on top of the tailplane carry through and he twisted onto his hands and knees. The view up the dark tunnel like fuselage was like one he had seen many times in his nightmares. Water was pouring in around the edges of the crew entrance door and forward of the tail carry through, where the floor was lower, water lapped back and forth. It was for all the world like the flooding coal mine that had nearly killed him years before. He was so shocked at the vision he nearly returned to his turret, but he knew there was no way out there and he had to go forward. Crawling forward, he turned and slid his feet off the carry through into the water. It was icy cold and knee deep. Pulling himself forward by the fuselage frames, he reached the mid upper turret, which he would have to go under. He looked at the water, which was almost up to the bottom of the turret. His heart pounded and his head throbbed, bile rose in his throat. He was going to drown, the Lancaster was going to slip beneath the waves and drag him down with it to the horrible bubbling lung-bursting death that had haunted his dreams for the last four years. He thought of Billy Procter, one of the two men that had been trapped

174

with him, and how when Billy had lost the use of his legs as they stood in the cold neck-high water he had held him upright and talked about when they had been at school together. They had listened to the rescue teams digging towards them from the other side of the pit fall and he could still see Billy's face in the glow of their one remaining Davy lamp as the water slowly climbed higher. Despite everything he did to maintain his circulation, eventually his arms had gone numb and his hands turned into unfeeling useless claws. Billy had slid lower and lower until he slipped silently out of George's arms and disappeared below the surface leaving a trail of bubbles, which suddenly stopped. Tears rolled down George's face as he realised that it was now his turn to follow Billy.

"George! George! Where the hell are you?" Harry was calling him.

"I'm stuck!" he yelled, unable to bring himself to dive under the turret.

"Hold on, I'm coming!"

"No!" Harry was not meant to die with him. "Get out! She's going down!"

"I'm on my way!"

Shit! The dozy little bugger will get trapped too, thought George. He looked again at the water. The only way to stop Harry was to go forward. Bollocks! He took a deep breath and pushed himself down into the water and forward under the turret. The water closed over his head like an icy shroud, stinging his face. His harness snagged on something and he was trapped. He was in total darkness, completely disoriented and didn't even know which way was up. Panic immediately arrived and he lashed out grabbing and wriggling in a whirlpool of uncontrollable thrashing until just as his lungs were about to burst he came to the surface. Where was he? Which way was he facing? Was he still in the tail? Then he realised someone had hold of him under his arms.

"I've got you, George, you can stop struggling now."

"Thanks," spluttered George, as they scrambled up onto the higher bomb bay floor, where the water was only a few inches deep. From there it was only a short straightforward scramble over the rear spar, then a quick wriggle up through the hatch into the fresh sea air that George had thought he would never breathe again.

The third impact had thrown Doug forward so violently his harness had stretched the full distance between his head and the top of the instrument panel. Although the edge of the panel was padded it had hit Doug hard enough on the bridge of his nose to knock him out and that was how Jimmy found him, hanging forward in his straps with blood running from his nose. Reaching up Jimmy jettisoned the escape hatch above Doug's head and supporting his pilot's torso with one arm pulled the seat harness release pin with the other. Then he turned the parachute harness release box a quarter turn anti-clockwise and squeezed it in his large hand until the click announced that the locking pins were free and the straps fell away. Throwing the straps aside he tried to lift Doug upwards out of the hatch, but Doug's limp dead weight was too much even for someone as strong and desperate as Jimmy.

"Help!" he shouted looking out of the cockpit into the darkness. Footsteps thumped up the fuselage roof onto the cockpit Perspex.

"What is it?" asked Bob.

"Doug's unconscious. I'll lift him from down here, you pull from above."

"No worries."

The hatch was small and Doug's bulky flying kit seemed to fill the space completely but slowly between the two of them they dragged him out into the dinghy that Alex held close to the edge of the cockpit. By the time Doug was out the water had just started to spill over the top of Jimmy's flying boots and he hurried up through the hatch himself. Jimmy was the last into the dinghy and once aboard Alex cut the line that held it to the aircraft and pushed them clear. The small circular yellow dinghy bobbed away as the Lancaster sank deeper by the nose. Eventually the water entered the cockpit hatch and within a few seconds the bomber started to slide quickly downwards, the cockpit disappearing first as the water worked its way up the fuselage. Air gurgled out of holes and hatches as the water rushed in and then it was gone, leaving a few bubbles to bob to the surface. Doug was still unconscious and Jimmy was fussing over him with a First Aid kit, but all the others stared at the sinking bomber until it had gone. Now they all turned and slouched with their backs to the edge of the dinghy, their knees up and their feet touching in the middle. Apart from the lapping of the water and the heavy breathing all was quiet.

10

The clear black winter sky stretched out above them to infinity. The myriad of stars sparkled brightly and provided just enough light to make out the pale blobs, which were the faces of the other people in the dinghy. A gentle breeze blew against the back of George's helmeted head where it stuck up above the edge of the dinghy. It was very cold, but for the moment, George was content to just lie back in the cramped, waterlogged dinghy and be glad that he was alive. After a few seconds that seemed like a lifetime he realised that they should be doing things and his mind turned to their training.

"Is everybody here?" In the dark he couldn't be sure and he was suddenly worried that he might have just watched one of the crew drown in the sinking aircraft.

"Yes," replied Alex, who had counted them all into the dinghy.

"We need to get this water out." They were sitting in three inches of icy water in the bottom of the dinghy and if they didn't get it out it would suck the heat out of their bodies.

"There's nothing to bale with," said Ron.

"We can use our flying helmets," replied George.

Slowly and laboriously they baled the water from the dinghy until although their flying clothing was wet up to at least their waists the dinghy was dry. Doug stirred then suddenly sat up.

"Where am I?"

"In a dinghy, skipper. We ditched," said Jimmy.

"Yeah, you made a bloody good job of it too skip," added Bob.

"But A wouldn't recommend you make a habit of it," said George.

"Is everyone alright?"

"You're the only one that was hurt skipper. You hit your head on the instrument panel," said Jimmy.

"How long have I been unconscious?"

"About ten minutes."

"Did anyone get our SOS, Harry?"

"I didn't get a reply skipper," said Harry disappointedly.

"Your receiver kept going off tune though, didn't it? Someone might have replied and you just didn't hear it," said Bob hopefully.

"Maybe. But I still have the standby communications system," grinned Harry, as he pulled two metal boxes from his flight bag, revelling in the full attention of the crew.

"What the hell are they?" asked Bob.

"Pigeons," replied Harry.

"Christ, I'd forgotten about them," said Bob. "Are they any good?"

"I've no idea," replied Harry.

"We'd be better off eatin' them," chipped in Alex.

"You lot have no idea, have yer?" said George, squirming to sit upright in the gently rolling dinghy. "My dad's been a pigeon fancier all his life."

"You can get arrested for that sort of thing," quipped Harry. George gave him a hard stare and carried on.

"Before the war he used to race them from all over Europe."

"Did he ever beat them?" asked Harry.

"I'll give you such a clip if you're not careful," said George.

"How fast do they fly?" asked Doug, who was intrigued by anything that flew, but knew very little about birds of any sort.

"Over 40 mph flat out, but over a distance about 30 mph."

Doug turned to Ron. "Where are we, Ron?"

"20 to 30 miles northeast of Cromer."

"So a pigeon could be at Cromer in an hour," said Harry.

"Yes," replied George. "But they'll fly back to where they come from and that's probably in the north of England."

"That's over 150 miles," said Ron. "They'll never make it."

"My dad's raced pigeons from France and Norway. They'll make it alright."

"It'll take them over five hours to fly that distance and that's not allowing for the wind," exclaimed Ron.

"It doesn't matter," retorted George. "They'll still make it."

"It's 02.00, if we set them off now they'll be home at about 08.00-ish," said Harry.

"I wouldn't do that," replied George.

"Why?" asked Harry.

"Because they're pigeons, not bloody owls!" said George, delighting in getting his own back on Harry. "We need to let them off at first light."

"That's not until about 08.00," said Bob.

"So they won't get home until at least 14.00," said Ron.

"And they might not be found until their owner comes home from work at 18.00, but the fact remains they will get home," said George emphatically.

"It will be dark again by then! They'll never find us in the dark!" exclaimed Ron, who was starting to feel seasick. The thought of spending not one day but two in the dinghy was almost unbearable. He also knew that Janice would probably get a telegram saying he was missing that evening and he was hoping he would be able to get in touch with her before it arrived.

"As long as the sea stays calm we'll be alright for a couple of nights," said Doug, wondering if that were really true in an open dinghy in the North Sea in winter.

"We're close to the east coast shipping lanes," said Alex. "We might get picked up by a ship."

"A mate of mine's on 254 Squadron flying Beaufighters out of North Coates. They get sent out on searches for ditched bomber crews all the time. I reckon we stand a good chance of being picked up," said Bob.

A thought suddenly occurred to Doug. "Do we have any flares?"

Everyone was silent until Harry grinned. "One Very pistol and twenty cartridges." He smiled, digging around in his bag. "And a torch, a flask of coffee, a chocolate bar, a note pad and a pencil and a First Aid kit."

"And two pigeons," added George.

"What's everyone else got?" asked Doug.

"I've got a revolver," said Bob.

"That'll be useful," said Harry sarcastically.

"It'll shut you up," retorted Bob.

Doug looked at Jimmy.

"I left everything behind," said Jimmy sheepishly.

"By the time me and Jimmy got you out she was about to go under," offered Bob.

"I've only got a pencil and paper," said Ron.

"I've got half a flask of coffee," said Alex.

"Where the hell did you get that?" asked George. "There's no space for it in a turret."

"I stole it off Ron," smiled Alex.

Ron took the resulting roar of laughter personally.

"I could have you charged," he said petulantly.

"Let's have a mouthful of coffee each now, and save the rest for later," said Doug, changing the subject quickly. One mouthful each finished the half flask, but in their chilled state the warm liquid's path could be felt down their throats and into their stomachs. Sleep crept up on them and Doug was aware they should stay awake, at least until daylight. The cold was penetrating to their very bones and sleep in those conditions could easily bring death with it. "Right! Nobody sleeps until daylight! Then at least three of us stay awake to look out for ships or aircraft."

"It's going to be easier said than done skipper," said George. "I can hardly keep me eyes open now."

"Well, tell us about yourself."

"What?" asked George, shocked by the request and a little embarrassed.

"Tell us your life story and then we'll all tell you ours. It'll pass the time and keep us awake."

"Yeah! Tell us a story, George, and spice it up a bit," laughed Harry.

"Where do I start?"

"Where were you born?"

"Half Moon Lane, Spennymoor."

"Well, start there and the rest of you have to ask questions."

One by one they took it in turns to tell their life stories and when anyone started to drift off to sleep Doug made them ask a question. They talked about where they lived and their families. They talked about their jobs and Doug quizzed them for details and prompted them when they faltered. Doug's crew came from a wide variety of backgrounds and although they were all reticent to start with, Doug's easy manner and coaxing brought them out of themselves and by the time the last of them had finished it was five o'clock.

"Let's all have another mouthful of coffee," said Doug, trying to stifle a yawn. Another three hours to dawn, he thought. How the hell was he going to stay awake until then? The warm coffee revived him slightly but it had the opposite effect on some of the others and they started to drift off to sleep. Doug was tempted to let them but this time George stepped in. He kicked his feet around the centre of the dinghy hitting everyone's ankles.

"It's not time to sleep yet, you lazy buggers! You've all got to name a song and we've all got to sing it." He was greeted with lots of curses but he wasn't put off. "Come on, Bob, you're first with Waltzing Matilda."

"Sod off, George, we just want to go to sleep."

"Do you ever want to see Perth again? If you do you'll sing Waltzing Matilda and stay awake!" His eyes glared bright in the starlight as he lashed out with another kick. "I've seen people give up on their life and once you stop fighting you're as good as dead! I nearly gave up meself tonight but I didn't and I'm still here and I'm going to survive this. Sleep is death and if you give in to it you're going to die and there's nothing anyone can do about it! You've got to fight it yourselves. Now sing bloody Waltzing Matilda, you Aussie bastard!" Reluctantly Bob started to sing and George immediately joined in. He was possibly the worst singer in the world but he was also the loudest and nobody was going to sleep when George was singing.

The singing took them past six o'clock when Doug took over again with competitions. First they had to take it in turns to name a country beginning with A. Anyone who couldn't think of a country or repeated a previous answer was out. Then they went on to B and so on. Teeth chattered uncontrollably and voices stammered answers as their bodies became numb with cold. More time was allowed to come up with an answer as their brains started to slow down. But with everyone prompting everyone else they kept going. This took them past seven o'clock and Doug stared at where he thought was east and dared to hope the sky was a shade lighter there. By now Ron was being sick regularly over the side of the dinghy. His stomach was empty and he stayed on his knees with his head over the side retching dryly.

"A should ha brought ya sick bag as well as ya flask," said Alex.

"No point," replied Ron. "It had frozen solid."

"Is it me or is it getting lighter over there?" asked Harry. They all looked towards where he was pointing and it did look as if the sky might be brighter there.

Jimmy reached into his flying clothing to his battledress and pulled off one of his buttons. Inside was a small compass and holding it steady he got Harry to shine his torch at it.

"That's east," he said. They all sat and stared at the start of the day, while the dinghy slowly rose and fell.

"Have any of you ever felt that we were bobbing up and down like this when we were on our takeoff run?" asked Jimmy.

"I have," said Bob.

"Me too," said Doug.

"Well, actually, sitting in the arse end, I am bloody bobbing up and down," said George.

"No," said Jimmy. "The whole Lancaster feels like it's bobbing up and down."

"I've often wondered about that," said Harry. "I thought it was just my imagination."

"Well, it isn't," continued Jimmy. "I was talking to one of the ground crew yesterday and I mentioned it to him. I thought it might be something wrong with the main wheel suspension but apparently most crews feel it. When they built the runway at Metheringham the ground was so boggy they put down a huge amount of aggregate and concrete, but they think that either a dodgy contractor sold them short or the ground was so wet that the aggregate sank into the ground and the concrete is now floating on the unstable soil below. So when we take off with a heavy load the runway flexes."

"So we are bobbing up and down," said Bob.

"Yes."

"I thought it was Doug's dodgy flying," said Harry.

"What's wrong with my flying?" asked Doug defensively.

"What's wrong with it? You take us all to bloody Berlin against our better judgement and then expect us to paddle home and you ask us what's wrong with your flying?"

"Oh shut up, you bloody fool," said George. "Let's have some chocolate while we watch the sun come up, skipper." They opened one of the bars of chocolate and broke it into equal pieces, then savoured it as they wished the sky lighter.

"This is a shameful waste of a chocolate bar," said Alex when he had finished.

"What do you mean?" asked Doug.

"Well, it's an awful waste eatin' it."

"What the hell do you normally do with it?" asked Bob.

"Och, ya would be surprised what a WAAF a'll do for a bar of chocolate," smiled Alex.

"You crafty sod," said Harry. "I'd never have thought of that! I've been eating mine!"

In war rationed Britain very few people could get their hands on chocolate and those that could, could name their price. Doug was shocked by the revelation and could feel himself blushing, but in the darkness nobody could see. Would WAAFs really do anything for a bar of chocolate?

Sally suddenly woke up and looked around in the darkness. She was immediately aware of where she was but didn't know why she had suddenly woken up. She was curled up in the two armchairs she pushed together to sleep on in the flying control tower office. She wasn't cold, which was the usual reason she woke up. Her long johns, trousers, vest, shirt, pullover, scarf, battledress top, and two pairs of thick wool socks under the greatcoat she was using as a blanket saw to that. Then she knew what had woken her as a Lancaster roared low overhead. Reaching out in the dark she fumbled for her boots and dragged them on as the cold air found its way under the greatcoat and made her shiver. Her crew could not have checked in yet or Uncle Bill would have let her know. This didn't worry her because they were flying V for Victor and everyone knew that it was a clapped out old crate and always came back last. Pulling her coat on she made her way outside and up the stairs to the glass room on the roof of the flying control building. The runway lights were on and the first Lancaster had already touched down and was taxiing clear of the end of the runway, its navigating lights like red and green fireflies in the darkness. Another bomber was on its final approach as she reached the roof and she watched the white landing lights touch down to the screech of tyres. Inside flying control Uncle Bill had the radio microphone in one hand and was just finishing speaking to one of his WAAF assistants.

"Mark it up on the board and don't tell Sally, there's nothing she can do and she'll only worry. Ops take more out of that poor girl than they take out of the crews."

Sally's hair stood on end. "Don't tell me what, sir?" she asked, dreading the answer.

"Sally! I didn't see you there… We've just had a message from Group. V for Victor sent an SOS a few minutes ago… They're ditching off the Norfolk coast." Although he could not see anything in the dark he could sense the look on Sally's face. Why the hell did she let herself get so involved? "Conditions for ditching are good and they gave a position which isn't too far off the coast so they stand a fair chance. Of course there will be a full search starting at first light." His voice trailed away as he knew he couldn't say anything to make her feel any better and he turned back to his radio.

Sally walked over to the glass wall of flying control and watched the next Lancaster land. Then she raised her eyes to the dark line of trees on the far edge of the airfield and the lighter starlit sky above them to the east. Out there somewhere her crew were fighting to survive on the North Sea. Or maybe they were already under it. She should have warned them about V for Victor, everyone hated flying it. Behind her she heard Uncle Bill's voice whisper, "Get her out of here, get her a brew and get her to bed. She looks done in." Silent tears rolled down her face. She had lost three other crews in the last six months and although she tried not to become attached to them she couldn't help it. They were all so young and full of life with so much to live for. She sniffed at her running nose as she allowed one of her WAAF friends to lead her away.

"Is it light enough yet?" Doug asked George.

George looked around. The sun was not yet above the horizon but the sky was a pale blue in the east heralding a crisp clear winter's day. It was also light enough to see the damage the instrument panel had done to Doug's face. Crusted blood stuck to his top lip and round his nostrils. His eyes were so black the bruising looked like a bar across his face or Zorro's mask, George thought.

He nodded. "It'll do."

Harry fished out the pigeons' boxes and Ron got out his note pad and pencil.

"What shall I write?" he asked.

"ZNV, ditched, then the position, the time we ditched, seven survivors. Anything else?" asked Doug.

They all shook their heads. Harry handed the first box to George who opened it and coaxed the pigeon out so that he could hold it with its wings folded in his palms and its feet resting on his little fingers. The small message cylinder sat on the bird's back like a rucksack and Ron unscrewed the top and inserted the message. George kissed the pigeon on the back of its head and threw it upwards. The bird flapped away and circled the dinghy gaining height. They repeated the procedure with the second pigeon and watched as they both circled them.

"They're bloody lost already!" said Harry.

"Well, if they land back here I'm going to shoot the little bastards!" said Bob.

"Give them a chance, they're just getting their bearings," replied George. After a few minutes the pigeons headed off into the distance while the crew watched them until they were out of sight, utterly convinced that their fate was in the hands of two birds.

Ten o'clock saw Doug, Jimmy and Bob on watch while George, Alex and Harry dozed between bouts of shivering. Ron was still retching over the side and even Harry was feeling sorry for him. The sky was pale blue with not a cloud to be seen. The sun shone brightly but with only imagined warmth and it was bitterly cold. The wind was starting to increase and occasionally spray came over the side of the dinghy. Doug was starting to get worried. If this continued they would not survive another night and they would be lucky if there was another six hours of daylight left. Jimmy turned and was sick over the side. The smell, before it was blown away, reached Doug and his stomach turned, but he managed to hold it, although he too was feeling far from well. Bob suddenly sat upright and scanned the horizon.

"Listen!" There was a pause and Bob continued to scan. "There!" He pointed. A black dot was moving from left to right in the distance and between wave splashes there was a barely audible drone.

"Harry!" He kicked the radio operator. "Harry! Quick, the flares!" Harry shook himself to full consciousness and realising what was happening pulled out the Very pistol, loaded it and fired a flare. The red flare soared upwards and was snatched by the wind in a large arch the brilliant flame leaving a trail of pink smoke.

"Fire another!" yelled Bob and a second flare rose skyward. Two more followed it but as they all watched the black dot continued on its way. "Bollocks!" said Bob.

"Do you think they were looking for us?" asked Jimmy.

"Possibly," said Bob, "I think it was a Beaufighter."

"If it was a Beaufighter it was probably going on a rover to the Dutch coast," replied Ron pessimistically. Rovers were anti shipping patrols against targets of opportunity.

"By himself, in this weather, with no cloud cover?" asked George sceptically.

"It's not the weather for rovers," agreed Doug. Lone anti shipping aircraft needed poor weather and plenty of cloud cover to hide from German fighters if they were to last long close to the Dutch coast.

"Well, it was definitely a Beaufighter," said Alex, who had the best eyes in the crew.

At eleven o'clock George, Alex and Harry were on watch when the Beaufighter returned. It was at about 1,000 feet and closer, but it would still pass them to the north by more than 2 miles. This time the fighter was heading west but the dinghy was up sun and the fighter crew would have to stare into the reflected glare on the water to see the tiny dinghy. Six more flares arced through the air but once more the aircraft continued on its way. This time the morale in the dinghy sank to somewhere below hopeless.

"The blind bastards!" said Bob.

"It's very difficult to see a dinghy," offered Doug.

"But they were right on top of us," complained Ron. "We'll never get them closer to us than that."

"We were up sun of them, that was the problem," said Alex. "There was nae much chance of them seein' us against that glare." He nodded towards the sun. Silence and despondency descended on the crew and they were all left to their own thoughts.

Half an hour later Bob spoke again, breaking the silence.

"I've had a thought."

"Don't worry, it'll soon get lonely and leave," said Harry.

Bob ignored him. "That Beaufighter was probably on a line search and next time he comes back he'll be further south than the last twice and that will put us down sun of him."

"He'll also probably be further away than he was last time," said Ron unhelpfully.

"It'll make a big difference him not havin' tae stare intae the sun," added Alex.

"We'll have to look into the sun to see him though," said George.

"But we're expecting him and he's easier tae see," replied Alex.

"When's he next due back?" asked Doug.

Ron thought for a second.

"Could be anytime now, depending on the length of his search legs."

"Right! Sharp lookout everyone." Doug was glad of something to do.

The swell increased and shortened, tossing the dinghy around more. Doug, Harry and George were all sick. Jimmy was sick a second time and Ron retched continually.

"There!" yelled Alex pointing. They all followed Alex's finger and after a few seconds spotted the black dot.

"Get the Very pistol ready, Harry," said Doug, but Harry was already kneeling up in the rolling dinghy. "Let him get closer." Doug was suddenly very aware they only had ten flares left. "Now, fire!"

The Beaufighter was at least 3 miles away, crossing them right to left and they had to squint to see it against the low winter's sun. Flare after flare soared skywards. George flashed Harry's torch and Jimmy took out his stainless steel cigarette case and used it as a heliograph in the sunlight. The Beaufighter was level with them now and still over 2 miles away. Bob blew the whistle attached to his battledress blouse collar. They were all shouting wildly now and waving their arms, as if either would help them. On the Beaufighter purred, the distinctive sound of its sleeve valve radial engines starting to fade.

"Come back!" wailed Ron in complete despair, as their last real hope flew on. Then the Beaufighter turned. At first they hardly dared to hope the slight change of course was a turn, but then it became obvious that the big fighter was in a steep banked turn. Harry fired another flare, and then saved the last two while George and Jimmy continued with the torch and heliograph. The Beaufighter headed towards them in a slow descent, passing close to the north of them so the pilot could look down at them through his left side cockpit window. They could see the crew clearly as the pilot continued to circle and the navigator waved at them. After one low level circuit the fighter climbed and keeping the dinghy in sight, continued to circle.

"He's radioing for a ship!" yelled Harry, as they all cheered themselves hoarse.

"Stop blowing that bloody whistle!" yelled George. Bob grinned and continued to blow.

After getting his message through the Beaufighter descended again and kept circling at about 1,000 feet and the crew lay back in the dinghy and watched it. Time wore on and the fighter stayed with them. For two hours the Beaufighter circled and Doug started to worry that it would soon run short of fuel and have to leave them.

"Ship!" yelled Alex making everyone jump.

Doug turned away from the fighter to look for the ship and at first saw nothing. Screwing up his eyes he tried again and saw a dot on the horizon. Soon the dot grew bigger, it had a large bow wave and was obviously going fast. It looked low and grey.

"It's an MTB," said Alex. "We'll be home in no time in that." A bang behind them made them jump but it was only Harry firing one of their last two flares.

"Just making certain," he said. A light flashed from the rapidly approaching boat. "Do you need a lift?" Harry read.

The low grey 110-foot-long Fairmile MTB bounced towards them over the shortening sea, the four 4,800 bhp petrol engines giving a distinctive roar. When the boat got close the engines cut and the bow wave shrank, as the boat quickly lost way to glide smoothly past them at a snail's pace twenty feet downwind of them. A group of sailors gathered by the port torpedo tube and one threw a line squarely over the dinghy. As they were being hauled in a white-capped officer stuck his head over the side of the bridge.

"Are any of you chaps hurt?"

"No!" replied Doug.

"Good! We don't have a doctor and I hate playing nurse!"

The sailors dragged them aboard while the Beaufighter made a low pass overhead and headed for home. The young officer, who had shouted to them, appeared off the bridge. He had the double wavy gold stripes of a Royal Naval Reserve Lieutenant and Doug realised that he must be the captain. The man's dark eyes flashed around them and assessing Doug as the man in charge offered his hand.

"Matthew Bell, you seem to have taken a bit of a knock, old boy, we'll get someone to look at that."

"Doug Jackson, yes, I had a bit of an argument with the instrument panel, but I think it probably looks worse than it is."

"Well, we'll get you all below and out of those wet things and I'm sure that the Chief will have some rum to spare." He nodded towards a large square dark skinned Chief Petty Officer with a full set beard.

"Where are you taking us?" asked Doug.

"We're to drop you off in King's Lynn. We'll be there in about four hours. I've promised my chaps a night ashore before we head back south. Now get yourselves below. I'll be down to see you later"

The four hours to King's Lynn passed quickly for most of Doug's crew. The warm dry clothes and large measure of rum made most of them fall fast asleep. Ron on the other hand retched all the way to port.

Sally had slept soundly until midday and now she was feeling guilty about it. How could she have slept like that when her crew were fighting to survive? Mind you, the coffee Jane had given her was partly to blame, it had been mainly whiskey. She dragged herself out of bed, washed and dressed and not feeling hungry went straight to work to see if there were any jobs that needed doing. There were no Ops on that night therefore no crews needed to be driven around so the MT Corporal set her to work washing lorries. It was a job she hated, but it was better than just worrying. At 1500 hours she took a break for a mug of tea and as she stood by the NAAFI wagon with her tea the MT Corporal called her over to the MT office.

"What have you been up to, Sally? Flight Lieutenant Forrester wants to talk to you," he said, holding up the telephone.

Sally quickly snatched the phone; she knew the Squadron Adjutant would only want to talk to her to tell her about her crew. The worry would soon be over but she dreaded what the message might be. She felt they were all still alive and she was usually right. She had been right about her other crews in that she had been certain they were dead, but this had felt different. Although she was confident of her instincts she needed to know for sure.

"Yes, Sir?"

"Sally we've just got word from the Navy. They picked up Pilot Officer Jackson and his crew an hour ago. They're all fit and well and they're going to drop them off at King's Lynn at about 18.00 hours. The docs will want to have a look at them but when they've finished I'd like you to pick them up from the hospital and drive them back here."

"Yes, Sir." She looked at the clock. "I'll set off in an hour."

"Very good." The phone went dead and Sally breathed out heavily. They were still alive; she walked out of the office and round the corner of the hut out of sight. There she allowed herself five minutes to cry with relief.

Sally hated hospitals. The stark cold white walls were characterless and harsh. The smell of disinfectant stuck in her throat and she wished the doctors would hurry up and let her crew go. It was half past seven and it had been dark outside for some time. Brief rain showers had made the streets wet although it was not raining now. She was sitting on a row of chairs in a corridor. Nobody else was waiting there and nurses walked by busily. With no one to talk to Sally soon got bored and sat staring at the wall.

"All done, lass, let's get out a here."

Alex's voice made her jump and she realized she had been caught daydreaming and smiled.

"You were longer than I expected." Then she saw Doug. "Oh my God!"

"It looks a lot worse than it is," he said, touching his bruised face gently.

"Yeah, you should have seen him before nurse Jimmy got him cleaned up," teased Harry. They were all dressed in their own battledress uniforms again. They had been very efficiently dried in the engine room of the MTB while it headed at high speed for King's Lynn, so that its crew could maximise their drinking time ashore. Only their fur lined jackets and boots were still damp and their feet squelched inside them.

"Where's the wagon?" asked Doug, trying to change the subject.

"Just outside," said Sally, turning to lead the way.

"What about a beer, skip, before we head back?" asked Bob. "Harry still owes me one."

"Yeah, go on, skipper!" chorused the other sergeants like a group of school children.

"All right," relented Doug. "If it's alright with Sally."

Sally knew she wasn't supposed to but who would know?

"Yes, no problem."

They dumped their parachute harnesses and damp flying kit in the back of Sally's truck and found a small pub near the hospital. The half a dozen locals in the bar gave them some curious glances but left them alone as they pooled their money and found they had enough for seven pints of bitter and a port and lemon for Sally. She had only wanted lemonade but Alex had talked her around. Once they had settled down in a corner of the bar Sally could contain herself no longer.

"So how did you come to have to ditch?"

"We got clobbered by a Jerry night fighter," replied Harry.

"But we clobbered him too," added George.

"He probably wouldn't have got us if we hadn't already been on three engines," said Doug.

"How did you lose the first engine?" asked Sally.

"We just lost all the oil pressure on it," said Jimmy. "I don't think we were hit."

"Was it number four?"

"Yes. How did you know that?" Jimmy looked surprised.

"That's what happened to Victor last time. Did you not see it in the 700?"

"Yes, but the fault had been signed off as fixed," said Jimmy.

"What Sergeant Allen signs as being fixed and what has been fixed, or more to the point, what has been fixed properly, can sometimes be two different things."

"I'll kill the bastard when we get back!" said Bob with a glint in his eye that said that while he wouldn't actually kill him he would probably do him very serious harm.

"No, you won't," said Doug.

"Don't worry, skip, I won't get caught."

"Leave him, it's not worth it, we just won't trust him in future." Bob snorted and took a drink of his pint but said nothing.

"So what happened when the fighter attacked?" asked Sally quickly.

"We had a massive fire in number three and it wouldn't go out. We had to put it down before we lost the wing," said Doug. "If it hadn't been for the fire we would have still made it back on two engines." He had thought about this a lot in the dinghy and he was convinced that he could have flown them home on the two left-hand engines.

"That's what makes the Yanks green with envy," said Sally. "Their Flying Fortresses can't fly on two engines if the two dead engines are both on the same side, whereas our Lancs can."

Doug didn't know that about the American bomber.

"It's hard work on your legs to keep straight when you try it in a Lanc." He added, "When did you hear we'd ditched?"

"About three o'clock this morning."

"So you got our SOS?" asked Harry.

"Yes, Group passed it on to us."

Harry smiled in a self-satisfied manner at George.

"So we didn't need those bloody pigeons anyway."

George put the end of his amputated middle finger to his nostril so that it looked like he had his finger three inches up his nose and pulled a face.

"Do you know when the Adj sent off the telegrams saying we were missing?" asked Ron.

"He didn't send them, sir." Sally didn't trust Ron and thought it best to treat him formally.

"Why not?" asked Ron, looking puzzled and alarmed.

"I think it was because you didn't ditch far off the coast and there was a good chance of you being picked up, so he didn't want to worry anyone. He would have probably sent them if you hadn't been picked up today."

"Oh shit!" said Ron. "I've just sent my wife a telegram telling her I'm alright and not to worry."

"Well, it won't matter," said Doug.

"You're obviously not married," said Ron. "Tell a woman not to worry when she hasn't got a reason to worry and she'll go mad with worry. God, I wish I hadn't sent it."

"And she'll probably get woken up when it's delivered," Sally added.

"Oh shit!" groaned Ron again. The sergeants were almost exploding with suppressed laughter at Ron's dilemma.

"Can you phone her from a call box?" asked Sally.

"We don't know anyone with a phone."

"Well, I hear you're all going on leave when you get back, so you'll be able to see her."

"Yes." Ron felt that once again, in his haste to do the right thing, he had made a mess of things. Janice would not let him forget it and even the thought of leave couldn't lift the depression he felt descending on him. Seeing the change in Ron even the sergeants stopped finding his predicament funny. Maybe there were reasons behind him being the way he was.

"Do any of you carry a mirror?" asked Sally, changing the subject.

The crew looked at each other. "No, why?" asked Doug.

"Well, I asked around at Metheringham and found out about the search for you. There were two Beaufighters from North Coats, the Cromer lifeboat and an MTB from a coastal convoy looking for you. When I heard one of the Beaufighters had found you I rang them up to thank them and I spoke to the crew. It's amazing how friendly you aircrew types are when you find out it's a WAAF calling." She smiled mischievously.

"It wasn't a bloke called Mick Holt was it?" asked Bob, thinking it might have been his friend.

"No, these were both Norwegian and they said they would have missed you if it hadn't been for the flashing mirror."

"Didn't they see our flares?" asked Harry.

"Only after they saw the flashing mirror."

"Bugger me, Jimmy!" exclaimed George. "We were saved by a bloody cigarette case!"

11

Doug sat in the pilots' specialist briefing waiting for the other pilots to take their seats and settle down. The previous two weeks had gone past so quickly it seemed like only yesterday he was floating around the North Sea. As soon as they had got back to the Squadron Nigel had dispatched them on seven day's leave and his crew had gone their separate ways.

Doug had spent his leave at home with his parents. His mother had fussed over him, after getting over the shock of his bruised face, which had now completely recovered. The large old familiar vicarage that had been his home for as long as he could remember made him feel safe and secure. His father talked to him about flying and his life on the Squadron. But it was so far removed from everyday life Doug found it difficult to get across what it was like to fly on operations and he took care to keep tales of burning bombers and ditchings out of the conversation. There had only been two occasions during his leave when he had really thought about flying.

The first was when he lit the living room fire one morning and a gust of wind blew smoke down the chimney into his face. A picture of the burning Halifax at Manston sprang to his mind and he relived the whole crash and rescue in vivid detail. It could only have taken a few seconds, because his mother was watching him and asked him if he was alright, as he knelt frozen in front of the fire holding a smouldering taper. He had quickly recovered and he didn't think his mother had noticed anything. But mothers always see far more than they let on and she took care to fit as much mothering into seven days as is possible.

The second time he thought about flying was towards the end of his leave. It was dark and the stars lit the clear sky above him, while the smooth black sea rushed past just below him. Yellow orange flames reflected off his instrument panel and the engines were silent. He was alone and the sea got closer and closer. Back and back he pulled the control column, they were nearing stalling speed and would hit the sea at any time now!

"Brace! Brace! Brace!"

Suddenly he was wide awake. He was covered in sweat and staring wide eyed at the ceiling of his bedroom. Instantly he realised it had been a dream, but had he shouted aloud or had he just dreamt it? He lay still and listened intently to the silence. There were no sounds of movement in the house and after a minute of holding his breath in total silence he relaxed, while his heart pounded inside his chest. The dream had shocked him at the time, but he soon forgot it and it didn't spoil his leave.

When he returned to the Squadron F for Freddy was back and its scars barely showed. Sergeant Green fussed over Freddy like it was his own personal property and in doing so filled the crew with confidence in the Lancaster and its ground crew. Sergeant Allen, on the other hand, had been mysteriously set upon on his way back to his billet from the sergeants' mess one night and was recovering from a broken jaw and fractured cheek bone in Lincoln hospital. About the same time a door had blown shut on Bob's hand badly bruising his knuckles, or so he said, and as long as he stuck to his story nobody could prove different.

Bob had spent his leave with Harry in London. They had stayed at Harry's parents' house, although it sounded like they had spent very little time there. From the stories Harry kept coming out with it seemed they had spent most of the time in various pubs or gutters and they were both glad to come back to the Squadron for a rest.

Jimmy had returned to the Squadron on his gleaming Triumph motorbike grinning from ear to ear, an engaged man. Doug always looked on Jimmy as a quiet and serious person who was very competent and reliable. But before they went on leave he had noticed Jimmy becoming withdrawn and it had worried him. Now he was back to his old self and if anything happier. Even Ron couldn't change his mood when he pointed out that happiness in a marriage doesn't last much beyond the honeymoon.

Doug was worried about Ron who had returned from leave more miserable than when he left. He looked tired, but that wasn't all, he had definitely changed. There had always been aggression in Ron, whether it was complaining about an aircraft's faults or bullying an airman. Now that aggression had gone and he seemed empty. He had always been quick to complain and it had made Doug's life difficult on more than one occasion, but now he mildly agreed to anything. He only spoke when he had to and was the very picture of misery. Any attempt Doug made to find out what the problem was met with a denial that there was anything wrong or a change of subject. Doug had no idea how to get around this and make him open up.

Alex, on the other hand, had come back from Scotland with a spring in his step and a few more notches on his bedpost, while George seemed to have spent his time walking his Dad's dog or drinking with his coal miner mates.

For the last week they had been flying practice sorties everyday. Airfield circuits one day, navigation exercises the next, then towards the end of the week dropping practice bombs on the coastal ranges and fighter affiliation. Doug had enjoyed the fighter affiliation best, because it gave him an excuse to throw the Lancaster around and with no bombs on board and only a light fuel load F for Freddy was a delight to fly. They had exercised with a Spitfire from nearby RAF Digby, which would follow them to the exercise area then come barrelling in to the attack from the bright blue sky. Harry would stand with his head in the astrodome and together with the three gunners would call in the fighter's position and shout evasive manoeuvre instructions while Doug twisted and turned the bomber around the sky. The gunners would practise tracking the wildly turning fighter with their sights, while the Lancaster corkscrewed in front of it. It was all good fun and very exciting but they all agreed it bore little resemblance to how they fought fighters in the dark. Ron, on the other hand, with nothing to do during the manoeuvring and no window to look out of was constantly airsick, but strangely silent and uncomplaining.

Doug looked out of the small square office window. Outside it was overcast but the heavy rain, which had been constant throughout the morning, had now stopped. The grey layer of cloud seemed lighter than it had been when he cycled to the Squadron Office, down the puddle soaked lanes. The gusty wind had also dropped and it looked like it would be a far better night than everyone had been predicting throughout the day. The general feeling on the Squadron had been that the night's Op would be cancelled because of the weather, but now Doug thought that looked unlikely.

Squadron Leader "Dinger" Bell strode into the office and with a loud, "Settle down, chaps!" called the captains' roll, then, "Bet you all thought this would be a scrub, didn't you?" He grinned over his large moustache. "Well, I'm sorry to disappoint you but I think we're going. That said, it won't be plain sailing. The front that gave us all the rain this morning and last night is now over the North Sea and the Low Countries, so we're in for a bumpy time and quite a bit of ice too. That's not all either! By the time we're due back the Met man says there might be fog about. So those of you who have been complaining to me over the last week about the FIDO engineers getting in the way while you taxi might well be glad of them tonight! Yes, that's right, the damn thing is ready! It hasn't been tested yet but they have assured the Station Commander that it will work, so if they're wrong he'll have their guts for garters! The good news is the target should be clear and there's no moon, however, once again it's full fuel tanks." There was a groan. "I don't know the target!" Dinger held up his hands. "But you all know Butch's favourite and he hasn't had us visit it for two weeks.

"Your engineers will have the details of your takeoff weights and your navs will have your routes so I just want to say a few words about the FIDO system in case we need it." He turned to a blackboard in the corner of the small office, which was now filling with smoke as most of the pilots drew deeply on their cigarettes. "FIDO, Fog Intensive Dispersal Operation. It's really a very simple idea. There are over seventy forty-yard burner units, these are basically pipes laid along the side of the runway and joined together. Every few yards along these pipes there is a nozzle pointing up." He pointed to the appropriate sketches on the blackboard as he talked. "Fuel from the storage tanks opposite the messes is fed to the burners at a pressure of 75 pounds per square inch and when it squirts out of the nozzles it's ignited. This, I'm told, results in jets of flame between two and three feet long and burns 1500 gallons of petrol a minute." He paused to let this sink in. "The heat generated either disperses the fog altogether, or lifts it off the surface so that you can get in below it." He looked around at the silent pilots and found himself thinking how young they looked, until he realised that he wasn't much older himself.

"How close do you get to the flames when you land?" asked one of the other pilots.

Dinger smiled; no aircrew liked fire. "If you land on the runway centreline you'll be nowhere near the flames, but I'm told they look closer than they really are."

"Well, that's you buggered, Flinty," ribbed Charlie. "You usually land with one wheel on the grass." He turned and winked at Doug while the others laughed.

"The thing to remember," continued Dinger, "is the heat FIDO produces to clear the fog also produces turbulence on the approach and if you come in too fast the hot air rising will hold you in the air all the way down the runway and you won't get in. So watch your approach speeds!"

"What are the extra burners for around the threshold of runway zero two?" asked Charlie.

The three extra burners were placed one across the approach end of runway zero two and the other two were placed outside of the runway edge burners, angling outwards away from the runway.

"That's the approach box," answered Dinger. "It's to give the fog there an extra boost and give you a better view of your touchdown area. Are there any other questions?" He looked around. "Well, that's it from me, see you at the main briefing."

"Landing between two rows of fire sounds a bit dodgy to me," said one of the other pilots, when he was out of Dinger's earshot.

"Not as dodgy as landing in fog," replied Charlie. Doug wasn't fond of either option.

At the main briefing room Doug found all of his crew sitting in their usual seats, four rows from the front on the left. Ron was the only one missing, because the navigators hadn't yet finished their specialist briefing.

"Where are we going then, Bob?" he asked, as he sat down beside his bomb aimer, who would have seen target maps at his specialist briefing.

"The big city again," whispered Bob, blowing cigarette smoke up away from Doug's face.

Ron arrived and sat down the other side of Bob to unpack his maps and navigation equipment.

"Everything alright, Ron?" asked Doug.

"Yes," replied Ron, then adding, "it's a long trip tonight."

The room was called to attention and they all stood up. The Station Commander, Wing Commander and Nigel walked down the centre aisle to the front of the room and the Station Commander told them all to sit down. Nigel called the roll and the Station Commander called for the curtain to be pulled aside to reveal the map. It was, again, Berlin and it was a long looping route. The crews let out a small sigh and started whispering, which was cut short by the Station Commander's booming voice.

"Yes, gentlemen! Berlin, and by a long route, but when you see the Met forecast you'll see why! We haven't been to Berlin for a while and it's about time we let Jerry know that we haven't forgotten it."

Doug half listened to the Station Commander while his eyes followed the route. South from Metheringham to Beachy Head, east-southeast to the French coast, then along the Somme valley before turning east. After another 70 or so miles the route turned south of east again towards Strasbourg, before jinking northeast between Mannheim and Karlsruhe to threaten Nuremberg. Short of Nuremberg the route turned further northward towards Erfurt, then again jinking eastwards towards Leipzig and Dresden. Finally, just short of Dresden, the route turned north to Berlin. It was a complex route that would hopefully keep the Germans guessing, but it took them a long way out of their way and would mean a long time over enemy territory. The route home was over 200 miles shorter, going northwest to the Baltic coast before turning west to pass south of Kiel and cross the south of the Jutland peninsular into the North Sea. Once over the sea the route again turned northwest into the middle of the North Sea before turning southwest towards the Humber and back to Metheringham. It was a huge circle of a route and Doug didn't like it. 1,425 miles, why the hell did it have to go so far north and south, he wondered?

"The Pathfinders are providing a Master Bomber for this raid so listen out for him on RT over the target and he will direct you where to bomb," continued the Station Commander. "The Bomber Leader and Signals Officer have the details. You're quite a long way down the bomber stream tonight so the target should be well marked by the time you arrive. Met!" The Station Commander got down from the stage and the Met man climbed up and pulled the captain's board to one side to reveal the meteorological chart.

It was immediately obvious why the route went so far north and south. A strong cold front ran down the middle of the North Sea and the circuitous route would hopefully keep them clear of the worst of the weather associated with it. Along the front there would be dense cumulonimbus clouds stretching from medium to low level up to the heavens. Below them would be heavy rainstorms, while inside there would be severe turbulence, hailstones the size of golf balls and lightning. The turbulence would throw the bombers around like toys and could, if it was bad enough, tear them apart. Hailstones, if they were big enough, could cause enormous damage, while lightning, apart from blinding the crew with its brilliant flashes, would damage electrical equipment and make radios unusable. But the thing aircrew feared most about flying in cumulonimbus clouds was the risk of ice. Violent updraughts in cumulonimbus clouds could support larger water droplets than other clouds and these droplets would be carried up to the tops of the clouds, where they would be supercooled to freezing point, but because of their rapid movement in the turbulence they would remain liquid. If an aircraft were to fly into these droplets however, they would smear onto the nose and leading edges of the wings and tail and the cold metal of the airframe would be enough to cause the droplets to freeze solid. Not only would this increase the aircraft's weight but also the ice building up on the wings would disrupt the airflow and destroy the wing's lift, making it impossible for an aircraft to fly. The Met man was saying that the icing index in the cumulonimbus clouds was very severe and they should be avoided at all costs. Fortunately the front was slow moving and the route took them around the southern and northern ends of the belt of clouds. Ahead of the cold front there would be scattered cumulus clouds giving rain showers while the warm front over the Baltic and Denmark was less pronounced and would give far less severe weather. The final Met warning was that there was expected to be clear skies behind the cold front, with a possibility of fog forming or icy runways towards dawn.

The Flying Controller gave the engine start and taxi times. He pointed out that FIDO was now serviceable, but had not been operationally tested, so if fog did form it would be better to divert to a fog free airfield if possible.

The Signals Officer gave his usual briefing but included the additional Master Bomber VHF frequency. The tension in the room had been increasing as the briefing progressed and most of the men were on at least their second cigarette, filling the room with a haze of smoke. Doug could feel the smoke irritating his throat but he hardly noticed it over the butterflies in his stomach.

The Intelligence Officer outlined the raid; it was a big one. Over 500 Lancasters and over 300 Halifaxes would drop 2,600 tons of bombs on Berlin. The fighter threat would be significant but there was no moon and the route took them around the ends of the main fighter airfield belt.

The various leaders talked through the different aspects of the raid with the Bomber Leader concentrating on the roll and tactics that would be used by the Master Bomber to keep the raid concentrated on the aiming point and stopping it creeping back.

When the last leader had finished Wing Commander Baxter stood up.

"Big raid tonight, chaps, we're fielding nineteen ourselves." Three additional crews had been posted into the Squadron over the two weeks since their last Op and for the first time in weeks Group Captain McKechnie had left himself off the flying programme. "Keep it tight, hit them hard and watch out for the weather on the way home. Good luck."

A time check at 15.00 ended the formal part of the briefing and each crew started its own individual planning. The planning went smoothly and they were soon ready to leave. The three new crews, on the other hand, were still working hard and Doug was glad his crew weren't the new boys anymore.

Cycling over to the crew room with the rest of his crew he noticed that only Ron wasn't chatting, so there was no change there, all must be well he thought. He waved to Sally waiting in her truck outside the crew room and went inside to kit up. He emptied his pockets into his hat and put it into his locker. Taking off his shoes he pulled on two pairs of thick socks and his thick fur lined flying boots. Next, he struggled into his Irving flying jacket, hampered by the fact that he was already wearing a vest, shirt, woollen pullover and battledress. Around him the other aircrew chatted and teased each other with friendly banter. In some cases, like between Alex and George, the banter was cutting and vicious. Anyone not used to it could be excused for thinking they hated each other, but nothing could be further from the truth. Doug had noticed that the harder the banter, the closer the bond, and it was the people who weren't included in the banter that were unpopular or disliked.

"Right skipper," said Harry. "I think you should make a real effort to bring us back here by air this time. I'm sick of coming back by train or boat."

"Yeah, skip, let's be conventional and fly back this time," echoed Bob.

"You ungrateful lot," replied Doug. "I take you on a train to see the sights of London and on a cruise and all you do is complain!" Banter knew no rank barriers in a crew, but nobody bantered Ron.

Locking his locker Doug went to the counter at the end of the building, where half a dozen airmen were handing out parachutes and rations. A young airman handed a parachute and harness to the man in front of Doug, and then looked at him.

"Seat parachute," said Doug. Pilots sat on their parachutes the same way fighter pilots did, while the rest of the crew had chest parachutes, which could be stored in the aircraft and quickly clipped to its harness in an emergency. The advantage of the seat parachute was you were always wearing it and it was always ready to use, but the disadvantage was it was bulky and heavy. It would have been impossible to move around inside a Lancaster wearing one, but to a pilot, who could never leave his seat, that was not a problem. However, the constant complaint pilots had about their parachutes was that they were like sitting on concrete. After an hour or two most pilots were numb from the waist down. Chest parachutes were much more comfortable, with just the harness straps worn in the aircraft. But their very real disadvantage was you had to grab your parachute pack and clip it to your harness in the dark, in an emergency, in a damaged aircraft, with time at a premium, before you could bale out.

"Do you want a revolver, sir?" asked the airman. Doug declined. Like the parachute, he had to sign for a revolver and he was afraid he might lose it. He picked up his corned beef sandwiches wrapped in paper and his bar of chocolate. Would WAAFs really do anything for a bar of chocolate? he wondered, as he stuffed the sandwiches and chocolate into his pockets. He had never had a girlfriend and they were a bit of a mystery to him. He had gone to an all boys' school and the only girls he knew were in his father's congregation and while they seemed to like him he found he was shy in their presence and never knew what to say. He hoisted his parachute onto his shoulder, slipping his arm through the gap between the back padding and the actual parachute pack, which he would sit on, so that the straps hung down in front of him, and he walked outside. As the name suggests, seat parachutes are meant to be sat on and are very uncomfortable and awkward to walk in, so pilots carried them over their shoulders and only put them on inside the aircraft. With his Mae West life jacket in his free hand he went outside.

As he strolled over to Sally's truck he took a good look at the weather. The grey overcast cloud stretched out to the horizon in all directions, but it looked very thin and it might break up at any time. There didn't seem to be any wind, which surprised him and he was glad they were carrying a slightly smaller bomb load, because without a wind it would be a longer takeoff run. The first shades of night were beginning to descend but they would be getting airborne at dusk, which was safer than a night takeoff. There were no signs of the forecast thunderclouds, which had passed over Metheringham earlier that morning and he hoped he would manage to avoid them altogether.

"Afternoon, sir," smiled Sally, saluting.

"Hello, Sally, I suppose you know where we're going?" She was a cracking girl, even dressed in multiple layers of heavy clothes; surely she wouldn't do anything for a bar of chocolate?

"Of course, sir, and it's a long route." She was showing off now.

"How do you know that?"

"They've lightened your bomb loads." She grinned.

"Afternoon, Sally!" called Bob, Jimmy and Harry as they threw their parachutes and flight bags into the back of the wagon and clambered in.

"You're all happy," she commented.

"Most of them are," said Doug, as Ron walked past looking at the ground and ignoring them. "It's amazing what some leave will do."

"Here you are, bonny lass," said George, as he handed Sally a large envelope and waddled to the back of the truck in his bulky suit.

"Thanks, sarge."

"Fit like!" Alex called to Sally as he too waddled to the back of the truck. "That suits ya!" He nodded at her heavy greatcoat stretched tight over the other layers of heavy clothes.

"I think yours has the edge on mine, sarge!" she retorted.

"If she played her cards right," Doug heard Alex say before George cut in.

"She's not your type and a reckon she's out a yer league an all." And he pushed Alex up over the tailboard.

"Sorry about that," said Doug.

"I've heard a lot worse, sir, shall we go?"

As they drove around the perimeter track, following the other crew buses, Sally looked at the sky for a while before speaking.

"This cloud will break up later."

"That's what the Met man said," replied Doug.

"Did he say there would be fog by dawn?"

"He said there might be."

"There will be, and it will be thick." She looked over at him, staring straight into his eyes and looking very serious.

"We've got FIDO to help us if we need it," smiled Doug, trying to lighten the situation, because his neck hairs had started to stand on end.

"Get back as soon as you can," warned Sally. "It will get thicker towards dawn."

They pulled into Freddy's dispersal and Sally wished them good luck as they climbed out and made their way to the aircraft or dispersal shack. Then she stared again at the sky. It looked so calm after the torrential rain from last night and that morning. But Sally was not fooled, tonight was a bad night for flying and she was worried.

As usual, Sergeant Green was standing at his post in the shack doorway.

"Evening, sir, everything's ready for you."

Doug and Jimmy scanned the form 700. Freddy was in good health, with no faults and Doug signed as taking charge, then they strolled over and carried out their external checks. There was plenty of time and in the pleasant winter's evening they felt no need to rush. As they completed the checks and prepared to climb aboard Sergeant Green walked up to them while his men removed the protective covers from the main wheels.

"Everything alright, sir?"

"Yes, sarge, no problems." The sergeant had something to say but was taking his time and looking around at the sky.

"Get back as quick as you can tonight, sir."

"We will," nodded Doug, as he turned to climb up the short ladder into the bomber. Inside he scrambled forward uphill in the dark fuselage, ducking under the mid-upper turret and climbing up onto the top of the bomb bay. He was wearing his Mae West now but clambering over the rear spar the parachute on his right shoulder seemed to catch on everything. Between the spars he slid it off, gathering up the straps so that they wouldn't dangle and trip him and he held it in front of him. From here forward the left side of the fuselage was full of radio and navigation equipment leaving only a narrow passage on the right. Climbing over the main spar Harry winked at him as he squeezed past. Forward of that Ron sighed as he moved, so Doug could pass and then he was in the cockpit. He moved the seat harness straps to the sides of his seat out of the way and placed his parachute in the tray that formed the base of the seat. Then he straightened out the parachute straps and slid over sideways behind the control column onto the parachute that was now his very hard seat cushion. Jimmy appeared beside him and held his parachute shoulder straps for him while he clipped in and tightened the lap straps. Then taking the shoulder straps from Jimmy he clipped these into the parachute locking box and adjusted them until they were comfortably tight. Jimmy was now holding the seat harness shoulder straps and Doug repeated the process. These straps had metal ringed holes in them, which fitted over a stud in one of the lower straps and were held in place on the stud by a locking pin. It was a fiddly operation to lock the harness in place but very quick to release with one swift pull of the locking pin. Now that he was strapped in securely he pulled on his flying helmet and fastened the chinstrap. Plugging in the intercom lead on his left side he connected his oxygen tube and holding the mask to his face, he turned on the oxygen and breathed deeply. The cold gas entered his lungs, telling him all was well. Then, letting the mask fall to hang to the left of his face, he started his pre engine start checks.

DR compass on, undercarriage and flap indicator switches on and indicators checked. He looked at his watch, five minutes to engine start time. He switched on his intercom and spoke into his mask.

"Check in front to back ready for engine start." The crew all responded ready and he nodded to Jimmy to start the engine's start checklist.

Outside, Sergeant Green looked up at the lofty cockpit, from his station to the left of the bomber's nose. He could see the pilot and flight engineer had started their checks and he scanned the area around the dispersal to ensure he was ready. The covers were off the tyres and stowed away, so they wouldn't take flight in the bombers slipstream. There were no little red and white striped flags hanging from locking pins or Pitot head covers which should be removed before flight and the trolley acc was in place by the right wheel.

"Tim, you've got the right! Frank, you've got the left! Bob and Sid, you're on the extinguisher!" The airmen ran to their posts, Tim standing by the trolley acc under the right wing root, holding the cable ready to climb up onto the right main wheel and connect it to the aircraft inside the right main wheel bay. Frank climbed straight up onto the left wheel and stood on the two-foot plates on the landing gear oleo legs and squatted down so that he could still see Sergeant Green. Doug opened the left side cockpit window and putting his hands out extended his index and fore finger of his right hand as a child would if pretending they were a gun and forming a ring with his thumb and fore finger of his left brought them together in the signal to connect ground power. Sergeant Green repeated the signal to Tim who climbed up on the wheel, dragging the trolley acc cable behind him, and plugging it in gave the sergeant a thumbs up, who repeated it to Doug.

"How many pumps, sarge?" asked Frank, who had not been on the Squadron long.

Sergeant Green considered it for a few seconds. It was a cold evening, only a few degrees above freezing, so the book said twelve pumps on the primers, but Freddy seemed to like more.

"Sixteen!"

In the right wheel bay Tim heard the instruction and smiled. He had been an engine fitter for years and he knew how to handle aero engines. The sarge was a good engineer but his background was airframes not engines and Tim reckoned he knew more than the sarge about Merlins. The starboard inner, which would be started first, was almost new, having just been replaced at Manston and that one he would give sixteen primes, but the starboard outer had done more hours and Tim knew it liked more priming, so despite what the sarge said he would give it twenty-one for luck. Standing up, with his head and shoulders inside the right wheel bay, he selected the priming tap to the starboard inner engine and pulled out the primer, which looked like a large brass syringe in the front bulkhead of the wheel bay. In and out he pushed the syringe sixteen times, before turning the tap to the starboard outer engine and giving another twenty-one pumps. While he was doing this the pilot and flight engineer were completing their engine start checklist and he finished just as he heard Doug shout down to Sergeant Green.

"Clear start three!"

Tim turned the priming tap back to number three engine and squatted down so that Sergeant Green could see him and gave a thumbs up. Sergeant Green repeated the instruction and Tim stood up inside the wheel bay holding onto the main wheel leg with one hand and the primer with the other. In front of his face, on the other side of the bulkhead sat 1,460 horses and they were about to be set free. He heard the starter coils activate, then the starter whine, the engine turned over and he drew the primer back ready to pump more neat fuel into the engine. The engine coughed and he pushed the primer home. It turned over three or four times then coughed again and he gave it another shot and it ran smoothly. He turned the tap to the number four engine while the slipstream from the started engine tugged at his overall trousers and tried to push him from his perch. The noise was deafening as it echoed inside the wheel bay, but worse was yet to come as he squatted down again to see the sergeant and was met by the full force of the slipstream in the face. He squinted through the tornado and saw the sergeant look at him and hold up four fingers. Tim gave a thumbs up with his free hand, while he clung on with the other and stood up again. The whole bay was vibrating and the noise was mind numbing. There was no way he could hear the number four starter motor, he could only wait until he heard, or rather sensed the other engine fire. There it was! A subtle secondary vibration laid on top of that from the first engine; he gave it a prime and waited. It would probably be enough, but he waited poised and ready. No, it was fine, it was still running smoothly and if it had needed any more priming it would have asked for it by now. Smiling smugly to himself at his knowledge of his engines he wire locked the priming pump and again squatted, squinting through watery eyes at the sergeant for the next signal while engines number one and two were started. There it was, disconnect the trolley acc. He pulled out the large black plug attached to the heavy cable and climbed down onto the main wheel before jumping to the ground, expertly keeping his balance in the 100 mph wind. He coiled the cable onto the trolley and as he finished Frank arrived to help him pull it clear of the bomber. They manoeuvred it out under the rear of the wing away from the propellers, Tim pulling the heavy cart by the handles while Frank pushed. By the time they got it well out of the way on the edge of the dispersal they were out of breath. Now they jogged back to the wheels, Tim returning the wave from the mid-upper gunner. The crew were running up the engines in turn now and the noise rose and fell as each was tested. Tim took hold of the rough soaking wet rope attached to the large wooden chocks either side of the right wheel and, stooping against the slipstream, readied himself to pull it clear. Above him the engines roared and four feet to his right an invisible propeller whirled round at 2,000 rpm. He had once seen a man walk into a turning propeller and his head had simply vaporised in a red mist, while the headless trunk had slumped to its knees before falling onto what would have been its face. The engine, on the other hand, hadn't missed a beat. With the mind numbing noise assaulting your ears from all directions and the rapidly moving propellers invisible to the eye, it only took a moment of carelessness. Tim reminded himself he was going to pull the chocks away from the wheels and continue out under the wingtips, away from the propellers. Sergeant Green crossed his hands in front of his crotch and swung them apart, chocks away. Tim pulled and nothing happened. He tugged at the rope, but it still wouldn't move. Then he realised that the chocks had been in place when the Lancaster was empty and since then it had had a thousand gallons of fuel and over five tons of bombs loaded aboard, making it sit low and heavy on its tyres and chocks. Normally this would have been allowed for, but for some reason this time it hadn't. He moved to the chocks and kicked them several times, freeing them slightly, and then he moved around to the other side and did the same there. Now he needed to get a good kick in at the right angle. He lay down on the still damp ground and slid in front of the wheel, the number three propeller whirling around above his head as he kicked at the wedged chock. He could see the flight engineer looking down at him from the cockpit and hoped the brakes were firmly on because he was right in front of the wheel. Eventually the chock gave in and Tim slid back under the wing, away from the propeller. Now taking a firm grip of the rope he yanked the front chock free and then ran towards the back of the wing, wrenching the rear chock free with his body weight and dragging them both to the edge of the dispersal.

"God, he had to work hard at that," said Jimmy, looking down out of the right side of the cockpit and seeing Tim appear at the trailing edge of the wing, dragging the chocks to the edge of the dispersal.

"Brake pressure 280 pounds per square inch, ready to taxi." Sergeant Green was looking over his shoulder, judging when Freddy would need to start to move to slot neatly into the procession of aircraft making their way to the end of the runway. Now he raised his hands like a conductor readying an orchestra. Doug took hold of the control column in his left hand and held it back into his stomach, gripping the curved brake lever and holding Freddy stationary. His right hand caressed the four throttles as he too judged the progress of the other bombers. Now was the time, Sergeant Green was waving his arms over his head and Doug advanced the four throttles and let go of the brake lever. The popping Merlins settled into a more comfortable rumble as the revs increased and Freddy moved slowly forward. Doug immediately closed the throttles and gripped the brake lever to bring Freddy to a halt. Satisfied the brakes worked, he set Freddy moving again and entering the taxiway pushed on full right rudder, to line up behind another Lancaster. As he did, he checked that the magnetic, gyro and DR compasses all turned the right way, the turn needle of the turn and slip indicator showed a right turn and the slip pointer showed left slip, while the artificial horizon remained level. Now he juggled the throttle settings and occasional applications of brake to keep station on the other bomber. He often thought that this was the most difficult part of piloting a Lancaster and kept a close eye on the brake pressure while he coaxed Freddy along. He was steering with a mixture of slipstream over the rudders, power to the outer engines and jabs of brake. Through the soles of his feet he could feel Freddy's tail twisting slightly and realised that George was rotating his turret from side to side as he tested it. Jimmy waved at the two boys who were regulars on the gate by the perimeter fence, but Doug was too busy. The grass either side of the taxi track was being blown flat by the bomber in front and Doug thought that it must be the same behind Freddy. They were in a left turn now and Doug checked that the compasses turned the other way and the turn and slip indicator and artificial horizon gave the correct indications. Tonight they were a long way down the queue of bombers and they stopped a long way from the end of the runway, with the rest of the Squadron stretching out in front of them.

"Before takeoff checklist," said Doug, over the intercom.

"Auto controls," replied Jimmy.

"Clutch in, cock out."

"DR compass."

Doug looked down at the bottom of the instrument panel between his knees.

"Normal."

"Pitot head heater on," said Jimmy, checking on his side panel. "Trim tabs."

Doug reached down with his right hand by the right side of his seat moving the elevator trimming wheel to the slightly nose down position and checked both the rudder and aileron trimmers were neutral. These controls looked like bath taps, one vertical and one horizontal and the thought always amused Doug.

"Elevator forward, rudder and aileron neutral."

"Propeller controls."

Doug brought his right hand forward onto the central throttle pedestal, and grasping the four levers below the throttles made sure they were fully up, in the fine pitch position.

"Fully up."

"Fuel. Master engine cocks on, number two tanks selected, cross feed off, booster pumps on for number one and two tanks," said Jimmy, checking as he went through the list. "Superchargers."

Doug checked the lever to the left of the throttle pedestal was set. "In M ratio."

"Air intake."

Doug checked on the left of his seat.

"Cold."

"Radiator shutters."

They had moved forward twice during the check, but were still quite a way from the end of the runway.

"We'll leave them in override for now, we don't want to overheat the engines."

"Flaps."

"20 degrees," said Doug, reaching down just in front of the trim controls, taking hold of the ring lever and pushing it down, holding it against a spring until the flap indicator showed 20 degrees, then releasing it. Now all they had to do was wait their turn to take off.

Dusk was just falling, but it was still light enough to see all the details of the airfield. The runway lights were on but weren't really required and the green light flashed from the runway caravan releasing another bomber, which roared down the runway and staggered into the air. It seemed unusual to Doug to be taking off for an Op while it was so light, but it was a long trip and at this time of year darkness would come quickly. Slowly they moved closer to the end of the runway and as usual Doug started to feel more nervous. He was about to take six men's lives in his hands and it always worried him. He knew he was a very average pilot with serious limitations when it came to flying on instruments and tonight, with bad weather in the offing he might need more skill than he possessed. On the other hand, he comforted himself, he had landed on three engines and pulled off a ditching, so he couldn't be that bad. Or had he just been lucky?

Slowly they edged up as one by one the Lancasters took off. The butterflies inside him whirled like a tornado and his heart pounded while he concentrated on taking long deep breaths. The Lancaster in front of them moved onto the runway and Doug fastened his oxygen mask over his face, adjusted it, and checked the microphone was switched off, so the crew wouldn't be able to hear his heavy breathing. Freddy stopped at the holding point, Doug squirmed himself as comfortable as he was likely to get and had a final check of all things vital. One of his instructors had called it the wife and kids check. When Doug had said he didn't have a wife or kids his instructor had replied that if he one day wanted to have them he should get into the habit of doing the check. Altimeter set to QFE and reading zero. DR compass heading bug set to runway heading and cross checked with the gyro and magnetic compasses. Auto pilot off, propellers fully fine, M ratio on the superchargers, flaps 20 degrees, radiator shutters! Thank God he checked! They were still in override, and while it was not vital, it hammered home to him the dangers of splitting checks or deciding to do things out of sequence. He switched on his microphone and left it on.

"Radiator shutter switches to automatic." Jimmy made the selection on the right side on the cockpit, hoping it looked like he hadn't forgotten.

"Everybody ready for takeoff?" he asked and listened as they checked in ready.

"Remember to look both ways before you cross the road," said Bob, referring to the truck they had nearly hit on their last Op. As he had promised he was behind the main spar, not in the nose.

The other Lancaster started to move and Doug released Freddy's brakes and edged it onto the runway, checking the approach was clear as he did so. Slowly he reached the centreline and put on left rudder and increased power to the starboard outer to pull Freddy round. Anticipating the stopping of the turn he closed the throttles and put on right rudder to stop Freddy's swing, then opened the throttles slightly to pull them forward a few feet to ensure the castoring tailwheel was straight for takeoff. Now he closed the throttles and squeezed the brake, bringing Freddy to a halt. He looked across at the chequered runway caravan and for the first time got a clear view of the group of people standing beside it. He saw Sally waving madly and Jimmy waving back. Then he saw the green light and looking straight down the white lines of the runway centreline said, "Here we go."

He eased the four throttles forward, the outer engines' curved levers being controlled by his little finger and thumb, while the two inners fitted neatly into the palm of his hand. The engines responded evenly and when the four red rimmed boost gauges showed zero boost on all engines he released the brakes. Freddy started to move and he smoothly moved the throttles further and further forward. He advanced the two port engines slightly ahead of the starboard to counter the propellers' pull to the left. The slipstream over the elevator was pulling at the control column and he fought to hold it aft of neutral with his left hand. Jimmy put his left hand under Doug's right on the throttles as they reached the gate and Doug felt the added resistance. His feet were automatically working on the rudder peddles to keep them running straight down the runway and he increased the pressure with his right hand to force the throttles through the gate into full boost.

"Your throttles!" he yelled to Jimmy over the thundering engines and took his right hand away, as Jimmy replied,

"My throttles!"

Now with both hands on the control column he felt more able to control Freddy as they accelerated down the runway under full power.

"14 pounds of boost 3,000 rpm on all engines!" yelled Jimmy.

"30!" said Ron.

Doug started to ease the control column forward, feeling the pressures from it into his hands, which told him whether Freddy was ready to raise its tail. Slowly he eased it further forward until he felt it lift.

"Tail up!" reported George.

"60!" yelled Ron.

Now Freddy started to swing from side to side and Doug worked hard on the rudders to keep straight. The end of the runway was in sight and moving slowly nearer. They didn't seem to be moving that quickly while Doug looked down the runway, but out of the corner of his eyes the grass was whizzing by.

"90!"

With no wind it would be a long run he thought, casting his mind back to their last Op, when they had nearly crashed on takeoff. We'll be alright in Freddy, he thought, trying to reassure himself. He started to feel, with pressure through his fingertips on the control column, to see if Freddy was ready to fly, but it was too early yet.

"100!"

Now he could see the white lines and upside down 02 of the end of the runway, as it suddenly seemed to rush towards him from 300 yards away.

"105!"

He eased the stick back and felt Freddy easily respond. The ground fell away slightly and the swinging stopped. He centred the rudders, checked the altimeter was showing a positive climb and checked forwards a little on the stick to fly parallel to the ground while they accelerated. Holding that attitude and not taking his eyes from the windscreen he moved his right hand down behind the trimmers to the T-shaped undercarriage lever. Pushing aside the bolt shaped safety lock he pulled the lever up and back, at the same time giving a swift application of brake with his left hand to stop the wheels spinning in the bays as they retracted. The end of the runway shot underneath them and then the boundary fence. Doug always had the instinctive urge to lift his feet up as they passed low over it. Easing the loaded bomber into a slight climb his eyes flicked quickly between the outside world and the airspeed indicator. 120 mph, still too slow to survive an engine failure. Timberland village church flashed past, a dull grey shape moving down their left hand side. 125 mph and 100 feet, he noted the next time he glanced in at his instruments. Hold it level there, he thought, let the speed build up. 130 mph and 150 feet, now they could cope with an engine failure, if they were quick.

"Course one seven zero degrees compass," said Ron.

Doug repeated it back and set it on the heading bug of the DR compass repeater, which was mounted centrally on the top on the instrument panel. The brown winter ploughed fields slid by underneath them. 140 mph, 300 feet and he eased on a few degrees of left bank to bring the nose slowly round onto one seven zero.

"Steady on one seven zero." At 160 mph and 500 feet he raised the flaps slowly and in stages. When they were fully retracted the Lancaster's trim was altered and he needed to hold the stick back against a heavy forward pressure to maintain their climbing attitude. Reaching down he moved the elevator-trimming wheel back until Freddy maintained the climb without any help. 160 mph and 1,000 feet. Doug brought the power back to plus 7 pounds of boost and the revs fell to 2,650 rpm. They were on course, in the climb, on range climbing power and the first of the difficult parts of the flight was over.

He could see two other Lancasters in front of him, black dots against the grey sky as they too climbed up towards the layer of cloud. Suddenly the first Lancaster disappeared into the cloud and Doug prepared himself to go onto instruments with a quick check that all the instruments made sense and crosschecked with each other. When he looked out again the second Lancaster had gone and the light grey cloud had taken on a wispy look, while Doug could see patches moving past them as they got close to entering it. Then the world went white and Doug stared at his instruments. Artificial horizon, airspeed, artificial horizon, altimeter, artificial horizon, compass, went the scan, God, he hated instrument flying. After less than a minute they were suddenly out of the cloud, emerging into a different world. Above them was a bright blue sky, with the sun a bright yellow ball to their right, low on the horizon. Just below them the cloud tops were so white they hurt the eyes and here and there Lancasters broke through the cloud, like submarines surfacing in a foamy sea.

"It's a better day up here than down there," said Bob, standing behind Doug's seat.

"Keep your eyes peeled for other aircraft and call out any that come close," reminded Doug, as Bob made his way through the cockpit into the nose.

Slowly the sun sank below the horizon and the clouds took on an almost unreal phosphorescent pink glow, while the sky turned from bright blue to red. The route took them between Cambridge and Bedford and here the cloud started to break up. First, sporadic gaps appeared here and there. These became more frequent, until there were more gaps than clouds. They went onto oxygen at 10,000 feet and by the time they reached 20,000 feet London was right under their nose in the darkness, which had now descended. Normally they would have been routed around the capital but tonight they had been deliberately sent directly over it, so that the people could hear the sound of the hundreds of friendly aircraft, on their way to pound Berlin. Levelling out at 20,000 feet Doug set up the Lancaster to cruise at its most economical, by bringing the rpm back to as low as he could get it while maintaining 160 mph. In Freddy that was 1,800 and that was as good as you would ever get.

Just south of London they spotted a solitary stationary searchlight pointing directly upwards ahead of them. This was Beachy Head and the light fixed their position as they turned off their navigation lights and set course over the channel towards France. The channel looked dark and foreboding, but it was a much shorter sea crossing than they were used to and they hardly seemed to have time to test their guns and arm the bombs before they were approaching the coastal flak and searchlight belt of France. Doug started to weave his usual pattern of turns around their base course and aimed for a gap between two clusters of lazily sweeping searchlights, while the twinkling flak sparkled ahead of them. Soon they were among it, but while it was unpleasant it was random and none came close. After a few minutes they were through and the route took them north of Amiens along the Somme valley. The meandering river was easy to spot in the clear night, as it reflected the starlight. How many men died there in a sea of mud less than thirty years ago? thought Doug. What was the point of them going through all that if it was just going to happen over and over again?

Ahead grey cloud showed up in the darkness, spreading out across their path and reaching from low level up to over 20,000 feet. Doug was not happy. The Met man had not forecast this and if this was wrong what about the rest of his forecast? The cold front had extended further south than forecast and they would have to try and go over it. As the cloudbank approached the enormous size of it became apparent. The cloud seemed to boil as it bubbled upwards, almost as if it was alive. Occasionally it would light up with a blue green flash of lightning before fading back to its dull grey in the black night. Doug eased up the revs and lifted the nose slightly into a slow climb.

"We'll try and get above it," he announced. At 24,500 feet Freddy could go no higher, but it looked like it would be enough and they slipped over the peaks of the mountainous clouds while they boiled and flashed below them.

"Bloody good job we're not in a Halifax," said Bob. "They'll never get over this."

Doug thought of the other crews who were right now having to fly through the heart of the clouds below them. They would be getting thrown around, hammered by hail and rain, static making the radio and even the intercom useless, pilots fighting the controls to keep them on course or even the right way up, while their eyes were screwed up staring at their instruments.

There had been no sign of any opposition so far and Doug wondered if the Germans were going to leave them to the bad weather and stay safely on the ground themselves. He certainly hoped so, because any fighter that got above them at the moment couldn't help but see them silhouetted against the grey cloud below. "Keep a good lookout, we're very visible above this cloud." As soon as he said it he regretted it. Everyone onboard was well aware of the danger and would be as alert as possible. Half an hour later the mountain range of cloud started to get lower and the lightning stopped. The cold had seeped through Doug's clothes and he shivered as he lowered the nose and descended again to 20,000 feet while the solid bank of clouds was left behind them, to be replaced by patches of cumulus. Now they were over Germany, heading roughly northeast, in the general direction of Nuremberg and still all was quiet.

There was a flash ahead of them. Was it lightning or had a bomber just exploded? They stared intently into the dark. The patches of grey cumulus clouds looked like giant icebergs, suspended in the air. One of them lit up, changing from red to blue to green. That's definitely lightning, thought Doug, as it passed down their right side. Then green light sprang forward ahead of them and flames appeared in the air. It was a long way off and they could only see a patch of yellow in the sky slowly descending, followed by a flash. And that's definitely not lightning, he thought.

"Bomber going down ahead."

"Roger," replied Ron.

Searchlights appeared over Nuremberg. They swept slowly to and fro, occasionally illuminating a patch of cloud that would diffuse the light over a large area. The route turned north before they got near Nuremberg and kept them well away from the lights. Now the German fighter controllers would be repositioning their fighters, reassessing what the target was and where the route would take the bombers next. Doug realised that he had not felt any bumps since they left England. The bumps were the slipstream of other invisible aircraft in the stream and while they reminded him of how close he was to other aircraft he could not see, now that they weren't there he felt very alone and naked. He felt like asking Ron if they were still on track, but he didn't want to question his navigator's ability, especially as he knew how Ron would react. They were probably in the right place but the weather must have dispersed the bomber stream so that it was spread over a larger area than normal. That shouldn't be too much of a problem, because they would all converge again on the run in to the Pathfinder's flares over the target.

They were just passing a towering cumulus to their left, which reached almost up to their level when Doug saw a green flash out of the corner of his eye. He assumed it was lightning from the cloud until Alex called, "Bomber being attacked 9 o'clock low!" When Doug looked it was the closest combat he had seen. It was perfectly backlit by the tall light grey cloud and the dark shadow of the bomber could be seen outlined against it, no more than 200 yards away. Below and behind the bomber was a smaller shadow, the nose of which suddenly lit up with yellow flashes; green darts of light flew towards the bomber. Some of the green darts ended at the bomber in bright yellow flashes on its wings, while others continued on into the night. Fire back, you idiot! thought Doug, willing the bomber to retaliate, but flames were already showing from the wings of what could now be identified, by its own funeral pyres, as a Halifax.

"Permission to open fire?" asked Alex. The German fighter was within range, they could even tell it was a Junkers 88, but the Halifax was finished and to open fire now would give their position away to a fighter who would probably quickly turn the tables on them.

"No, hold your fire unless he attacks us." And Doug rolled on 30 degrees of right bank and turned away from the Halifax, whose right wing was now a mass of flames as it went into a shallow dive.

"One parachute!" exclaimed George.

"Two!" called Alex.

A blinding flash suddenly lit up the whole area turning night into day and Freddy shuddered and jumped.

"What the hell was that?" asked Bob.

"The Halifax just blew up," replied George.

"Where's the fighter?" asked Doug.

"Don't know, skipper, I can't see a thing," said George, trying to rub a sea of thousands of green blue stars from his dazzled eyes.

"Alex?"

"It's nae good, skipper, a cannae see a thing either. But if he didnae turn away he'll a gone up wi' the Halifax!"

Once more alone Freddy continued on its way towards the target, through an empty sky that was far from empty.

12

Berlin had scared Doug the first time he saw it and it didn't scare him any less now. If anything the sight tonight was more spectacular than ever before because being further down the bomber stream instead of at the front, the attack was well underway. They were still twenty miles away, and all that could be seen of the city itself were the red and yellow fires. Hundreds of searchlights swept over the area and the white sparkling flak bursts were incessant. The cloud cover had increased as they had approached and though the clouds weren't as high as before, the tops barely reaching 10,000 feet, there were more of them and they covered about fifty percent of the ground. Through the large holes in the grey carpet the ground was still visible and it was possible to fix a position using rivers and lakes, but anything else would be invisible under the shadows of the clouds. Doug was observing Berlin through one of these large holes at the moment, which allowed him the right angle to see forward to the city. Soon he would lose sight of the target again as they overtook the clouds and changed the angle.

The crackly voice of the Master Bomber scratched its way into Doug's headphones.

"Bomb on the reds! Bomb on the reds! Ignore the greens! Ignore the greens! You're creeping back! You're creeping back!"

They flew over the next bank of cloud and the target disappeared behind it. Doug imagined what was happening. The red TIs would have been dropped visually in the light of yellow parachute flares, between the clouds, and they would be the most likely to be accurate. The green TIs would have been dropped using H2S during a period when the target was obscured by cloud. Now the Master Bomber would be circling the aiming point, assessing how accurately the markers had been placed and correcting the aim of the main force bombers while they dropped their loads.

"Course to target zero six zero degrees compass, six minutes," said Ron.

Doug turned onto the course and things started to happen quickly. Yellow sky markers burst ahead of them over the cloudbank.

"Start dropping window at the sky markers, Jimmy, the ground markers are under the clouds," said Bob, who had a far better view of things close under the bomber's nose. "What's the current wind?"

"One eight zero at 20," replied Ron.

211

The cloud underneath them was suddenly lit up by a searchlight shining on it from below, turning it from a dull to a light grey. Another gap in the clouds was coming up and by leaning as far to the left as he could and straining his neck, Doug could just see red TIs slightly to the left of the nose, while the fires spread out on either side.

"Bomb doors open, master switch on, bombs fused and selected, skipper," said Bob. Doug reached behind him to the lever by his left hip.

"Bomb doors open, master switch on, bombs fused and selected," he repeated. They were in the flak now and the yellow flashes left light grey clouds of their own in the sky around them. As yet, none had come close, but they were still only over the outskirts of the city.

"Bomb doors fully open," confirmed Harry. A yellow searchlight beam flashed across them flooding the cockpit with light for an instant before passing on. Doug knew it would soon be hauled back towards them and threw Freddy into a left turn and dived. The beam did return, but passed behind them and finding nothing moved on.

"Pathfinders top up the red markers! Top up the red markers!" crackled the Master Bomber.

Bringing Freddy back onto course Doug could see, below and in front of his right knee, the shadowy shape of Jimmy in the nose, throwing out window down the chute. Until then he hadn't realised he was alone in the cockpit. He looked to the right, where Jimmy usually stood, and out of the side window saw another Lancaster caught by a lone searchlight. It started to turn, but before it could wriggle free three more lights latched onto it and a storm of flak burst around it.

"Single-engined fighter 8 o'clock high!" yelled Alex. "He's coming in. Corkscrew port! Corkscrew port!" Forcing the throttles through the gate into full boost with his right hand he put on full left aileron and pushed the stick forward with his left. Freddy dived left, its engines screaming and Doug felt himself being lifted out of his seat as the nose fell away. The burning city appeared through the windscreen and Doug reversed the control column and using both hands pulled up Freddy's nose so that the fires once again disappeared behind the front turret, while he was forced down onto the solid pack of his parachute.

"He's gone over the top of us!" shouted Alex.

Looking right Doug saw the single blue exhaust flame, short blunt nose and square tipped wings of a Focke Wolf 190 heading straight for the illuminated Lancaster. Yellow flames shot from the leading edges of the German's wings and dull blue flashes appeared under them. Doug guessed these came from the cartridge ejection ports. Small explosions erupted along the mid-section of the Lancaster's fuselage and the Wild Boar fighter was gone. Doug levelled out and throttled back while staring at the other bomber. It was just flying straight on through the hail of flak; it didn't manoeuvre, it didn't fire back at the fighter. He almost yelled at it in frustration. Then something fell from the nose and whipped back in the slipstream. Just as he was about to lose it in the dark he saw a parachute open and another black dot fell from the nose while the Lancaster started a slow descending turn to the right, away from them.

"Commencing bomb run," said Bob, bringing Doug back to the task in hand. "Left, left...Steady."

Now Doug could no longer see the TIs, only the edge of the fires, which also reflected from the underside of a layer of cloud ahead of them. He eased Freddy up another 200 feet back to 20,000 feet and steadied the speed at 160mph. Now he needed to concentrate on following Bob's instructions and flying accurately.

"Illuminators, more light on the target! More light on the target!" urged the Master Bomber.

Most of the flak seemed to have been aimed at the coned Lancaster, but now it was back and some dull red flashes sent a rattle along the sides of the fuselage audible over the engines. They were approaching the bank of cloud and it was starting to cut out his view of the fires.

"Will we be able to see the TIs?" he asked Bob.

"I'm hoping we'll be over the other side of the cloud before we get to the release point," said Bob. "We're lined up alright." Now they were above the cloud and while they were safe from the lights, the gunners still fired their flak up through the clouds at random to cause the Lancaster to bounce around in the turbulent air. Looking down the left side of the nose Doug could see a glow through the cloud and the far side of the cloud was nearly below them.

"Damn it!" exclaimed Bob. "Dummy run! Dummy run! We missed the aiming point below the clouds."

"Aw shit!" said Alex, who had had some large pieces of flak rattle off his turret and didn't want to stay over the target any longer.

"Just drop them anyway," said Ron.

But Bob was having none of that. "We'll have to go around, skipper."

The thought of turning around and flying into the oncoming bomber stream terrified Doug so much for a second he couldn't speak. His mind searched for a reason why they couldn't do it; although it was extremely dangerous, it was also standard practice. Eventually, he closed the bomb doors and cleared his throat enough to say,

"Roger, turning port, keep a sharp lookout, I'm going to try and climb above the bombing altitude." It would have been quicker to descend below the bombing altitude, but then there would have been the danger of bombs falling on them from above and any bomber having difficulties would be more likely to be below the bombing altitude than above it. So opening the throttles, Freddy clawed for height once more.

Flying back over the city at 20,500 feet Doug was surprised at how many bombers he saw outlined against the fires below them. Even single seat fighters, without radar, couldn't help but find targets when they were backlit like this. He was thankful he had turned left because most of the searchlights and flak seemed to be off to the right side of the bomb run, which was now to their left. He was soaked with sweat; he could feel it running down his back and the sides of his face. His chest was heaving as he breathed heavily and he checked his oxygen to see if it was still connected. All was well, but his body seemed to be demanding more air than his lungs could supply.

"Break right!" yelled Bob. Doug reacted immediately and Freddy a second later and Doug glimpsed a large black shadow flash down their left side.

"How long do you think that cloud will take to pass over the aiming point?" Doug asked Bob.

"Not sure, skipper, but to be safe I think we should set up again from the run in point."

"That'll put us ten minutes behind schedule."

"You can't hurry a cloud, skipper," was the casual reply.

Five nerve shattering minutes later they turned again onto the bomb run. Doug let down slowly to 20,000 feet. He could feel his hands shaking on the control column while his heart thumped inside him with the same effect as if someone the size of Jimmy was hitting him rhythmically in the chest with the heel of his hand. The pulsing pounded in his head, causing intense stabbing pains in his temples. His body was boiling hot and his clothes were wet through, whereas his face felt ice cold and clammy. What the hell was happening to him? It must be at least minus 20 up here, he couldn't possibly be hot.

The target looked much as it had done before and Doug dreaded the thought that they might have to go around again. We must get back, he thought, everyone wanted them to get back as soon as possible and they were already ten minutes behind schedule. There was the bad weather in the North Sea too, that would probably be worse than forecast, and if they took longer than expected to get through that they would be well behind schedule. What if there was fog? They would have to divert and they might not have the fuel. They entered the city again, over another large bank of cloud, and Bob started to line Freddy up on the markers. The raid was nearly over now and there were few Pathfinder aircraft left to keep the TIs topped up.

"This is the Master Bomber! This is the Master Bomber! I want more red TIs 400 yards north of the greens! I repeat! I want more red TIs 400 yards north of the greens!"

Freddy emerged from over the bank of cloud and the run-in to the target looked clear with the cloud that had spoiled their last run now well beyond the release point.

"Can you see any red TIs?" asked Doug.

"No, just greens," said Bob. "If they don't drop any before we arrive I'll drop about 400 yards north of the greens."

"Roger."

A white flash lit up the sky. Scarecrow, thought Doug, imagining the disintegrating bomber. If any of the crew had survived the explosion they would be falling to their deaths right now. He did a quick calculation: the human body falls at about 120 mph or 2 miles a minute. Bombing altitude was 20,000 feet or about three and a third miles, so it would take a falling man one minute and forty seconds to reach the ground. A long time to watch your death approaching. He shuddered and realised he didn't feel warm anymore. The sweat was freezing on him and while his adrenalin would keep him warm over the target he knew it was going to be a long cold flight home.

"Left, left... Steady. There still aren't any reds, skipper, and I reckon we're less than a minute from the drop point."

"Any Pathfinder aircraft! Any Pathfinder aircraft! This is the Master Bomber! This is the Master Bomber! I need illuminators and red TIs 400 yards north of the green TIs."

"It doesn't sound like there are any Pathfinders left, Bob, just go ahead and drop 400 yards north of the greens."

"Roger... Left, left... Steady... Steady...Bombs gone!" Freddy leapt upwards, freed of over five tons of bombs. "Hold her steady for the photoflash, skipper."

"Sod the photo!" shouted Harry. "We've spent long enough over this damned flak trap! We're not getting paid by the hour, you know!" But Doug held Freddy steady for the photoflash fifty-three seconds after the bomb release.

"Bugger me!" exclaimed Bob. "A Pathfinder just dropped a red TI right where I aimed our bombs."

"This is the Master Bomber! This is the Master Bomber! Good marking! Good marking! Drop on the red TI! Drop on the red TI!"

"I should be with the Pathfinders," said Bob proudly.

"To hell with that," said George. "They do forty-five Op tours."

"Well, we should definitely get an aiming point certificate out of that," said Bob. Any crew who got a photoflash photograph which showed they had dropped their bombs on the aiming point, got a certificate.

"Can we get out of here yet?" asked Ron.

"Any time... Now!" said Bob, hearing the camera click.

"Good! Course three two five degrees compass," said Ron quickly.

Doug turned sharply left and pushed Freddy's nose down to increase their speed and get them clear of the target more quickly. Although the raid was all but over the flak was just as intense and they weaved their way between searchlights and explosions until they were clear of the suburbs. Doug levelled off and then started a long slow economical climb back up to height. They would need to get as high as they could if they were to stand any chance of getting over the front Doug suspected they would find in the North Sea.

Group Captain McKechnie had watched the Squadron depart from the top of flying control. Then after a quick tour around his station to see that all was well he had gone home to spend the evening with his wife. It was the first time he had allowed himself a night off in weeks and he spent it with his pregnant wife in the commandeered farm that had become the RAF Metheringham Station Commander's house. It had been a pleasant evening but he had not been able to completely stop himself thinking of the crews flying to Berlin and back. His wife, of course, had noticed his restlessness and she was also thinking about them. As usual she planned to go to the interrogation and hand out the sandwiches and mugs of tea. She had heard them take off at five, but for once she had not watched them; the baby was due soon and she was feeling very tired. She knew it was to be a long trip, her husband had said he expected them back around midnight and he told her she should get some rest tonight rather than helping at the interrogation. She had nodded in agreement but said nothing; she knew it was not worth arguing with him. However, she was the only person on the station who would dare to openly defy him and when midnight came she would appear in the interrogation room and there would be nothing he could do about it.

As the mantelpiece clock struck ten McKechnie stood up and walked slowly to the fire. He prodded it once or twice with the wrought iron poker and then turned to face her.

"They should be starting back across the North Sea now." He looked towards the heavy blackout curtain over the window. He had been fighting the urge to look outside at the weather all evening and now he could bear it no longer. "I'm going to go over to flying control for a while. I think you should turn in, you look tired."

"Yes, I think I'll do that," she replied, knowing she could get a full hour and a half's sleep and still get to the interrogation room before the first crews got back. As he pulled on his greatcoat and picked up his hat she kissed him. He said goodnight and as she climbed the stairs she heard him close the front door.

Driving his car down the dark deserted country lane that had originally joined the villages of Metheringham and Walcott and was now closed to the public, because it ran right through the middle of his station, McKechnie scanned the sky. It was a clear crisp starry night and most people would have looked on it as a beautiful winter's evening, but McKechnie knew it for what it was: an evening that could decimate a squadron and leave his station covered with mangled Lancasters and broken bodies.

The solid bank of cloud stretched as far as the eye could see to the right and left of their track. The bottom of it was somewhere near the black surface of the North Sea and invisible in the dark, while the tops, white in the starlight, towered above them, up to what must have been well over 40,000 feet.

"There's no way we can get over that," said Bob from the front turret as he stared at the mountainous clouds.

"Are you sure that's not the Alps?" asked Harry, sarcastically with his head in the astrodome.

Doug had climbed Freddy to 25,000 feet for the flight back across Germany, which was a comfortable and economical height for an unladen Lancaster. But when he saw the clouds towering above them he had climbed as high as Freddy could go. This had turned out to be 29,500 feet and at this height Freddy wallowed around in the thin air and refused to go any higher.

The huge range of clouds did indeed look as big and as solid as a range of snow covered mountains. Doug had been shivering all the way from Berlin, but the sight of the clouds in the distance had taken his mind off the cold. He had hoped against hope that they would be able to get over the weather front but now all hope of that was gone and he knew the only option was to fly through it. Maybe it wouldn't be as bad as it looked, he lied to himself, as they neared the white wall of cloud.

"Hold on everybody, it's probably going to get a bit rough," he announced, just before they entered the clouds.

The starlit sky vanished instantly as the white wall enveloped them and for a second all was still as the total darkness wrapped itself around them. Doug stopped looking out of the windscreen and stared at his instruments. They were level at 29,500 feet with a steady speed of 160 mph heading two nine five degrees compass. Then the nose shot up so violently the fuselage shuddered and it was all that Doug could do to hold it down. The right wing jumped upwards and the nose dropped so sharply Jimmy, who was standing beside him, found himself suspended between the cockpit floor and the Perspex canopy. His arms flailed around wildly, until they caught hold of the back of Doug's seat and he hauled himself back down. As he did the nose shot up again and he fell to the floor before he eventually struggled to his knees. Curses and exclamations came over the intercom from all quarters while Doug fought with the controls just to keep Freddy approximately straight and level.

"Good to have you back," he said to Jimmy, as the engineer finally managed to get back to his feet. "The pressure on the controls is going to be too much for me one handed. I'll need both hands on the stick, tighten up the throttle friction nuts and keep an eye on the boost and revs while I try to keep us the right way up!" Jimmy did as he was told and the mad roller coaster continued. Doug found he was being mesmerised by the instruments, as they shook themselves and blurred in front of him. He was looking too long at the artificial horizon, he told himself, but he needed to concentrate on it to try and keep them level. You must do a quick scan, his mind urged him. Speed, Christ, the pointer was fluctuating anywhere between 120 and 180 mph. Back to the artificial horizon, get the left wing up! Height, 31,000 feet! Impossible, the ceiling for a Lancaster was about 29,500, if you were lucky! The turbulence is flinging us up, he realised. Heading, the DR compass alternated about 15 degrees either side of three zero zero, while the gyrocompass had long since given up and was slowly rotating. The magnetic compass he didn't even waste his time checking, because it too would be completely useless.

A loud bang and brilliant flash made him jump.

"Lightning strike!" yelled Jimmy, as he disappeared to check his panel. Doug felt he had been in the cloud forever – it was his picture of what hell was like.

"New course…compass!" crackled Ron, as the static from outside Freddy started to interfere with the electrics.

"Say again!" said Doug.

"New…degrees…pass!" repeated Ron.

"I can't hear you, Ron, you're breaking up!"

Five seconds later Ron appeared at his side, looking green even in the darkness and hanging onto anything that appeared solid. He handed Doug a piece of paper with two four zero written on it, which Doug read in the dull green glow of the instruments while Ron disappeared back behind his curtain. Doug set two four zero on the compass and wrestled Freddy round onto an approximation of that heading.

"Jimmy, the boost's down to 6 pounds per square inch, the throttles must be sliding shut!"

Jimmy reappeared at his elbow and scanned the gauges before easing the throttles further forward and tightening the throttle friction nut again.

Now they were doing somewhere between 110 and 170 mph and were at 27,000 feet, but if they took the average reading, they were on course. Doug's arms were starting to ache from the constant battle with the elements and he wished he had Jimmy's strength. A wall of water hit the windscreen with such force Doug thought they had flown into the sea and his mind flashed back to their ditching. The sheets of water lashed the outsides of the Lancaster so hard it was impossible to be heard inside. Another blinding flash and Doug tried to blink away the green haze that hung in front of his eyes. He was near panic; he was blinded and could not see the instruments. Anything could be happening to them at the moment and he could do nothing to save them. He blinked hard and stared with all his might, his arms and wrists locking the controls in a neutral position and his mind praying the violently jostling turbulence would even itself out and they would remain approximately level. Slowly the green mist cleared and he found Freddy in a shallow dive with the right wing up 30 degrees. Once again he fought to get Freddy level and back on course. 100 to 160 mph and 25,000 feet, the speed was dropping, the boost was down to 6 pounds per square inch again. Now the turbulence is forcing us downwards, thought Doug.

"Jimmy, the boost's down again!" Jimmy didn't respond, he had his back to Doug and was kneeling at his panel on the right cockpit wall. Doug reached over, nudged him and pointed at the boost gauges.

Jimmy said something, but Doug couldn't hear him. He moved the throttles up again to restore the power, then held his mouth close to Doug's right ear and shouted, "Carburettor ice!"

Of course, why hadn't he thought of it? As the air entered the carburettor it speeded up and was therefore also cooled and the moisture was now freezing and blocking the carburettors. Doug reached to the left of his seat and selected hot air to the carburettors. At that moment the rain eased, just as the starboard inner coughed and spluttered, followed by the starboard outer. The warm air was melting the ice in the carburettors and water was entering the Merlins' cylinders. Freddy wallowed in the air, and then with one or two loud backfires, the engines ran smoothly again.

"We need to get out of this level!" yelled Jimmy, over the noise of the rain and static. "If we run on hot air we'll be very short of fuel when we get back!" Hot air, being less dense, was less efficient and the engines produced less power for a given throttle setting.

They were down to 20,000 feet and Doug increased the power to 9 pounds of boost and lifted the propeller controls to fully fine, to give 2850 rpm. This should give them the best climb performance. He heaved Freddy into a climb out of the carburettor freezing level and hopefully away from the powerful down draughts that had dragged them down about 10,000 feet.

Doug's eyes felt like they were trying to pull themselves out of his head as he strained to concentrate on the instruments. His head was pounding and his arms and legs were now on fire while he struggled to keep Freddy under control. Now they were in the climb and with the rain easing off he could hear the engines more clearly. At least they sounded healthy enough now the ice had gone. The turbulence was as bad as ever and he could only hope to keep to an approximate course, speed and height. But at least the artificial horizon had not let him down and by staring at it and keeping the aircraft on the climb bar, with the wings level, he should stay on course and climb out of the ice. The unusual thing about carburettor ice is it will only form in a certain temperature range and if it gets too cold the ice won't form, so climbing to a colder level would stop the ice.

Hold the climb attitude, Doug thought to himself, his arms like lead. This can't go on much longer, he must have been in the cloud for hours.

"How long to the coast, Ron?"

"Say again!" The rain was still lashing the fuselage.

"How long to the coast?" he shouted, feeling he needed something to hold on to in his mind to keep him going, despite the pain in his arms and legs and the terrible headache that made him just want to close his eyes and sleep.

"About an hour! But in this we could be anywhere and the GEE is useless since the lightning strike!"

"What about the radio?"

"Nothing but static, but I think it's still working! We might get something when we get clear of the storm!" yelled Harry.

If we get clear of the storm, thought Doug pessimistically. Did they really still have an hour to go the coast? That only put them halfway across the North Sea; surely they must have been in the storm longer than that! He forced himself to concentrate on the instruments again, even though he was at the point of exhaustion.

What the hell was happening? The speed was low, 130 ish, they were still in the climb but they were only at 21,000 feet! The engines, he could hear, were still giving climbing power, the artificial horizon was showing the correct climbing attitude, the speed should be 160 mph and the altimeter wasn't moving. For a second he was confused, then he realised that the altimeter must be jammed. He hit it, but it wouldn't budge.

"Ron, what's our altitude?"

"21,000 feet!" came the shouted reply.

Ron's was jammed as well; it could only be ice over the static vent.

"Jimmy, is the Pitot head heater on?"

Jimmy checked. "Yes!"

Doug's tired mind searched for another explanation, while his aching arms and legs continued their fight semi automatically. No, there was no other explanation, the Pitot head was blocked, the heater must have failed and ice had formed in the tube. Now he would have no altimeter or airspeed indicator. To a pilot who hated instrument flying at the best of times the prospect was so scary Doug felt sick and his stomach actually heaved but, with some difficulty, he kept the contents of his stomach down.

"Jimmy, we have a serious problem! We've got ice in the Pitot tube and we've lost the altimeter and airspeed indicator! I daren't climb any more without the airspeed indicator in case we stall! We'll fly level using the power settings and the artificial horizon, but we might be in the freezing level, so look out for airframe ice!" He brought the throttles back to 7 pounds of boost but kept the propellers in fine pitch and selected cold air on the carburettors. If the airframe was starting to ice up it was probably too cold for carburettor ice.

"How much fuel have we got left, Jimmy?" That would be the next problem now they couldn't fly economically.

"Enough for about an hour and three quarters!"

"How long to Metheringham, Ron?"

There was a pause. "About an hour!"

About an hour. For Ron to be vague about timings meant he couldn't be sure of his position, but then again, how could he be in these conditions? Hadn't it been an hour last time he asked? He was sure it had and that was ages ago, or was it? No, that was an hour to the coast and it was another 30 miles or so to Metheringham from Spurn Head. His mind spun, he had to stay alert or they were all done for. What if this storm went on all the way to Metheringham? They couldn't land in this. They would have to bale out, he decided. They would fly as far west as the fuel allowed then, when they were sure they were over land, they would bale out. He was surprised that the idea did not frighten him. Perhaps because it was less frightening than the thought of having to try and land in the middle of the storm.

"I can see ice starting to form on the wings!" shouted Jimmy.

"It's building up on the nose too!" added Bob.

Doug wrenched his eyes from the artificial horizon and stole a rapid glance at the windscreen. It too was well on the way to freezing over completely. How much further was this cloud going to go on for?

McKechnie pulled up outside flying control and got out. He took a long deep breath of the cold night air and scanned the far side of the airfield. All he could see were the dark silhouettes of the trees at the far side of the perimeter track. He breathed out a long dense cloud of condensation, which only slowly drifted away from him in the still night. Above him the stars still shone brightly. This was not good, he thought. This was not good at all, and he went into the flying control building and climbed the stairs to the second floor. The bare light bulbs cast a harsh light on the magnolia painted walls of the corridor after the darkness of the blackout. Opening the first door on the right McKechnie entered the Senior Controller's Office. He knew it would be empty because Bill Fairclough never left the tower while the Squadron was airborne. Not because he had to stay there, but because he felt he should. He felt for the light switch in the darkness and turned on the light. Crossing to the desk he phoned the station exchange.

"Hello, this is the Station Commander, get me Group Operations."

Sally was in her usual armchair bed in the flying control office when she was woken by the sound of a raised voice. She was instantly fully conscious as her curiosity tuned her acute ears to what was being said.

"Well, that won't be much use if they're short of fuel," said the voice, which she knew she recognised but hadn't yet placed. Then she heard a phone being put down quite hard. It was the Station Commander, she realised. What was he doing at flying control? she wondered, as she quietly got up. Pulling on her boots she heard the office door opposite close and footsteps go along the corridor towards the tower. When she had tied her laces she followed. There was no sign of anyone in the corridor, but this was the only way he could have gone. So fixing the blackout she went outside onto the balcony and climbed the metal exterior staircase to the tower. Entering the little glass room she could instantly tell the atmosphere was not relaxed. Glancing around she soon picked out the shape of the Station Commander in the darkness, staring out across the airfield.

"Would you like a brew, sir?" asked Uncle Bill.

"Yes... Yes, I would. Thank you," said the Station Commander absent-mindedly.

"Patterson, is that you?" Uncle Bill asked.

Sally jumped. "Yes, sir," she replied.

"Could you sort a brew for everyone? You know where everything is and Williams will help you."

"Is that Patterson the driver?" asked the Station Commander suddenly.

"Yes, sir," said Sally quickly, amazed that the Station Commander had heard of her, let alone remembered her name.

"I've heard you wait for your crew here," he said, unusually quietly, as if he was already thinking of something else. "Good show." And he turned away again to stare across the airfield.

Sally and Jane Williams went out into the cold night and descended to the flying control building proper to put the kettle on.

"What's he doing here?" asked Sally.

"I don't know," replied Jane. "He just came in and said good evening, then stared out of the window."

"He was on the phone earlier, in Bill's office. I think it was to Group. I couldn't hear what it was about, but he seemed a bit annoyed."

When they returned to the tower with the tea the Station Commander hadn't moved.

"Thank you," said Bill, taking a mug for himself and one for the Station Commander. "Here you are, sir." He handed over the mug and the Station Commander nodded his thanks. Now they stood side by side looking into the night. Bill was older than McKechnie, but three ranks junior. Flying had been Bill's life and he had no interest in anything that took him away from it, so he had never pushed for promotion. He had been a flight sergeant when the war started and after a year of war he had risen to flight lieutenant, just by surviving. A crash had laid him up for two years and now he was too old to fly Ops, so he would probably be a flight lieutenant when the war ended. He had seen a lifetime's worth of senior officers struggling with a difficult decision and while the decision often seemed straightforward to Bill he was not the one who would have to carry the can as a result of it. So he knew it was not his place to offer advice unless it were asked for, but he also knew how to manoeuvre situations around and he had already manoeuvred himself to the Station Commander's side.

"It's a very clear night tonight, sir."

"Yes."

"Do Group have any news on the raid?"

"No."

"Oh well, the boys should be back in an hour or so." He wasn't quite ready to speak yet, so Bill waited a few minutes by his side. The silence in the tower was amplified by the stillness of the night and even the buzzing of the static over the RT seemed oppressive. The dark outline of the trees, on the far side of the airfield, seemed slightly less distinct than they had been before.

"Have you heard any aircraft since the Squadron left?" McKechnie suddenly asked.

"Only the other Squadron bombers joining the stream earlier, but nothing for hours, sir."

He was almost there, he would soon ask. Bill was pretty sure what the problem was and he had been considering the same problem himself for the past hour. He had already made his decision on what he thought should be done and he was sure McKechnie had decided too. But the difference was, it was McKechnie who had to make it, and live with the consequences. That made things much harder and required more thinking time.

"What's the latest Met forecast?"

"Fog by dawn, sir. It's less than an hour old."

"Fog by dawn," McKechnie echoed. "Typical of the Met men to come up with that." He snorted. "Anyone can see we're going to have fog by dawn. What we need to know is if we'll have fog in the next two hours."

"There's always the FIDO," said Bill, pushing him towards the decision he had made.

"Yes… If Group would let us use it."

This was something Bill had not seen. "Oh?" he said, prompting a response.

"Group say there are Jerry intruders about and we are not to light the FIDO."

So that was why the problem was so big. The easy solution was being denied them. If there were intruders around the FIDO would show up for miles and attract them all to Metheringham to pick off the bombers as they came in to land. But it's not intruder weather, thought Bill.

"It's a bit clear for intruders."

"Yes and with a weather front in the middle of the North Sea intruders won't have the legs to fly around it. You know that and I know that, but apparently Group don't know that." McKechnie gave vent to his frustrations before again lapsing into silence and staring into the night.

"If we get fogged in the Squadron could still divert," offered Bill, although he knew the fog was forecast for the whole east coast and the only clear airfields were likely to be well to the west. McKechnie said nothing and Bill knew it was a poor alternative.

Suddenly the phone rang, making more than one person jump. Jane answered it, took a message and hung up.

"Ops, sir, Group have been in touch and the first aircraft have checked in on WT. The front was worse than forecast and they had to fly through it. The aircraft that have checked in are all short of fuel."

McKechnie watched the first wispy white tendrils of mist form in a hollow halfway along the runway and slowly start to reach out across the airfield. So much for the diversion option, he thought. His mind was with the cold, tired and probably frightened young men heading for home and safety, only to be met by an even greater danger. The fog was starting to form and the Squadron was an hour from home. Could they get them down safely before the field was clamped?

"How long will it take you to get all the boys down, Bill?"

"If they were in the overhead now it would still take us at least thirty minutes to get them all down. But they're not due back for about an hour yet and with the bad weather they'll probably be late."

"So we're looking at an hour and a half from now," said McKechnie, staring at the night.

"At least, sir," Bill emphasized.

"Have you seen that?" McKechnie pointed into the night.

"Yes, sir," replied Bill, without even looking. He knew McKechnie was pointing at the ground mist and he wanted the Station Commander to know he'd already seen it.

"When do you think it will clamp us?"

Now Bill took a long look at the mist, as it slowly spread. He knew McKechnie had already made his own estimate and was just asking him to confirm his own suspicions. Bill had sat in the tower on many a long night and watched fogs like this form and he knew that once it had started it thickened very quickly.

"About an hour, sir. Maybe a little longer."

"So..." McKechnie turned and faced the flight lieutenant. The shielded lights of the tower cast a dull yellow light across Bill's face, which emphasized the deep wrinkles around his eyes caused by long hours of staring into a dazzling sun. He knew Bill had been reading his thoughts and had probably come to the same conclusion as he had some time ago, but he summed up anyway to make sure he had missed nothing. "The first of our aircraft won't be back for at least an hour and it will take us at least half an hour after that to get them all down. Meanwhile the fog will probably clamp us before we can get them down. They don't have the fuel to divert to clear airfields and Group won't let us use FIDO because of intruders." He looked Bill straight in the eyes. "I could do nothing, as ordered, and lose half the Squadron." Bill stared straight back at him, knowing that to do nothing was not in McKechnie's nature. "I don't really have much choice, do I?"

Both men had stared death in the face many times in the air, so tough decisions, and for that matter staff officers, held no fear for them. "No, sir," answered Bill quietly.

"Do it."

Bill turned and walked to the phone, dialled a number which was answered immediately.

"Ops, this is flying control, Station Commander's orders, light the FIDO."

Even in the dark cloud Doug could see Freddy's wings were white and he could no longer see through the windscreen. He had worked the windscreen de-icing pump for a few minutes but with no effect and the windscreen remained white. Freddy was starting to feel sluggish, as it had done when they were at 29,000 feet, but now they were much lower than that and Freddy was still struggling to fly.

"We're going to have to descend out of the ice!" yelled Jimmy.

"I daren't!" Doug replied. "With no altimeter I've no idea how high we are and in this weather we could fly straight into the sea without seeing it!" He was very scared and had no idea how they were going to get out of this mess. Despite his father's occupation he had never been very religious, but for the last two minutes he had been praying. In his tired, fear-numbed brain there was nothing he could do except keep fighting with his pain wracked arms and legs to keep them in the air. The ice was building up fast and they were obviously in the middle of the icing layer. They could no longer climb, weighted down as they were with ice, and if they descended the icing level might go all the way to sea level. Doug was suddenly aware that Jimmy had gone and he looked around quickly. He was lying on his back with only his wriggling feet visible on the cockpit floor. His upper body was out of sight behind the instrument panel.

"What are you doing?" asked Doug, but Jimmy couldn't hear him and Doug had to wait what seemed like an eternity for him to emerge. By the time he did Freddy was all but uncontrollable, with a thick layer of ice over both wings and the nose.

"What the hell were you doing down there?" yelled Doug, who was close to panic and feeling like Jimmy had deserted him.

"I've cut the pipes to the back of the altimeter so it can get air," replied Jimmy, as he closed a large clasp knife.

Doug looked and saw the altimeter was showing 19,000 feet and appeared to be working again. The moisture outside might have frozen over the vent, preventing the altimeter from working, but in an unpressurised aircraft so long as air pressure could get to the altimeter it made little difference whether the air came from inside or outside the aircraft.

"Brilliant!" exclaimed Doug, then for the rest of the crew, "We're going to start to descend. We're at 19,000 feet now and we're going to try and get below the icing level, which will probably mean going quite low, so keep your eyes open for the sea." Bringing the throttles back slightly he lowered the nose and tried to judge Freddy's speed from the sound of the slipstream above the noise of engines and the feel of the controls, because the airspeed indicator was still frozen up. Scared of stalling he let the speed build up to a point where he could feel by the pressure on the controls that the speed was about 250 mph and the altimeter was unwinding at about 1,000 feet a minute. The turbulence was still undiminished and they bucked and bounced around as they descended. Doug again tried to de-ice the windscreen but the de-icing jets could only clear two small patches on the windscreen, which soon iced over again when he stopped pumping. They passed 10,000 feet and while the ice was no worse it was no better either. Jimmy was staring out of the cockpit side window at the right wing and silently praying that the ice would start to melt. At 5,000 feet Doug was thinking the freezing level could well go down to sea level, in which case if they didn't get out of the storm in the next few minutes they would ice up completely and fall into the sea. 2,000 feet and Doug pulled up Freddy's nose to level flight on the artificial horizon and set the throttles back to plus 7 pounds of boost. When he guessed the speed had stabilized he lowered the nose very slightly and eased Freddy downwards very slowly. At the same time he warned everyone to look out below them for the sea and call out the second they saw anything. At 1,000 feet they were still in clouds and Doug knew they had very little hope left when there was a horrendous crack! He glanced quickly to his left fully expecting to see a wing breaking off, but all he saw were shards of white flying backwards away from him in the slipstream.

"It's breaking up!" yelled Jimmy, from behind Doug's seat, as he watched the ice breaking away from the upper surfaces of the wings.

"He means the ice is breaking up," added Doug, aware that the rest of the crew might think he meant Freddy was breaking up.

Two minutes later, without any warning, they emerged out of the cloud into as nice a crisp clear starlit night as anyone could have wished for. The turbulence stopped immediately and after the noise and thrashing around in the storm all was quiet and still. Freddy droned them homewards while Doug, with burning and throbbing arms, slowly climbed them back to 5,000 feet, where he felt more comfortable. It would take a long time for the Pitot tube to unfreeze and the airspeed indicator would be out of action until that happened so it was prudent to have some height in hand, just in case. In the meantime he put what energy he had left into clearing the ice off the windscreen with the de-icing jets. Beside him Jimmy was doing fuel calculations.

"We have an hour and a quarter's fuel left, if we're careful with it," he eventually announced.

While Doug was now breathing a sigh of relief, Ron's problems were only just starting. In the storm there was nothing he could do to fix his position, but now they were clear of the clouds he needed a quick fix so that he could lay in a direct course for Metheringham, because the storm had left them with little fuel to spare. Unfortunately, the lightning strikes had knocked out the GEE and H2S. He could fix his position with the stars, but he hated the long-drawn-out process of taking star shots with the bubble sextant, then the working through the astronomical tables to get what always seemed to be a very inaccurate fix. However, the only other way he could fix their position would be for Harry to take some radio bearings and he didn't like to ask Harry to do this because he knew Harry hated him and he did not want to admit he needed him.

"How long to the coast, Ron?" asked Doug, after giving him what he thought would be long enough to get at least a rough fix.

"Thirty-one minutes if we're still on track."

About thirty minutes to the coast, then another fifteen minutes to Metheringham, only thirty minutes to spare, thought Doug. And Ron was being vague, which meant he wasn't sure of his position. What if there was fog?

"We don't have much fuel to spare, so we'd better route straight to Metheringham. Have you got a fix?"

"I'm just working on it, the GEE is out of action."

We don't have time for this, thought Doug. "Harry, see if you can get a QDM from Metheringham."

"Wilco, skipper."

A QDM was a request for the magnetic heading to the requested station. It made no allowance for wind, but it did at least get the aircraft heading in the right direction. Harry tuned the transmitter to the RAF Metheringham HF frequency and started to rattle away at his Morse key. Through his headset came the crackling static of the electric storm and he had no idea if his message was being transmitted or not. After the first attempt he waited and received nothing. He checked his receiver and tried again. This time a very weak signal came back and he pressed his headset hard against his ear with his left hand to cut out as much aircraft noise as possible while he scribbled down the message with his right.

"QDM to Metheringham two three five degrees."

Ron plotted this on his map and checked it against their planned route.

"Are you sure about that? It puts us well north of track."

"The signal was weak but that's definitely what they said," replied Harry.

"Well, you'll have to get some more bearings to confirm it and give me a fix," said Ron, deciding that as Doug had asked Harry for the first bearing he might as well finish the job. At least it would mean he didn't have to take any star shots.

Doug decided he would head off any argument that might arise between Harry and Ron by cutting in quickly.

"I'll head two three five for Metheringham until you give me any course corrections, Ron."

"Alright," replied Ron, thinking quickly, knowing he was under pressure and allowing himself to be railroaded. "I need DF bearings from Middleton St George, West Raynham and Binbrook radio operator."

Harry bristled, but bit his tongue and started to take the bearings.

The first bearing, from Middleton St George near Teesside, put them 50 miles north of track and Ron didn't believe it. But the second and third bearings confirmed the fix; they were 50 miles further north than they should be. Doing some quick calculations with his Dalton computer he worked out they were actually 150 miles from Metheringham. Using the forecast wind of two seven zero degrees at 10 mph, which at 5,000 feet would hopefully not be too inaccurate, they would have to head two four zero degrees and with a ground speed of 160 mph it would take them fifty-six minutes to reach base, leaving nineteen minutes of fuel to spare. It wasn't a lot, but they had been in far worse situations.

"Navigator to pilot, the storm has blown us north of track by 50 miles. Head two four zero degrees compass ETA fifty-six minutes."

"Two four zero degrees compass," repeated Doug changing course slightly. What would they do if there was fog at Metheringham? he thought. With about twenty minutes of fuel left they couldn't go anywhere else. They would have to rely on the untested FIDO, or head Freddy out to sea, put on the autopilot and bale out.

"There you go, Sally," said Uncle Bill. The Station Commander was now standing outside looking at the FIDO and the atmosphere in the tower was much more relaxed. "F for Freddy have just requested a QDM, but they're quite weak, so they're probably still a long way out."

"Thank you, sir," she replied. "I'll go over to dispersal and wait for them there." She stepped outside and looked over at the FIDO. The Station Commander was leaning against the handrail staring at the twin lines of fire spurting skywards. The roaring of the flames could be clearly heard even at this distance. A Lancaster circled overhead setting itself up for an approach and Sally looked away from the FIDO across the dark side of the airfield over the technical site. There the fog had settled, and while she could still see the buildings it was getting thicker all the time. Soon it would be a real pea-souper, with the only clear space being around the runway. She decided she would watch the first aircraft land before driving over to the dispersal. It was on its final approach now, coming in from the south, its white landing light beams catching and being defused by the remaining patches of fog. The red and green navigation lights were only just visible marking the wing tips and showing the watchers whether the wings were level. The four Merlins were producing a low grumble, as they pulled the Lancaster towards the runway. As it crossed the threshold of fire to their right the engines were cut right back and they popped in protest. The dark shape of the bomber was now plainly outlined against the red flames while it floated along just above the runway. Yellow and red flashes of flame reflected off the Perspex cockpit and turrets, and then there was a screech of brakes as the tyres touched the runway and it was down. Other bombers rumbled overhead, circling to wait their turn to land. Sally turned and left the Station Commander to watch the Squadron return.

With ninety of the 150 miles behind them Bob had started to look for the coast, but instead of the usual dark line in the dark night he saw a band of grey. For a minute he watched it before being sure what it was, then he turned on his intercom and reported.

"Fog bank ahead. I think it's over the coast."

Damn it, thought Doug, maybe it won't go too far inland. But he knew it was a vain hope and as they crossed over the white blanket they could see it stretching on into the night ahead of them.

"How far are we from Metheringham, Ron?"

"40 miles."

Doug selected RT. "Coffee Stall, Coffee Stall, this is Hadnone F for Freddy, do you read me, over?"

"Hadnone F for Freddy, this is Coffee Stall answering. You are loud and clear. Set QFE nine nine four, runway in use zero two left hand, we have thick fog in the area and FIDO is active. Call at 10 miles, over."

"QFE nine nine four, runway zero two left hand, call at 10 miles, F for Freddy." Thank God for FIDO, thought Doug, as he started to descend, but it would still be very tricky because the airspeed indicator was still frozen up and he had no idea what it would be like landing with FIDO. At 2,000 feet the fog looked as solid as a crisp even fall of snow and it reflected the light from the millions of stars above them.

Just after Doug called 10 miles from Metheringham, Bob called, "Look at that in our 2 o'clock at about 2 miles." They all looked and saw three dark square towers sticking up out of the white carpet of fog. "Lincoln cathedral," said Bob, as they sailed slowly past. Perched high on its hill, dominating the landscape, as its Norman builders had intended it to, it was the only thing that was not completely enveloped in the dense fog. A minute later Bob saw a glow in the fog to the left of the nose and Doug, realizing it could only be the FIDO, called, "Airfield in sight."

"F for Freddy, this is Coffee Stall, orbit at 2,000 feet, you are number four to land, over."

Doug acknowledged, flying towards the glow so it would pass down the left side of the aircraft and he could get a good look at it. From above he could clearly see the flames along the sides of the runway, but as soon as he left the overhead and started to look obliquely through the fog all he could see once again was the glow. He started to worry; he would need to see more than that if he was to have any chance of landing, especially without an airspeed indicator. While Bob squeezed through the cockpit on his way to behind the main spar, Doug caught a glimpse of a dark shape below him against the fog, with two tiny red and green lights. Picking it up again he saw it was another Lancaster waiting to land. Turning back north he kept the glow in sight while all the time he thought of the fuel getting lower.

"F for Freddy, this is Coffee Stall, descend to orbit at 1,000 feet, you are number two."

"Fifteen minutes' fuel left," said Jimmy.

"Before landing checks," replied Doug. He was very tense and could not wait to get back on the ground. His arms and legs were sore, he was numb from the waist down because of the hard parachute, his back was so painful it felt like it was on fire and he had a splitting headache. But it was not over yet, he still had to get his crew down safely and he was not sure if he could do it. Of all the instruments he used during landing the airspeed indicator was the most vital. If you let the speed drop too much on the approach you would stall and with no height to recover in, a crash was inevitable. But if you went too fast you would float along the runway and not land in the space available. Doug always thought the lesser of the two evils was to go too fast, because if you overran the runway you had a much better chance of surviving than if you fell to earth before reaching it. As one of his flying instructors had once told him, "It's better to step out of the wreckage at the far end of the runway, than to get dug out at the near end!" Now as he waited his heart pounded.

"Auto pilot control cock."

"Out."

"Superchargers."

"M ratio."

"Air intake."

"Cold."

"Brake pressure."

"270."

"Speed below 200 mph?"

"I think so."

"Flaps."

"20 degrees." He held the nose down, fighting Freddy's tendency to raise the nose as the flaps lowered then he re-trimmed.

"Undercarriage."

"Down." Doug waited to check the green lights were illuminated, showing the wheels were locked down.

"Propellers."

"Fully fine."

"Fuel booster pumps on for number one tanks. Call for full flap on finals."

Doug had watched the other Lancaster disappear into the fog and knew their turn had come. Please God, get us down safely, he thought.

"F for Freddy you are clear to land, surface wind calm."

"Clear land, F for Freddy." Doug took Freddy a long way past the threshold of runway zero two to give himself plenty of time to line up with the runway and hopefully stabilize his speed. Looking back over his left shoulder he could see the flames and it took him an effort of will to make the turn back to the runway. During the turn he brought the power back to zero boost and let the nose drop slightly. The altimeter started to slowly unwind and he had to stop his eyes from habitually flicking from the fires to the useless airspeed indicator. Halfway round the turn he could see the fires along the runway clearly and started to feel more confident, if he could just keep the speed stable. Now they were lined up with the runway and it looked to Doug like they were flying down a tunnel with fog all around them and the runway edged with fire at the far end.

"Full Flap."

Jimmy lowered the flaps all the way and Doug felt the change in trim and tried to correct it. He was sure the nose was too high and the speed must be dropping. He edged on more power, up to plus 2 on the boost, to counter the extra drag of the flaps. The approach angle looked good and the flames were getting nearer, reaching up towards him, making him want to lift his feet away from them.

Then they hit the turbulence from the air rising off the fires. Freddy jumped up and Doug instinctively reacted by opening the throttles. Freddy surged forwards and the stabilized speed was lost. They were over the threshold at fifty feet and fast. Doug cut the throttles and, looking along the left side of the nose, used the rudders to keep on the centreline of the runway and away from the jets of flame, which looked huge as they flashed past the side of the cockpit below them. Down they glided towards the runway while Doug eased the control column back further and further to check their rate of descent. He didn't need an airspeed indicator now, he was just feeling for the ground, but they seemed to be floating forever along the runway without the wheels making contact. This was not right; they should have touched down long before now. Maybe he had badly misjudged the speed and they had been going a lot faster than he thought. He looked up from the spot a hundred yards in front of the nose he was using to judge his height above the ground, to see the end of the runway, which was closer than he thought.

"We're not going to get in skipper," said Jimmy, in a voice that was obviously calmer than he felt.

Hell! They had been so close, but there was nothing for it. Doug opened the throttles to plus 9 pounds of boost and overshot. "F for Freddy going around."

"Roger, F for Freddy," replied the tower calmly. "You are still number one and clear to land." Raising the undercarriage and bringing the flaps up to 25 degrees Doug was well aware that there were other aircraft waiting to land behind him and he was holding them up. Some would be short of fuel and cursing him. How long could flying control allow him to fly round in circles preventing others from landing?

"How much fuel have we got left?"

"Ten minutes, enough for another two approaches."

"Right, chaps, I don't know if I can do this without an airspeed indicator, so if we don't get in this time I'm going to climb and we'll all bale out, alright?"

"I don't believe this! He's brought us this far and now he's going to make us get out and walk!" exclaimed Harry.

"You'll be okay, skipper," said George, which was echoed by all the others.

"Alright, if you say so, but I want you all to put your parachutes on. We won't have fuel to climb very high before baling out."

Once again he flew Freddy downwind past the fires at what he hoped was a stable speed and turned in for another approach. He lowered the wheels and once lined up with the runway told Jimmy to lower full flap. The tunnel of fog closed around them and Doug started to talk to himself as he concentrated on the approach. This was their last chance and it was all up to him.

"We're too high, ease it down a bit, gently back on the throttles. We're still too high, power back further, lower the nose, feel for the stall and get ready for the turbulence."

The threshold approached and the first turbulence rocked Freddy, but Doug was ready and didn't overreact. They sailed over the threshold high at 100 feet and Doug cut the throttles early to try and get them down quicker. The runway rushed up to meet them and Doug, pulling the stick back too quickly to check the descent, ballooned Freddy into a slight climb. Doug held the slight nose up attitude and waited for Freddy to start to sink again. They were still at thirty feet and Doug knew they were near to stalling.

"Don't stall it! Don't stall it!" He knew he should open the throttles, but he had to get them in this time. Then he felt it, through the tips of his fingers on the control column, a slight buffeting from the elevators, and the stall had arrived. Doug pushed the throttles through the gate into full emergency boost while holding Freddy's level attitude as the Lancaster started to fall. The propellers bit deeply into the air but Freddy was falling faster and faster and with the engines racing they hit the ground hard jarring all their bones and internal fittings. After the one almighty impact Freddy bounced straight back into the air with a nose high attitude and Doug could not lower the nose or cut the throttles as that would have induced another, even more violent, stall. He could only overshoot and they would have to bale out.

"Oh shit! I'm sorry, chaps, I can't do it." He had a lump in his throat, he was exhausted, he had done his best, but it hadn't been good enough and there was a sob in his voice. Now his crew would have to take their chances in their parachutes. He brought the power back from emergency boost and set up for a normal climb, he would head northeast, he didn't want Freddy to land on any of the local villages. As he was about to tell flying control his intentions Ron cut in.

"Doug, my airspeed indicator's working!" Doug looked down and his airspeed indicator appeared to be working too. The combination of the heat from the FIDO and the jolt of the heavy landing had de-iced the Pitot head.

"How much fuel do we have?"

"Five minutes," said Jimmy, looking at the gauges that were showing just above zero, but Jimmy knew that Freddy would run on empty for a few minutes.

"F for Freddy overshooting, I have enough fuel for one more approach."

"Roger, you're clear to land."

"There are other people up here as well you know," crackled a voice from another Lancaster.

"B for Baker only has ten minutes' fuel left," called another.

"Shut up and give him a chance!" called another voice, which Doug recognised as Charlie's.

Doug flew downwind again and turned in to land. Again he was high, but bringing the power back to zero boost and lowering the nose to maintain 110 mph, he was soon on the glide path. Then he increased the power and raised the nose slightly to maintain the correct rate of descent and hold the speed. His eyes flashed from the runway to the airspeed indicator. The turbulence hit them and they soared over the threshold at fifty feet and with the throttles cut floated down the runway. The speed decayed to 105 mph, and Freddy started to settle towards the runway. 100 mph, then just above the runway the Lancaster didn't seem to want to sink any more.

"She's not sinking," said Doug, exasperated as 95 mph came and went on the airspeed indicator.

"Wheel her on skipper," said Jimmy.

So Doug stopped holding back on the stick and waited for the wheels to touch. When they did, with a screech, he gave a quick push on the stick, raising Freddy's tail to kill the angle of attack on the wings and destroy the last of its lift, preventing the Lancaster from bouncing back into the air. Then he watched as the red lights at the end of the runway approached them down the corridor of fire. The speed was 80 mph now and they could no longer fly so he lowered the tail heavily to the runway, producing a "Bloody Hell!" from George, before holding the control column right back, to keep the tail firmly on the ground, and pulling hard on the brakes. The end of the runway rushed at them and Jimmy braced himself against the instrument panel, but with the brakes full on and the tyres screeching Freddy skidded to a halt with 10 yards to spare.

Taxiing back to dispersal Doug started to shake. He tried to stop it but the more he tried the worse it seemed to get. He breathed deeply and tried to relax his muscles but the shaking continued. In their dispersal they opened the bomb doors, shut down the engines, checked the chocks were in, released the brakes and selected ground power. Jimmy was scribbling in his fuel log but Doug could not wait for him to finish, he had to get out. He threw off his straps and lifting his parachute pushed past Jimmy then Ron who was still packing away his navigation equipment. He scrambled down the dark tunnel of the fuselage to the door and his shaking arms and legs almost caused him to fall down the short ladder to the ground.

Bob, Alex and Harry were kissing the ground and laughing while George hurled derogatory comments at them. Doug stood and stared at them almost in a trance while his hands shook. When the sergeants had finished fooling around they all lit up cigarettes and Harry offered one to Doug.

"Christ, skipper! We didn't think you would get us in there."

"Yeah, skip, when you told us to put our parachutes on Harry nearly wet himself."

"Only because you grabbed my parachute in panic, you yellow Aussie bastard."

Doug tried to smile as he took one of the offered cigarettes, but it came across as more of a grimace.

"Are you alright?" asked Alex.

"Of course he's alright," said George, who had noticed Doug's hands shaking. "That was a bloody good bit of flying that, with no airspeed indicator. Well, give him a light somebody!" Then without waiting George took the cigarette from Doug's hand and lit it for him from his own cigarette, then handed it back.

Doug drew on the cigarette and his head swam. He felt colour come flushing to his cheeks and he wanted to cough but he suppressed it. Sally's wagon was at the edge of the dispersal and he walked slowly towards it.

"Everything alright with the aircraft, sir!" Sergeant Green called after him.

"See Jimmy about it," said George. He nodded towards Doug. "He's had a rough trip."

Sally was standing by the front of the truck and she watched him approach. He looked exhausted, she thought. His head hung down and his feet were dragging. The parachute over his shoulder looked like it might flatten him at any minute and she had never seen him smoke before.

"Welcome back, sir," she said cheerily. But after nodding a reply he just turned and stared back at the Lancaster. The rest of the crew came over chatting and joking and climbed into the back and Sally went to close the tailboard. When she came back Doug was on his hands and knees on the grass being violently sick. She knelt down beside him and put her hands on his shoulders.

"It's alright, sir, its just shock. You'll be as right as rain after a good night's sleep. This happens to most people at some time or another after a rough trip." Doug spat and looked round at her, his eyes full, but he couldn't speak. "Come on, sir. Let's get you in the wagon and we'll take a nice slow ride round to interrogation, so you'll have plenty of time to sort yourself out."

13

George opened his eyes. Damn these Wakey Wakey pills. They didn't seem to keep him awake in the air but now he was in bed he couldn't sleep. Somewhere in the billet someone was snoring loudly. Lucky bastard, thought George. He was just about to turn over and try to go to sleep when he heard a sound off to his left. He could have been mistaken so he lay still and strained his ears to the darkness. There it was, a tiny whimper to his left.

"Jimmy? Are you alright?" he whispered. The noise stopped. "Jimmy?"

"Yes?"

"Are you alright?"

"Yes."

"What's the matter?" George persisted.

"Nothing."

"Sure?" George was very perceptive and while they had all been shaken by their recent close shaves George knew that Jimmy had felt it more than most. There was a long silence before Jimmy answered.

"I've wet the bed." The quiet childlike voice was full of embarrassment and shame and for a second George was shocked and didn't know what to do. This had to be covered up. If word got out it would destroy Jimmy. He was a good lad and far too good an engineer to lose; he had to be straightened out. George swung his feet out of bed and felt for his boots; he was already wearing thick socks against the cold.

"Get up," he hissed to Jimmy, as he tied his laces. In the darkness he heard Jimmy get out of bed and through the stale airless hut he caught a whiff of Jimmy's embarrassment. "Bring a spare pair a pyjamas and yer wash kit and come with me." He pulled his greatcoat over his own pyjamas, checked the pockets for his cigarettes and lighter and silently opened the hut door. Jimmy followed him outside, into the thick pre-dawn mist, and down the row of huts to the ablution block. The grey wispy blanket swirled around the two figures in the darkness. One short and striding along in front through the mud, with obvious purpose, the other large and powerful, slowly bringing up the rear, with his head hung low. Inside George felt for the light switch.

"Right, you get yerself cleaned up and I'll have a tab and we'll think about this." He rummaged through his pockets and extracted his cigarettes and lighter.

Jimmy washed himself and changed into his dry pyjamas while George smoked, coughed and spat.

"I can't carry on," Jimmy eventually said, his eyes full of tears.

"Of course yer can," replied George, who had expected this, but was still unsure as to how he was going to get Jimmy to change his mind.

"How can I? Look at me! I'm so scared I wet myself." He stared at the floor and a couple of tears ran down his face.

"No yer didn't. Yer wet the bed; it's not the same thing. If yer wet yerself in the air that would be different, but yer fine then. As for this, yer were asleep, so it's not yer fault. Yer not responsible for yer actions when yer asleep. It says so in King's Regulations. That's why yer can't be charged for anything yer do within ten seconds of been woken up. If yer not properly awake yer not responsible."

"It is the same thing. I did it because I'm scared."

"Jimmy, we're all scared. I've been more scared in the last few weeks than I've ever been in me life. When that Jerry fighter nearly collided with us on our first Op I nearly shat meself and when we ditched I was so scared I nearly just curled up and let meself die. The thing is, yer just have to keep goin'. We've had it rough, but we'll get through it, we're a good crew."

"But look at me! I feel sick before every Op and my hands shake. What if I freeze? You can't rely on me, not when I'm like this. I might get you all killed."

"Yer don't have a monopoly on fear, yer know. Harry talks so much before Ops he nearly makes himself hoarse because he's scared. I once saw Alex praying when he thought nobody was lookin' and why do you think I smoke so much? So you've wet the bed, it could be any of us tomorrow night. There was a bloke I went through basic training with who wet the bed every time he got drunk and he didn't give a damn about it. Mind you, it pissed the rest of us in the billet off no end." He saw a hint of a smile on Jimmy's face. "You've saved our lives at least twice now, and yer too good an engineer to lose, you've got to keep going, what's the alternative? Are yer going to go AWOL, or refuse to fly? They'll send yer LMF if yer do, then what would Mary think?" For a second he thought he'd gone too far. The mention of Mary brought a far off look to Jimmy's eyes and another couple of tears rolled down his face.

"But I have nightmares."

"We all do, lad, it's nothin' unusual, yer could even say it's natural."

"But mine is always the same." At this George stopped and looked at Jimmy, remembering his own personal nightmare which visited him most nights, and his hair tingled. After what seemed like a long pause Jimmy continued. "We're flying along and I look behind Doug's seat at the port engines and they're both on fire. The flames are covering the wings and flying back over the top of the fuselage as far as I can see. I can't even see the upper turret. Everything is bright red and yellow and I reach for my parachute but it's not there. I fumble around but I can't find it and Doug's yelling at me to bale out and I know he won't go until I do and I can't find my chute." Jimmy's voice was getting higher as he relived the nightmare and the panic rose in him with the vivid pictures before his mind's eye.

"It's alright," soothed George, trying to calm him down.

"It's not alright. Doug will stay until I bale out and if I can't find my chute he'll die because of me!"

"But it's just a dream, Jimmy lad, it's all in yer head."

"But if it did happen? I don't want to let anybody down."

"Of course yer don't and yer won't, but yer have to keep goin', there's no other way out. Yer've seen engines on fire and it's scared yer, of course it has. Yer'd be mad if yer weren't scared, but just because it's happened before doesn't mean it's goin' to happen again. Yer'll only let us down if yer make us go on without yer. But I know you, Jimmy Wilson, and you won't let any of us down."

Jimmy opened his mouth to continue, but what was the use? George wasn't going to let him give up. He looked over at the defiant little man who was a foot shorter than him.

"How am I going to face them?" He jerked his head towards the billet.

"They don't ever need to know, bonny lad." George smiled looking at his watch.

"But they'll see and smell it."

"It's six o'clock, they won't wake us till late morning at the earliest. You get dressed and take yer blankets over to the laundry now and you'll probably have them back before the rest of us are up."

"But what about the smell and the wet mattress?"

"A diversion for the smell," said George, picking up an empty paint tin that had been left in the ablution block and pouring a pint of water into it. "And I'll light the stove before we leave the billet, you hang back and when everybody's gone put yer mattress next to the stove to dry. Then all yer have to do is be sure to get back before anyone else to put it back on yer bed when it's dry. That shouldn't be too difficult as yer the only one with a motorbike."

Back in the billet Jimmy dressed, rolled up his blankets and left for the laundry while George lay in bed smoking another cigarette and blowing the smoke towards Jimmy's mattress, which he had turned over so the wet side was on the bottom. After a while he drifted back off to sleep.

He was woken by the duty corporal shaking his feet.

"Ten o'clock, report to the Squadron Office for 11.30. Christ, it stinks in here, has somebody pissed themselves?"

Jimmy was sitting on the edge of his bed looking at George. His blankets were back and looked dry.

"Go and get washed and shaved," said George, wanting him out of the way. As soon as Jimmy had gone George swung his feet over the side of his bed and kicked over the paint tin.

"Aw hell!" he exclaimed, as the tin clattered over spilling water over the floor.

"What?" asked Bob, from his bed opposite George's.

"I've just kicked me bloody piss pot over."

"Aw shit, you haven't, have you? Christ, it smells like a sewer."

"Ya clumsy Geordie twat, that's goin' tae stink for days," said Alex.

"Well, pass us yer kilt and I'll wipe it up and nobody will be able to tell the difference," replied George defensively.

"We've all got to live in here you know," said someone from further down the billet.

"Alright, go and get washed and shaved. I'll clean it up and light a fire to dry the place out."

By the time the other occupants of the billet had got back George had mopped up the water and lit the stove.

"It still stinks in here," said one of Digger's crew.

"Well, there's not a lot I can bloody do about that, is there?" asked George aggressively enough to put a stop to any other comments, unless they wanted to risk getting physical. By 10.30 all the sergeants had left the hut to go for breakfast, leaving Jimmy to dry his mattress and George to get shaved. Fifteen minutes later, with George on pillion, Jimmy rode his motorbike to the mess for breakfast, arriving just after all the other sergeants.

11.25 saw all the sergeants arrive at the Squadron Office just as Doug and Ron were riding up on their bikes. A slight breeze had picked up since dawn and lifted the mist off the ground to form a continuous grey mass of cloud low overhead.

"Morning," said Doug, but his voice lacked its usual enthusiasm and he looked pale with deep red sunken eyes.

"Are you okay, skipper?" asked Bob.

"Yes, I'm just tired that's all." And he hurried into the Squadron Office, followed by the rest of his crew.

Inside Nigel looked up as they entered.

"Ah! Good morning! I hear you had some difficulty finding the ground last night. Still I suppose I should be grateful that you brought the kite back in one piece this time." Then he noticed Doug, but decided not to tell him he looked ghastly and moved straight on to business.

"You're on Ops again tonight. Specialist briefings at 14.00, main briefing at 15.00. Any problems?" This last comment was to the crew in general but aimed at Ron. Ron glared back at him but said nothing.

"I'm afraid there's no MT this morning so you'll have to do without the services of the delectable Sally. All the drivers are busy fitting snowploughs to their trucks; we're expecting bad weather in the next few days. Still you've got your bikes. See you at the briefing."

"Can we still operate with snow on the ground?" asked George, hoping the answer would be no and Doug and Jimmy could have a rest.

238

"That depends on how deep it is and how long we have to clear it. I dare say the Station Commander will not let a little thing like the elements put his station non-operational. He'll probably have you all out with shovels before that happens," smiled Nigel.

"I can't shovel snow," said Harry, as they left the office. "I've got a bad back."

"The only thing wrong with your back is yer can't get it out a bed in the morning," replied George.

"Well, pardon me, Your Highness, just because you're getting chauffeured around on a motorbike today. But just you remember, I knew you when you didn't have a pot to piss in." George blushed, Jimmy went quiet and the other three sergeants roared with laughter while Doug and Ron looked confused.

Jimmy rode slowly round the perimeter track to F for Freddy, trying to make his petrol go as far as possible, although he had already set up an arrangement with Sally. One bar of chocolate for one gallon of petrol, smuggled from MT. While some girls wouldn't do absolutely anything for a bar of chocolate, they would still do quite a lot.

Even so they arrived well ahead of the rest of the crew, pulling up beside the ground crew shack with Sergeant Green standing, as usual, in the doorway with his mug of tea.

"Morning, lads. She's all ready for you. Bombed and fuelled up and she's been rearmed. All that's left to do is load the window and that hasn't been delivered yet."

"Right," replied Jimmy. "Is the 700 ready?"

"Does Hitler only have one ball?" asked Sergeant Green, holding the canvas flap of a door to one side to allow them to enter the hut.

Jimmy ran through the 700 while George warmed his hands over the primus stove that always seemed to be lit on the hut's packing case table. Then they made their way over to Freddy as the rest of the crew rode up.

"Listen, George, I'm really grateful," Jimmy began as they got to the aircraft. The others were still parking their bikes at the edge of the dispersal and George cut in and stopped him.

"We're a crew, Jimmy, we help each other. Someday you'll probably have to help me. Are you okay now?"

"Yes, I think so but I'm still terrified."

"Yer not alone there, bonny lad." He winked as they walked under Freddy's bomb bay and looked up at the bomb load. "That makes a change," he said. "Nine 1,000 pounders as well as the Cookie."

"Yes, 13,000 pounds of bombs. The loads are getting heavier all the time," replied Jimmy.

"That's more like it," exclaimed Bob, walking up with the rest of the crew. "Plenty of high explosives. Why burn their houses down when you can blow them to bits?"

"You're a bloodthirsty bugger, aren't yer?" said George, walking down the length of the bomb bay checking the bombs. "I'm surprised yer don't empty yer revolver at them out of the front hatch when we're over the target."

Behind them there was a metallic ping overhead and they turned just in time to see one of the 1,000 pounders fall from its carrier and crash onto the dispersal concrete. For five seconds time stood still while they all stared at the large menacing parcel of explosive lying beside them. Harry was closest to the bomb. When it fell it had missed him by inches and now he stood mutely staring at it, his face white and his mouth open.

"Bob, was that one a delayed action?" asked Doug.

"They all were."

"How long were the delays?"

"Twelve to twenty-four hours."

"Sod that I'm out a here," said George, starting to run towards the edge of the dispersal. Before he reached it Alex and Jimmy had overtaken him and were well on their way towards a new 100-yard dash record, while the rest of the crew were close behind.

Sergeant Green heard the clatter and got to the hut doorway just in time to see the bomb lying under Freddy and the crew running across the airfield like a herd of startled gazelles.

"Oh shit," he said under his breath.

"What is it, sarge?" asked one of the ground crew, without getting out of his chair by the primus.

"Looks like a 1,000 pounder's fallen off and our brave heroes are going to get help," he replied sarcastically.

"Those bloody armourers, I thought they were rushing it. They're all delayed reactions, aren't they?"

"Yeah, twelve to twenty-fours, so even if the acetone is broken, if it hasn't gone off yet it's not going to go off for at least twelve hours. All the same I'll have to get the Squadron Armaments Officer out." He went to the field telephone in the corner of the hut and made the call.

British delayed action bombs used a fusing pistol containing acetone ampoules. When the bomb was dropped the propeller in the nose turned a crusher inside the fuse, which crushed the acetone ampoules releasing the acetone. This would then start to eat away at an acetone disc and when this had been eaten away it allowed a striker to move forward detonating the bomb. The length of delay was governed by the thickness of the acetone disc and the strength of the acetone. The bomb falling from Freddy would probably have broken at least some of the glass ampoules and in time the bomb would go off, but not for a few hours.

After 400 yards the crew came to a breathless wheezing halt and turned to look back at Freddy. "Is this far enough?" asked Jimmy.

"Probably not," said Bob.

"What are we going to do now?" asked Alex. They all looked at Doug.

Doug didn't have a clue what they should do and was starting to feel foolish at having run away in the first place because the ground crew were all still standing in the doorway of the hut looking over at them. He had only run because the rest of them had. How was he supposed to know what to do?

"We'll walk to the south side of the perimeter track and see what happens."

Slowly they walked to the track, their boots and trousers splashed with mud from the wet grass. To their right a motorcycle came around the track from the technical site. When it got close to them it slowed down and Doug was surprised to see the rider was sitting side-saddle. As the bike passed them it went into a turn to circle them on the wide concrete.

"Can't stop!" yelled the rider. "The clutch cable's broken! I'd wait here if I were you. A bomb's just fallen off F for Freddy!"

"No shit! It just bloody missed me!" replied Harry who had only just regained his voice.

"That was lucky!" yelled the rider as he rode off.

"It's the sort of luck I can do without," said Harry.

They stood and watched the motorcyclist get to Freddy and jump off his bike to let it crash on the grass by the edge of the dispersal. Then he walked up to the bomb, inspected it for a few minutes, turned and talked to Sergeant Green before getting back on his bike and riding back towards them.

"It's a delayed action!" he yelled, as he circled them again. "We'll put it back on!"

"But won't it be armed now?" asked Bob.

"Probably, but it won't go off for at least twelve hours, so as long as you don't bring it back it will be fine!" With that he waved and rode off.

"Who was that?" asked Doug.

"The Squadron Armaments Officer," replied Bob.

"He's bloody mad," said Harry.

"As a hatter," agreed Bob.

"We sit on tons of high explosive after he's had his hands on it?" said Alex.

"And now he wants us to sit on an armed delayed action bomb," added George.

"Well, he must know what he's doing," said Doug.

"Are you sure about that?" asked Ron.

They walked back along the perimeter track to Freddy's dispersal where Sergeant Green met them.

"That was a bit exciting for you, wasn't it?" he smiled.

Doug tried not to blush. "Yes, a little, I believe they're going to fix it back on."

"That's right, sir. But you'll have time for your ground checks before then. Just don't close the bomb doors."

Walking out to Freddy behind the rest of the crew George was amused to see they all walked in a large circle around the bomb lying on the concrete. Pulling himself up the short ladder into the rear fuselage he was met by the usual aircraft smell of paint, oil and petrol. The light green walls were damp with condensation and he turned to his left and headed towards the light coming from the rear turret. The oval frames around the inside of the fuselage always reminded him of ribs, as if he was in the belly of a great fish. Jonah and the whale, he scoffed to himself. Just above floor level on either side of him were the troughs carrying the long belts of .303-inch bullets to his four Brownings from the magazines either side on the fuselage above the rear of the bomb bay. Six feet aft of the entrance door, in the dark interior, was the circular tube of the Elsan toilet and immediately behind that the floor rose two feet over the tailplane carry through. From here he would have to crawl to the small double rear fuselage doors, which had been left open to let light into the rest of the fuselage. Squeezing through the doors he crawled the last three feet to his turret. Twisting around he sat on the cold damp metal and sliding his feet out in front of him, slid into the turret. Once in he squirmed himself comfortable on the thin foam sponge cushion and reached behind him to slide the twin black turret doors shut. They were pivoted behind his shoulders and curved to form the rear of the turret when they were shut. With both doors shut the catch behind his right shoulder clicked and he was secure in the turret. Now he pulled his flying helmet from the inside of his battle dress and slid it on. Feeling behind his right shoulder he located the intercom lead and plugged it in. His oxygen tube plugged in between his knees and he checked the oxygen contents gauge, which was in the same place. To his left was where the electrical lead that powered his heated suit was plugged in, but he didn't bother wearing that for ground checks. The intercom crackled as Harry turned it on. Doug and Jimmy must have finished their external checks by now and nearly be ready to start engines, he thought, as he looked through the turret Perspex at the grey overcast sky. The clouds looked higher now, the fresh breeze lifting them away from the surface. As usual, the Perspex of the turret was spotless and there were no signs of any hydraulic leaks. He unlocked the turret and tried the manual controls. The turret moved smoothly and freely, but much more slowly and with much more effort than when there was power applied to it. A hydraulic pump in the port outer engine powered the rear turret and until this engine was started George couldn't carry out any more of his turret checks. His reflector sight also looked in good condition, but until one of the inboard engines was started he wouldn't turn it on because the change from ground to air power could cause a power spike and blow the bulb. The turret was small but so was George and he didn't feel too cramped in it, although it was much worse in his bulky suit. The four guns were slightly more than shoulder width apart, two on each side, mounted one just above the other with their breeches about a foot in front of his shoulders. Between his feet and rising between his knees was the control column with the handgrip turret controls and triggers on the top. Hydraulic pipes and electrical wires ran down the control column and back under his seat. The control grips were at 45 degrees to the horizontal at chest height and George's hands rested naturally on them with his elbows bent at 90 degrees.

"Check in front to back ready for engine start," crackled Doug's voice over the intercom. One by one they checked in ready, then after a pause the number three engine whirled and fired. The vibrations travelled down the fuselage and shook the rear turret. Each time another engine started there was a subtle change to the vibration. The port outer would be the last engine started so George waited patiently. His checks would not take long.

He opened each of the four breech covers on his Brownings and removed the ammunition belts. Then closing the breeches he cocked each gun in turn, checking the breech was empty as he did so. When he finished he felt the fourth engine start and settle down to a steady tick over. As it did power was applied to his turret and he heard the hydraulic pressure increase. He waited a few seconds then pulled slowly back on the right hand grip. The pivot on the top of the control column meant that as he did this the left grip went forwards, just like bicycle handlebars and the turret slowly turned to the right. The more George pulled back the faster the turret rotated until at 90 degrees it hit the stops and stopped. George repeated the exercise to the left, and then rotated the turret as fast as he could in both directions.

Then he checked there was nothing that would snag on the breeches of the guns and elevated and depressed the guns at different rates, the rear ends of the guns moving up and down outside of his forearms. Next he pulled the right trigger and heard the double click as the firing pins flew forwards into the empty breeches of the two right-hand guns, then he repeated it with the left. He rotated the turret in both directions at different speeds, while at the same time elevating and depressing the guns to check full and free movement in all planes before leaving the turret pointing directly aft with the guns horizontal and turning on his gun sight. The sight was fixed to a horizontal tubular bar. This in turn was fixed to two vertical bars, just inboard of the guns. The four guns were pivoted on these bars for elevation, as was the gun sight. Because the vertical bars held the considerable weight of the four guns they in turn were supported by more tubular bars, which went from level with the top of the hand grips at 45 degrees back behind George to anchor points at the back of the turret. Many rear gunners felt they were in a tubular bar cage, but George didn't mind that. He knew as long as he kept his elbows inside the bars he wouldn't trap himself with his own guns, as had happened to many gunners, some being seriously injured. After losing a finger to heavy machinery in the dark of a coal mine George had a healthy respect for the powerful hydraulics of the turret.

Now George adjusted the brightness of the sight so that the red ring and spot were hardly visible. Then, seeing a truck driving around the perimeter track he swung the turret onto it and tracked it along the road, the red dot steady on the driver's cab. The turret moved smoothly and he was very pleased with it. He did a quick check of his oxygen, and then leaving the turret pointing aft, he turned off the sight, reloaded the guns and sat patiently waiting for everyone else to finish their checks. Eventually the engines throttled back and Doug asked if anyone had any problems. There were none and while the engines were shut down George reached behind his right shoulder and released the catch on the turret doors, slid them open and disconnecting his oxygen and intercom leads climbed backwards out of the turret.

Climbing down the ladder out of Freddy, with Alex close behind him, George walked towards the ground crew.

"Any faults, sarge?"

"No, lads, it all seems fine. I've still got one in five tracer in the top two guns and armour piercing de Wilde mix in the other two, haven't I?" Like most gunners he was fanatical about the type of ammunition he used. George thought the one tracer bullet in every five for the top two guns was good to indicate how close his fire was to a target that he wasn't yet hitting. This would give a pair of tracer rounds every quarter second, enough to show him where his fire was going, but not enough to blind him. The other two guns had an equal mix of armour piercing bullets, to punch through any armour plate the German night fighters might have, and the de Wilde bullets were incendiary bullets, to set them on fire. The added advantage of the de Wilde bullets was that they gave off a bright orange flash when they hit something, so once you were on target you could see exactly where you were hitting. The ground crew assured George that his ammunition was just as he liked it. Then Alex asked them the same question about his guns. Because he only had two guns, he used a different mix. The rest of the crew were all climbing out of Freddy now and they all seemed satisfied that the Lancaster was on top line.

"Right," said Doug. "Back to the Squadron Office to report in and see if they need us for anything else."

Jimmy and George rode slowly back to the Squadron Office, but were still well ahead of everyone else when they pulled up outside.

"We'll wait outside," said George. "And hang back when we all go in. That way we'll be the first out when they clear us off and we can get back to the billet with plenty of time to square everything away."

When the rest of the crew caught them up they were just finishing their cigarettes and this gave them the excuse to be the last two into the office. Doug reported Freddy fully serviceable and as expected the Adj cleared them off until their specialist briefings at 14.00. Jimmy and George left the office with suspicious haste and roared off on Jimmy's Triumph. By the time the other sergeants got to the billet Jimmy and George had replaced Jimmy's mattress and tidied everything up so that nobody would ever know about Jimmy's accident.

Because of the incident with the bomb they were slightly later than usual and it was already 12.45 and their flying meal would start at 13.00. They just had time to pull on their long johns and heavy woollen sweaters under their battle dress before going to the mess. George was glad there wasn't much time. He hated hanging around and he had noticed how Jimmy constantly looked at his watch when he had nothing to do and George didn't want him to have any time to think before this trip.

In the mess the aircrew meal was the usual bacon and eggs and the sergeant chef gave George the usual hate filled stare, but said nothing as George dipped his dry bread in the bacon fat in the bottom of the tray. While after only four Ops they were certainly not veterans, now they all knew the routine and so didn't stand out from the crowd as new boys. George looked around the other tables in the dining room; it was easy to spot the crew that was going on its first trip tonight. They were looking around their new surroundings nervously and were obviously unsure of themselves. George felt sorry for them; they still had the great unknown ahead of them.

But if they made it back, the next time he saw them in the dining room before an Op they would stand out a lot less and the time after that they would go unnoticed in the crowd. The surroundings would be familiar to them, the meal routine. They would just be one more crew on the Squadron, but inside, they would have changed forever. Each one of them would react to Ops in a different way. They would all feel the pressure and the fear, but some would cope better than others. Their bodies would react differently; their minds finding different ways to fight the fear.

George found it interesting how different people reacted to the stress of Ops. Somebody had once told him it had nothing to do with the common perception of bravery. A person was generally considered to be brave because of one or two distinct, significant acts. Like Harry coming to help him get out of the ditched Lancaster that could have sunk and drowned them both at any time. But while Harry's action was no doubt brave, it had been a spur of the moment instinctive thing, which happened so fast Harry would have had little time to think about it. It said a lot about Harry, that his instinct was to risk his life for his friends, but it was a completely different sort of bravery that was required to keep men flying dangerous bomber Ops night after night. That was not instinctive or spur of the moment. You had a long time to think about what you were about to do and it was far more wearing on the nerves. This however, was not really considered to be bravery; it was just your duty, what was expected of you.

George thought that in reality it took more bravery just to fly Op after Op than to do one or two instinctive brave acts. The fear eats away at your nerves, he thought. The bravest man in the world will crack up eventually, if he carries on long enough. Someone had once described it to him as courage being water in a bucket and Ops being a hole in the bucket. Eventually all the water will run out and you'll crack up. Some people start with more water in their bucket than others, but it will still run out eventually. You could have some scary trips and some close shaves and that would make the hole in your bucket bigger. You could go on leave or be rested and that would top up the level of the water, but the hole would still be there, draining your courage away.

The physical signs of the stress were also interesting and numerous. George had noticed how many of the more experienced crews had nervous twitches. Nothing big, just the occasional movement at the corner of the eye or mouth. In his own crew Harry always talked more before an Op and right now he was chattering away so quickly nobody else could get a word in. George was sure Ron was far more airsick now than he used to be and poor Jimmy wet the bed. He hoped that it had been a one off or it would tear Jimmy apart. Jimmy was a kind, quiet and sensitive bloke and not cut out for this sort of thing, thought George. But if he cracked up, through no fault of his own other than not being the right temperament for Ops, he would be sent LMF and have his life torn apart. As for himself, he smiled, his personal nemesis was his fear of drowning, which gripped him like an ice-cold hand round his throat and tormented his sleep every night.

But surprisingly, Ops didn't bother him that much. He knew that as a rear gunner he stood even less chance than most of surviving a tour, but he had come to terms with it. So long as it was quick and he didn't drown he accepted that there was nothing he could do about it and what would happen would happen. His body on the other hand didn't agree with this and since the ditching George had been plagued with diarrhoea. It had eased during his leave but as soon as he had come back to the Squadron it had returned. He hadn't mentioned it to anyone and hadn't been to see the doc. But now, looking around the table he wondered how many of the others were suffering from minor ailments that had never bothered them before. He looked around at them. Alex, Bob and Harry were outwardly the same as always, but who could tell what lay beneath? Jimmy was quiet, as usual, but was listening to Harry telling yet another story, rather than withdrawing into himself, which was good. Wouldn't it be great if we all got through this in one piece? he thought. Well, night fighters shoot down most bombers and to get into position they've got to get past me.

As usual the gunners' specialist briefing finished first and George and Alex found themselves waiting in the cold outside the main briefing room for the rest of their crew. George saw little point in the gunners having a specialist briefing because apart from occasional snippets of intelligence information about the German night fighters and their tactics there was very little to be said. Today however, had been different. There was an unsubstantiated report that the Germans now had night fighters with upward firing cannons. This had set all the gunners talking. A night fighter with upward firing cannons could fly directly below a bomber and fire up into its unprotected belly, without being seen or shot at. If the Germans really did have upward firing cannons it would be a nightmare for the bombers. For weeks now there had been talk among the gunners of new turrets, with heavy half-inch machine guns that could knock chunks off even the heaviest armoured night fighter. There was even talk of radar directed turrets that could shoot down night fighters that the gunner couldn't yet see. But if the Germans had upward firing cannons there would be no point to any of these, because the Germans would be in the bomber's only blind spot and immune.

"Well, a canae see it masel," said Alex.

"Why not?" asked George. "They would be easy enough to fit and the pilot would just have to look straight up through his canopy to aim them."

"The main danger," said one of the other Squadron gunners, "would be if he shot straight into the bomb bay. He would blow himself up with the bomber."

"That does nae mak me feel any better," replied Alex.

"During the last war we had night fighters with upward firing guns for use against Zeppelins, so it's nothing new," said another gunner.

"Shooting from directly below we're a massive target and because we can't see him he can take all the time he needs and shoot straight into our fuel tanks or engines," said George.

"So what do we do about it?" asked another gunner.

"We need turrets that can shoot downwards," said another. "Like the Yanks have on their Flying Fortresses and Liberators."

"Where would we put it?" asked yet another gunner. "We're all bomb bay and H2S underneath, there's no space."

"You could get rid of the H2S scanner and fit a turret instead."

"The navs would never allow that. And it would mean an end to blind bombing."

"You could put the turret behind the bomb bay and move the H2S back a bit."

"But then you'd have tae get rid o the mid upper turret," said Alex. "And who'd spot the Wild Boars comin' in on ya from above when we're over the target then?"

"You could put the mid upper turret further forward over the bomb bay," offered another gunner.

"You could rebuild the whole bloody aeroplane from scratch! But they won't do it!" said George. "The question is what are we goin' to do about these upward firing guns with what we have at the moment?"

There was a long pause before one of the older and most experienced gunners who hadn't spoken yet said, "All you can do is keep as good a lookout as you can and weave as much as possible so you can look nearly straight down from the mid upper turret."

"That's not ideal," said one of the new boys.

"Ideally we wouldn't be at war," replied the old hand.

Group by group the other crew specialities had arrived and joined their crews until they were all present and the briefing room doors were opened. George sat with the rest of the crew in their usual seats as the buzz about the new upward firing cannons spread around the room until they were called to attention for the start of the briefing. The briefing followed the usual format and the only surprise for George was the target, which was Leipzig. George was so used to going to Berlin he had almost forgotten there were other targets in Germany, but of course he thought, we can't hit the big city every night or the Germans will always know where we're going. As far as George was concerned one target was much the same as another. He didn't know anything about Leipzig and he didn't care, but what he had noticed was that Leipzig wasn't quite as far as Berlin, which had to be better. The route was again a southerly one. Out over the North Sea at Lowestoft, into Belgium, turning left onto east south of Liege, where there was known to be heavy flak. Skirting the bottom of the Ruhr until north of Koblenz, where they turned northeast towards Kassel, then just before they got there they turned east again direct to Leipzig. The route home was northwest, jinking around the built up areas, until they crossed back out into the North Sea west of Wilhelmshaven and once out of German radar cover turning west for home. George copied down in his notebook the times for crossing the coasts and turning points. He also noted the main towns and areas of flak and approximate times at these places. He had smoked a cigarette while waiting outside the briefing room, another as he noted down the route details and now was on his third as the specialists started their summing up. His throat was dry and the smoke was irritating it so that he was desperately trying to stifle a coughing fit and he could feel his face getting redder and redder with the effort. Most of the details of the briefing didn't concern him; as far as George was concerned other members of the crew were the brains, he was just a set of eyes. But even as just a set of eyes he had to know what to expect to see and when.

The briefing broke up into the individual crew planning and George exploded into his fit of coughing.

"You need tae cut down on the cigarettes, laddie, they'll kill yer if yer not careful," said Alex.

"If you can guarantee that it'll be the cigarettes that kill me I'll be a happy man," croaked George.

The crews started to drift out to the crew room to kit up and soon Freddy's crew joined them. In the crew room it was the usual crowded scramble. George emptied his pockets into his locker but kept his cigarettes and lighter. Then he took two rubber bands and held them in his mouth while he pulled on two pairs of thick socks then struggled into his heated suit. The suit was made from the same material as an electric blanket and was as stiff as cardboard. Over this he pulled a heavy rubberised buoyancy suit. Alex helped him into it and then George helped Alex on with his. Once inside the suit George paused to get his breath back, and tried to stop himself sweating.

"If you don't stop smoking those killer fags, George, you're not even going to be able to get dressed for an Op," bantered Harry.

"You should try them, Harry, it says on the packet that they stop you talking bollocks," retorted George.

"I wouldn't if I were you, Harry," said Bob. "They obviously stunt your growth."

"Aye," said Alex. "Yer might disappear altogether."

Now George pulled on his heavy flying boots and did up the zips at the front. The zip of the buoyancy suit was the next obstacle, which, if you tried to do it up yourself, usually turned into a kind of solo wrestling match. So George tried to hold his suit tight while Alex pulled up the zip, and then George pulled up Alex's zip for him. The trick seemed to be to take your time and not to fight the suit; that way you didn't sweat as much. Now, with the suit on, George pulled on his left thin, inner, leather glove followed by his heated glove, then finally his heavy leather gauntlet. Now he took one of the rubber bands from his mouth and bending the glove's empty second finger over the stump of his amputated finger he used the rubber band to secure it out of the way. Next, using the second rubber band, he secured the page of noted route times that he had torn from his note pad to his left sleeve. Finally, he adjusted his watch so that it sat comfortably over his inner and heated gloves but under the high wristlet of the gauntlet, where he could see it if he needed to. Pulling on his three right hand gloves and picking up his flying helmet he was now finished at his locker. Locking the door, he went to the crew room counter. The airman took one look at his ball-shaped figure and knowing he was a gunner handed him a Mae West life jacket and a chest parachute and harness.

"Do you want a gun?" he asked.

"No thanks, it's dangerous enough without one," George replied.

As usual, George and Alex were the last two to arrive at Sally's wagon, which looked strangely agricultural with its massive snowplough blade fitted. George pulled an envelope from a pocket of his buoyancy suit.

"Same routine, bonny lass."

"Same routine, sarge." She smiled as she took the envelope.

The first shades of night were falling and the sun was only just visible above the horizon, but the sky was clear as they drove around the perimeter track. As usual, now that Ron was with them, they sat in silence. Or was it that they were now thinking of what lay head? Suddenly the wagon's brakes screeched and they jerked to a stop.

"Sorry," called Sally, as they climbed out. "I can't get used to the weight of the snowplough on the front wheels."

Doug and Jimmy went to check the 700 while the rest of them walked straight to Freddy, calling insulting comments about women drivers back to Sally, as they went. George and Alex were bringing up the rear.

"It's always the bloody same," said George. "I get all this kit on and then I want to take a leak."

"Do you not think it might be your age?" asked Harry.

"You want ta watch yer lip, young un," said George, as he put down his Mae West, parachute and harness next to Freddy's tail and started to search through his layers of clothing.

"Like looking for a needle in a haystack," said Bob, while he climbed aboard.

Harry stood by the door and helped Alex scramble into his Mae West and parachute harness before climbing the ladder.

"I don't know," he said, as George started to anoint the tailwheel. "You have the whole airfield and you piss on our bloody aeroplane!"

"It's lucky," George replied.

"Not for the tailwheel," said Harry, disappearing inside.

"Weak bladder?" asked Alex, climbing the ladder.

"There's nothing weak about my bladder. I reckon I could hit you from here!" But before he could prove it Alex took the hint and ducked inside. When he had finished George adjusted his dress and struggled into his Mae West. Then he expertly flicked his parachute harness over his shoulders and clipped the upper straps into place before reaching between his knees to do up the lower straps. When he was happy that all was done up and adjusted, he picked up his parachute pack and climbed inside. With the heavy clothing on everything seemed half the size and twice the effort as he crawled down to the tail turret pushing his parachute in front of him. On the left hand side of the fuselage between the fuselage rear doors and the entrance doors to the tail turret was the rear gunner's parachute stowage. George slid his parachute pack in and fastened the retaining strap across it. Then he squirmed round so that he was sitting feet towards the tail and slid into his turret. He shuffled himself comfortable and fumbled for the leads to his heated suit and intercom. Once located he plugged them in and reaching round behind his shoulders slid the turret rear doors shut. Finally he connected and turned on his oxygen. He was now cut off in his own little world, far away from the rest of the crew with his only contact through the intercom.

Doug and Jimmy had walked past, doing their external checks while he was settling into his turret. Now the intercom crackled to life and Doug asked if they were ready for engine start. The crew all checked in and one by one the engines were started. The gunner's heated suits were powered from either of the two generators, one on each inboard engine. Soon after the number three engine fired George felt the suit start to heat up. The suits were supposed to be thermostatically controlled, but the thermostats frequently failed and the suits were often either off or on. George turned his off; he would turn it on again later, when he really needed it. As the number one engine fired George's turret came to life and he carried out the same checks as he had earlier that day. Then the engines were throttled back and after a pause they started to move forward. A quick check of the brakes and they were out onto the taxiway and heading for the runway, with other Lancasters coming up behind them.

It was now well into dusk and the other aircraft had their navigation lights on, so George reached down between his knees and turned on the white tail-light. Now he looked to his left to see if the two boys were sitting on the gate to wave them off. Yes, they were there and George waved back and dipped his guns at them. Then they stopped, they must be in the queue to take off, he thought. The other Lancasters closed up to them and stopped. The bomb aimer of the Lancaster behind waved at him. George realised that it was the crew on their first Op. He'll learn, thought George. Bob was not in the nose, he was behind the main spar. Quickly George slipped off his right-hand gloves and rummaged around in a pocket of his buoyancy suit, popped a Wakey Wakey pill into his mouth and replaced his gloves. It was highly unlikely that they would be scrubbed now. After half a dozen moves forward Doug asked if everyone was ready and taxied onto the runway. They lined up, there was a pause, then the engines roared and with a slight jerk they were off. The white lines moved away from under him as the speed increased. The sky behind them was clear and he could just make out Sally waving them off.

"30!" said Ron.

The vibrations of the straining engines ran through the fuselage and he could feel the rumble from the tailwheel. Then the rumble stopped and he felt the tail lift.

"Tail up!" he called. Now he was bobbing up and down slightly as Doug held Freddy level and swinging from side to side as Doug fought to keep them straight and on the runway centreline.

"60!"

He could see the next Lancaster already taxiing onto the runway as the lines raced away from him quicker all the time.

"90!" He guessed that they were about two thirds of the way down the runway now.

"100!" Anytime now he should feel them lift.

"105!" Very slowly the ground dropped away from him, and then stayed about twenty feet below him. Suddenly the runway was gone and they were over grass, then the Martin village road, then a brown ploughed field and slowly climbing away. George reached down and turned off the tail-light to signal that they were clear of the runway and on their way.

14

Not long after crossing the Wash Freddy reached 10,000 feet and they all went onto oxygen. It was now below freezing in the rear turret, but under his layers of clothes George was still comfortable. Only breathing the cold oxygen brought on a brief shiver, but his body soon adjusted to it. By the time they approached Lowestoft they were nearing 20,000 feet and the temperature had now dropped to minus 25 degrees centigrade. It was completely dark now, but the bombers still had their navigation lights on, so they were easy to see and avoid. It was a clear night with no cloud cover and thousands of stars twinkled brightly above them. There was no moon and while it looked a bright night above them and the ground stood out well below, it was difficult to tell how far you could see horizontally. Twice George had had to call the position of bombers to Doug because they strayed too close, but there was never any real risk of a collision. As they crossed the coast however, they would all turn off their lights and the risk of collision would increase enormously. George lifted the wristlet of his gauntlet and looked at the luminous dial of his watch. Two minutes to the coast, he thought. The cold was just starting to seep through his clothes and he considered turning on his heated suit, but decided to leave it a little while yet.

"Crossing the coast at Lowestoft now," said Bob.

"Roger," replied Ron. "On track, on time."

"Roger," acknowledged Doug.

The dark blacked-out land of East Anglia slowly drifted away behind them, giving way to the silvery edged darkness of the North Sea. Behind Freddy George watched the red and green pin pricks of the bombers' navigation lights one by one disappearing as they crossed the coast. Now was when he really started to earn his pay. Keeping a good lookout from an aircraft is not a natural thing, it has to be taught and practised. It was a major part of air gunner training and George now fell into the routine, which had become second nature. Quartering the sky, first he started in his top left quarter and scanned his eyes through that quarter left to right, right to left from top to bottom. He concentrated on the corners of his eyes, which are more sensitive to light, shade and movement. This was where he was most likely to spot other aircraft at night. Looking directly at the area you are trying to search you are using the part of your eye that is sensitive to colour and that is not much use at night, when everything is black or shades of grey. When he had scanned the first quarter he moved to the top right quarter, or Freddy's 6 to 9 o'clock high position, and repeated the search there. Then he searched the bottom left and finally the bottom right. After one complete scan he paused for a second and then gave the whole area a quick once over scan. The pause was vital. If the eyes have nothing to focus on, as is the case on a dark night or in cloud or fog, after a while the eye muscles will relax into their natural position and without realising it your eyes will be focused at a point about six inches in front of your face. Anything further away, like a night fighter at 400 yards, will be blurred and invisible. When he had finished his all over scan he started again in the top left, and so it went on.

"Level at 20,000 feet," said Doug.

Now George's feet were cold and it was starting to creep through his gloves too, so he switched on his heated suit and felt it start to heat up. They were now well away from the coast.

"Permission to test guns, skipper?"

"Carry on."

George reached forward and pulled back the four cocking handles, checked the safety catches were off, and looking through his reflector sight he eased the brightness of the already barely visible ring and bead down a little more. Then looking through the sight he turned his turret fully right and depressing the guns all the way, he gave both triggers a brief squeeze. Even above the constant droning roar of the Merlins the short staccato rattle of the four Brownings was deafening. Blue flashes came from the sides of the guns as the cocking handles flew back and forth and small yellow flashes, which were soon swallowed in the darkness, decorated the muzzles. Four red tracer rounds raced off into the night, to be dowsed in the dark waters below. As he finished he felt the vibration and short rattle of Alex's guns and a few seconds later Bob's in the front turret.

"Rear turret fully serviceable."

"Mid-upper fully serviceable."

"Front turret likewise."

"Roger," replied Doug.

Well, that's that excitement over with, thought George, returning to the drudgery of quartering the blackness. Now he was suffering from what appeared to be Freddy's only fault. His electric suit was getting hotter and hotter. He had reported it before but despite all the ground crew's efforts they had not been able to locate the fault or fix it. So now George was in the unusual position of being probably the only gunner in Bomber Command that was too hot. It was especially true of his feet, which were now so hot it was beginning to hurt and he had to turn off his suit. He glanced at his watch, five minutes to the enemy coast. Back to the search, a dark shape caught his eye in their level 4 o'clock. As he looked at it, it disappeared, but in the corner of his eye it was still there. George gave it two seconds of assessment before being certain it was a bomber at about 400 yards and no threat. After completing a scan it was still there and now at about 300 yards, back to the scan. One minute and another scan later the bomber was at 200 yards and clearly a Lancaster.

"Skipper, rear gunner, there's a Lancaster 200 yards in our 4 o'clock. He's been there a while but he's closing in and I don't think he's seen us. Can we climb fifty feet?"

"Wilco, George."

Freddy eased into a slow climb while the other Lancaster continued to slowly approach. George continued his scan, keeping one eye on the other bomber until it slid majestically out of sight fifty feet directly below them.

"Ten miles to the enemy coast," said Ron.

"Roger, starting to drop window," said Bob.

Now Freddy smoothly went into a left turn and George took advantage of this to take a good look to his right, directly below them. Then the weave turned to the right and George checked the other side. It was mainly Alex's responsibility but two pairs of eyes are better than one and while it was still early for night fighters George liked to check underneath regularly, especially since hearing about the upward firing guns. Back to the scan.

A dark shape rushed at him from the darkness directly behind and slightly above.

"Dive skipper! Bomber directly behind!" Starlight glinted off the Perspex of the Lancaster's nose, as it grew rapidly bigger, less than 100 yards and closing fast. The shadow rapidly developed distinctive features in the monochrome light. Engines grew out of the wings, blue exhaust flames glowing either side of them. Freddy was dipping away now and George was being lifted from his seat, but the other bomber was now right on top of them. Now he could see the pilot's and flight engineer's faces, green in the reflected glow of the instrument panel. Then they disappeared behind their aircraft's nose as Freddy dived away and the Lancaster swept over the top of them.

"Jesus!" blasphemed Alex, as the bomber roared over his turret and the other aircraft's engines produced a rhythmical buffeting through Freddy's fuselage.

"You can level out now, skipper, he's over the top of us."

"Roger, George, I can see him, and good spot."

The weaving started again and George went back to his scan.

"Crossing the enemy coast now," said Bob.

A white flash went off to George's left leaving a patch of grey where it had been. Then another directly behind them. George tried not to look at them. Not because he was particularly scared of flak but because he didn't want to spoil his night vision by looking at the light. It takes thirty minutes for the human eye to fully accustom itself to the dark and only a second to totally destroy that sensitivity. For that reason it was constantly hammered into gunners not to look at any lights, whether it was flak, searchlights, burning aircraft or the fires over the target. A dozen or so flashes later and they were through the coastal flak belt and into Belgium. Once again the black earth slid past below them, rivers and canals reflected the starlight from the clear skies like silver ribbons. Far behind, three coastal searchlights waved lazily back and forth.

"Navigator to bomb aimer and rear gunner, we're going to pass directly over a junction of two canals and I want to take a back bearing. Bomb aimer, tell me when we're directly over the junction, rear gunner, call the angle on my mark."

"Roger," replied Bob.

"Roger." This was unusual, thought George. Ron usually used the GEE equipment to work out the wind and find their drift. It must have been jammed sooner than usual because Ron would not normally ask for help from anyone unless he felt he really had to.

"Over the junction in 3… 2… 1… mark," said Bob. Ron would now have started his stopwatch and after a few minutes George would see the canal junction appear behind them. He would aim his guns at it and keep tracking it until Ron called mark and then George would read off the angle from a graduated scale on the traversing ring of his turret. If the angle was zero there was no drift, but that was highly unlikely. What Ron did with the drift angle he would find, George didn't know. He hated maths and it was Ron's problem. All he knew was that it was distracting him from searching for fighters. The junction of the two silver ribbons appeared and George put his sights on them, and then started to scan the sky again.

"Mark!"

George checked his sights and traversed his turret slightly left back onto the junction, then bent down to read the scale.

"Four degrees left drift," he reported.

"Roger, four degrees left drift."

Most people would have said thank you, thought George, as he once again started to scan the sky.

"Bomber going down 8 o'clock," reported Alex.

George took a quick glance in that direction and saw the yellow streak in the sky. It was a long way off, probably a bomber that had stayed out of the main bomber stream. There was no doubt about it; bad navigation or inaccurate flying would get you killed. Ron might well be a pain in the arse, but he seemed to be a good nav so it was worth putting up with him. There was no flak around at the moment so that bomber must have been the victim of a fighter; George redoubled his efforts searching the sky.

George thought about what he had been taught about the German night fighter air defence system. It relied for its early warning on a system of Freya long-range early warning radars, each of which had a range of about 120 miles. These were placed at intervals all along the European coast. There was one at Ostend and they had just passed less than 20 miles north of there, so at this very moment they were on a German radar screen and had been for some time. There was a second line of Freyas along the German border and a third line around Berlin. This was known as the Kammhuber line, after General Kammhuber who was in charge of its construction. The Germans however, called it the Himmelbett line, meaning heavenly bed or four-poster. These radars each searched a designated box of airspace and had their own command centre responsible for that area. In addition to the Freya radar each box had two Giant Wurzburg radars, which although having a shorter range than the Freyas were more accurate.

The procedure for countering a raid was simple. The coastal Freyas detected the bomber stream while it was still far out over the North Sea and predicted forward to where and when they estimated it would cross the European coast. Fighter controllers would then scramble night fighters to patrol the boxes of airspace through which the bombers must pass. When the bomber stream entered a box that box's Freya radar would select a portion of the bomber stream and track the aircraft in that section. Within that section of about thirty aircraft the sector's fighter controller would select one as his target and direct one of the accurate Giant Wurzburg radars onto it. The second Wurzburg would be used to track the German night fighter. Inside the command centre the position of the target and the night fighter would be projected as two beams of light onto a frosted glass plotting board. The fighter controller would give instructions to the fighter to turn right or left and increase or decrease speed or height until the two beams of light came together. The target should then be nicely lined up in front of the fighter and within the 2,000-metre range of the fighter's own Lichtenstein radar. From this point the night fighter's radar operator should be able to take over the intercept and talk his pilot to within visual range of his target. It was very simple and straightforward. But while it worked well early in the war, when bombers would take off as a bunch of individuals and make their own way to the target by their own routes, on their way wandering through the fighter boxes one or two at a time and getting casually picked off as they went, unfortunately for the Germans, by 1944 Bomber Command was much more professional and now the whole of the bombing raid would fly in a dense stream through one of the fighter boxes in a few minutes, completely swamping it. The German controller could only direct one intercept at a time so, if he was quick, he might manage to get in two intercepts before the 500 or so bombers on the raid passed through his area. Possibly two bombers shot down out of 500. A raid could expect to pass through half a dozen fighter boxes and which two bombers got shot down in each box was pure luck. Obviously up to twelve bombers shot down out of 500 wasn't enough to have a serious effect on the raid and more fighters needed to be brought into contact with the bomber stream. Of course if a bomber wandered out of the stream due to an error in navigation it was likely to pass through a fighter box where it was the only target and it was almost certain to be attacked. This was why a good navigator was so valuable. The system also relied strongly on the Giant Wurzburg radars, which were now badly jammed by the dropping of window.

To improve the efficiency of their air defence system the Germans were using two new additional systems. The first was a form of loose control, letting the fighters hunt freely; this was "Tame Boar." The German controllers would plot the course of the raid as normal and try to predict the bomber's route. But instead of talking to individual night fighters the controller with the best radar picture of the raid at that time would give a broadcast on a specific radio frequency to all the night fighters, giving the details of where the bomber stream was, where it was heading and if possible what the target was. It was then up to the night fighters to find their own way into the bomber stream and hunt for their targets with their own radar or visually. Now instead of one controller directing one intercept, one controller was directing all the night fighters simultaneously. The important thing was for the controller to get the fighters into the bomber stream as soon as possible. To this end the Germans set up a network of fighter beacons all over Europe. Each beacon consisted of a radio navigation beacon for the night fighters and a visual flashing light using Morse code to identify each beacon for single-seat fighters. When a raid was plotted the controller would make a guess at its route and target and send his fighters to a beacon ahead of and close to the bombers' route. It was then much easier for the fighter crews to find the bombers because they were starting from a known location close to the bombers. And if they were lucky the bombers might well stumble into the fighters by accident as they pushed east to their target.

The second new system was "Wild Boar." These were single-seat day fighters sent up at night to hunt visually for the bombers. They would fly to the fighter beacons and listen to the fighter controller's broadcast to direct them to the bombers. Because they had to hunt visually their main chance of success was over the bombers' target, when they could fly above the bombers and silhouette them against the fires of the burning city.

What George had not thought about and knew nothing of, was what Bomber Command was doing to counter the new German tactics. While window hampered the German radars, the operators quickly learned to work through the jamming and with broadcast control, the controller with the best radar picture gave the broadcast. So to stop the broadcast you would have to jam all the German radars all the time, which was impossible. By far the easier target was to jam the controller's radio. This task was given to 101 Squadron, flying specially modified Lancasters out of RAF Ludford Magna in north Lincolnshire. These Lancasters had extra radio equipment and an eighth crewmember. The eighth crewman would scan the radio frequencies until he located the German fighter broadcast. Then he would either use a microphone fitted into one of the Lancaster's engine nasals to transmit very loud Rolls Royce Merlin engine noise over the frequency, totally obliterating the controller's instructions, or better still, all eighth crewmen were fluent German speakers and they could give the fighters false instructions, sending them all the wrong way. The German controllers, who could also hear the false instructions, would try to countermand them and there would usually lead to an argument between the German controller and the British crewman as to who was the real controller. On one occasion the German got so angry he started to curse the British spoofer who calmly replied, "The Englishman is now swearing." To which the German replied, "It's not the Englishman, it's me!" Naturally the German fighters got very confused and many went the wrong way.

To counter these tactics the Germans started to change the broadcast control frequency in a pre arranged sequence every few minutes. But this caused problems for the fighters, who had enough work to do without having to constantly change radio frequency. They also installed many high power radio transmitters so that they could "out shout" the spoofers. But perhaps the best tactic they used against spoofing was to use female controllers. Women's voices are clearer over radios and all the eighth crewmembers were men so the female voice was always the real controller.

Other electronic warfare aircraft protecting the bomber stream were a British Squadron of American B17 Flying Fortresses. The B17 was used because the jamming equipment was fitted into the bomb bay, which in a B17 is in the fuselage and easy to get to. British bombers had their bomb bays under the floor and any equipment stored there would have been very difficult to get at. These Flying Fortresses of 214 Squadron flying from RAF Sculthorpe in Norfolk were part of 100 Group and they carried "Jostle" which was a far more effective radio jammer than the microphone in the engine of the 101 Squadron Lancasters. They also carried "Piperack" which jammed night fighters' radars. Altogether this equipment weighed 6,000 pounds and had to be carried to the target and back again, unlike the main force bombers who could get rid of their load halfway.

Freddy was now passing close to Brussels and ten searchlight beams weaved lazily back and forth around the city. Soon they turned left passing north of Charleroi then south of Liege and into Germany.

George was cold again and had turned on his suit. But while the body part of the suit started to heat up slowly the feet got hot very quickly and George knew it wouldn't be long before they would be burning and he would have to turn the suit off again. He just hoped he would be able to stand it long enough so that he could warm his body up a bit.

Without taking his eyes off the sky he felt for his oxygen tube and ran his hands up and down it, squeezing it flat along its length. While he did this it restricted his breathing, but each time he breathed in he could feel the sting of small shards of ice hitting him in the face. If he didn't keep doing this his breath would freeze in the tube, blocking it and he would pass out. The first indication the rest of the crew would get that all was not well would probably be when they landed and found him dead in his turret, he thought. It was not a pleasant thought, but that and the knowledge that it had happened to some unfortunate gunners served to make him concentrate. It was easy to spot a gunner, thought George, they were the ones with the red sore patches around their nose and mouth. Alex was particularly prone to this and it brought out his acne, but still he always seemed to be able to get the girls. The crew inside the fuselage were slightly warmer than the gunners and didn't have a problem with freezing oxygen systems, unless it was a particularly cold night.

As he weaved his turret from side to side quartering the sky he tried hard to ignore how cold he was. He was lucky that, like Alex, his body seemed more able to adjust to the cold. He felt sorry for Bob. Bob hated the cold and it seemed to affect him more than anyone else on the crew. But one thing George couldn't shut his mind to was the fact that his feet were now painfully hot and he could stand it no longer. He had to turn the suit off again and his body had only just started to get semi-comfortable.

A large river appeared below heading north, which had to be the Rhine and they turned to head northeast. Green tracer flashed far in the distance drawing George's eye instantly to it. There was a yellow patch there now, far off and slowly getting bigger. It was too far away and to dull to damage his night vision so he watched it for a few seconds as it slowly started to descend, getting further away all the time.

"Aircraft going down 6 o'clock, it's a long way astern."

"Roger."

He had said aircraft because it could have been a bomber shooting down an attacking fighter but George knew it was highly unlikely and he was sure it was green tracer he saw. All the German tracer he had seen was green, whereas the British tracer always looked red.

God, he was cold again! But his feet still hadn't cooled down from their last roasting and they felt sore. He decided he couldn't take the heat on his feet again just yet and instead rubbed his hands up and down his thighs and arms to try and warm up. It didn't do any good, it was too cold. He stamped his feet up and down, not because they were cold but because he was starting to get cramp behind his knees from sitting in the same position. The stamping made his feet feel even more sore and he thought he might have burnt them with the overheating suit. He was also starting to go numb from the waist down because of the hard turret seat. Fortunately George could do something about this that most other gunners couldn't. He stood up. He had to stoop well forward, curving his back around the roof of the turret, but for most gunners even this was impossible in the confines of a turret. After a quick stretch and wriggle to restore the circulation he sat back down, shuffled himself comfortable, or as close as he could get to it and went back to his routine.

After what seemed like an age George heard Ron order a course change and felt them alter course to the right. Soon he could see the searchlights around Kassel to his left; they were now on the final leg to Leipzig. Using the forecast winds this 110-mile leg should take thirty minutes, he remembered from the briefing. Good, he was shivering now and he had to turn his suit back on. After five minutes he had stopped shivering but his feet were burning and again he had to turn the suit off. His feet were very painful now and he kept getting cramp behind his knees that he couldn't seem to ease. God, he wished they would reach the target. They would still have about 560 miles to fly back to Metheringham, which would take them around three hours, but the journey home never seemed so bad somehow.

Now that they were well into Germany there was a steady stream of fires in the sky and it was obvious that a large number of fighters had found the bomber stream. This of course concentrated George's mind and the thirty minutes passed far more quickly than he thought they would. The next thing he knew was Bob reporting fires over the target and they were starting to line up for the bomb run. They were well down the bomber stream so the target should be well alight by now. Behind them was darkness, but this was the most dangerous part of the Op. All the bombers would converge on the target and while it was planned to get as many bombers over the target as quickly as possible to swamp the defences, it was also true that the more bombers there were in a small area of sky the more likely there was to be a collision. There was also the danger of being hit by bombs falling from above as well as the night fighters, Wild Boars, flak and searchlights. They passed over some green target markers, dropped short of the city. Jimmy would now be dropping the window, I wonder how he's holding up, thought George. Now the flak started, red, yellow and white flashes, leaving grey clouds in the black sky. As yet none of it was close, but that would change as they went over the target on their straight predictable course.

Emil Kahn hated his new job. He was a bomber pilot and had been since 1940. He had bombed London, Birmingham, Manchester and many other British cities. He had also taken part in the great raid on Coventry. He had no business in a fighter! He had never wanted to be a fighter pilot! When he joined up it had been his goal to fly Stukas, but he had been sent to Junkers 88s instead. That had been for the best, he thought; when the Stukas had come up against the RAF fighters they had proved to be death traps. But he liked bombers, in a bomber you were part of a team who worked closely together and helped each other. In a bomber you were on the attack, taking the war to the enemy. Now here he was, alone in a Messerschmitt 109 flying around in circles 21,000 feet above Leipzig on a clear but dark night.

This was all the fault of Oberst Hans-Joachim Herrmann, thought Emil. Herrmann was a bomber pilot who had come up with the idea that Germany had lots of day fighters that were considered to be unsuitable for night fighting and lots of under-used bomber pilots who were all experienced at instrument flying, which was essential for night flying. So why not put bomber pilots into fighters and send them out at night to try and find the bombers as they flew over the burning cities? The fighters could fly above the bombers and it should be easy to see the bombers against the fires below them. And he had been right, thought Emil. The bombers were easy to see, but day fighters had a very short range and you could not stay over a target for very long. The fighter had no navigation aids and if the weather closed in it was almost impossible to land safely. As it was, all the single-seat fighters tended to be scrambled together, so they all ran out of fuel together, resulting in a mad scramble to get down again after the raid. This often resulted in collisions over fighter bases or crashes on landing and many good bomber pilots were killed doing a job they were not properly trained or equipped for. To top it all, as a bomber pilot, he had had no training in air-to-air tactics or shooting. He had flown these missions five times now and seen bombers each occasion. But as he had dived on them he had either misjudged the range and overshot or lost the bomber in the dark as he approached its level and the fires no longer silhouetted it. On the one occasion he had actually managed to fire his guns it had been one quick wild burst as he raced over the top on a bomber that had been a lot closer than he thought. He hadn't seen any hits and he suspected he had scared himself far more than the bomber crew.

Tonight was turning out to be the same as the others; he had tried to attack two bombers already. The first had been below and to the left, a perfect black shape against the orange fires. He had lowered the Messerschmitt's nose and turned towards the bomber, but in the dive his speed had increased so quickly he had found himself rapidly closing on the bomber and having to push the fighter into a steeper and steeper dive to keep his guns on target. This of course made his speed increase faster still and he had to pull away violently to avoid colliding with the Halifax, which had completely filled his vision.

The second attack he had taken much more slowly. He had spotted the bomber and moved into its high 7 o'clock, keeping it backlit by the fires. Then he had throttled back and lowered the fighter's nose, maintaining the same speed as the bomber and slowly descending to the bomber's level. Unfortunately, as he got down to the bomber's level the fires no longer silhouetted it and it melted away into the darkness. Emil had opened the throttle fully and charged after it, but it had just gone.

Now the raid had been underway for twenty minutes and the city was well alight. He had been in the air thirty-five minutes and he had enough fuel for one more attack, then he would have to try and find his airfield and land. Lining up to the west of Leipzig heading in the direction that the bombers seemed to be flying he again started to search the sky above the fires. He had the Messerschmitt's engine throttled back so that he was flying at about the same speed as the bombers. Flak burst around but mainly below him; that was another problem for the Wild Boars, they were as likely to get shot down by their own flak as the bombers were. Then he saw it, another stark black outline just like those in the recognition charts, against the fires. This one he would make sure of and he started to close in slowly, keeping the bomber in sight below and to his right. Keeping his speed down to that of the bomber's he eased the fighter down until he was only 300 metres away from it, in its 8 o'clock and very slightly above.

Now he was too close to lose it in the dark when he put his nose down to attack. All he had to do was make sure he hit it.

Freddy was well established on the bomb run and the flak seemed to be worse than Berlin. The Lancaster jumped and bounced around the sky in the man-made turbulence. George tried not to look at the bursts, but they were everywhere. He could see the start of the glow of the burning city appearing below Freddy's tail and he tried to keep his eyes away from it. Bob was giving his instructions to Doug over the intercom and a minute before he had felt the bomb doors open. Not long now and they would be on their way home, instead of flying in a dead straight line through a wall of flak.

"Fighter! 8 o'clock high!" yelled Alex.

George felt Freddy twitch, then Doug asked, "Is he attacking?"

"No, he's just sitting there at about 300 yards."

George could see him too now.

"We're nearly at the release point," warned Bob.

Doug didn't want to have to corkscrew to lose the fighter but then have to fly back against the stream to start the bomb run again, unless he absolutely had to. George sensed this and the thought of it didn't thrill him either.

"I've got him too, skipper. I don't know if he's seen us yet, but we've got him covered," said George.

"Roger, we'll carry on with the bomb run, shout out if he starts to attack."

"We're about fifteen seconds to the release point," called Bob.

"He's turnin' in!" warned Alex.

"Don't shoot yet!" said George. "Hold her steady, skipper." He had recognised the black shape's square-tipped wings and long thin nose as a Messerschmitt 109 when it turned in. He had also seen the fighter's nose drop and he realised he had seen this sort of attack before. The fighter wasn't heading straight at them to make a quick slashing attack; it was setting up to do a curve of pursuit attack. It passed down through their level in a slow descent, crossing the Lancaster's tail at about a 30-degree angle to their course, 200 yards behind, and started to pull up. Now it would roll slowly into a left climbing turn and as its nose started to drop it would be lined up perfectly to fire into Freddy's cockpit. George had seen it many times during the fighter affiliation training and he knew exactly when to make his move. His hands were no longer cold, they were damp with sweat and his breathing was short and shallow. Inside his chest his heart thumped noisily and the blood roared louder in his ears than the Merlins, but outwardly he was completely calm. The dim red circle and dot of his reflector sight tracked the fighter through Freddy's low 6 o'clock and into its slight climb. The red dot was on the cockpit, but George knew he would have to pull some lead on that or by the time the bullets had gone the short distance to the Messerschmitt it would have moved and he would probably hit it somewhere around the tail. The red circle neatly surrounded the dark fighter, which would put a night fighter at about 400 yards, but for a smaller day fighter to fill the ring like that it had to be about 200 yards away. Too close to miss he thought, pushing to the back of his mind the night fighter he had missed from ten yards on their first Op. This time he couldn't afford to miss because it was unlikely that the fighter would. His time was just a couple of seconds away, this would stop them laughing at his shooting, he thought… he hoped.

"Not yet, Alex, not yet, wait… wait…" He knew Alex would be tracking the fighter just as he was. Its nose was coming round and starting to fall. Gently his hands eased the turret controls to the left, very slightly increasing its rate of rotation, slowly moving the red dot from the cockpit along the nose to the propeller. There would be one split second when everything would be right, just before the fighter opened fire, and it was now!

"FIRE!" George tried to remember to squeeze the twin triggers and not jerk them as if the extra pressure would give added destruction to his guns. His four Brownings exploded in blue and yellow flashes, the noise deafening. Every corner of his turret was lit up by the flickering light and the red tracer streaked towards the target. Instantly a mass of yellow sparks splattered the side of the fighter behind the engine and it seemed to stagger in mid air.

Emil had finally got it right, he was set up perfectly and this bomber was as good as dead. His sight was falling just in front of the bomber's nose while his finger started to increase the pressure on the trigger that would fire the two 13 mm MG131 machine guns above the Messerschmitt's engine. His thumb rested on the button that would unleash the 30 mm MK108 cannon firing through the propeller hub and the two 20 mm MG151 cannons mounted in bolt on fairings under the wings. But just as Emil was about to send a mass of explosive shells into Freddy he saw a bunch of yellow flashes from Freddy's tail, there was a loud bang and then nothing.

A .303 Browning fires twenty bullets a second and George was firing four of them. He fired a two-second burst but it was all over in the first tenth of a second. Of the 160 bullets fired, fifty-six hit, most of them in the first second, because the longer a machine gun fires the more it vibrates and the less accurate it gets. That is why gunners are always told to fire short bursts. Single-seat fighters carry very little armour and most of that is behind the pilot's seat to protect him from a traditional attack from the rear. There was no armour to protect Emil from the wall of bullets entering the side of his cockpit. Four came through the left side of the fuselage, smashed the instrument panel and left through the right side. Twelve whizzed through the cockpit turning it into a mass of flying glass and broken metal shards. Ten slammed into Emil so hard he was forced sideways out of his seat harness into the right side of the cockpit. He didn't care; the two bullets that had blown off most of his head meant he didn't feel anything. Twenty of the other bullets hit the L-shaped fuel tank that Messerschmitt pilots sat on, while the rest passed harmlessly through the rear fuselage. Fuel gushed out of the tank and four de Wilde incendiary bullets flashed and ignited it in a massive yellow sheet of flame.

"Got him!" screamed George, in delight.
"Bombs gone!" called Bob.
"Where is he?" asked Doug.
"5 o'clock low, going down in a spin, a mass of flames!" As far as George was concerned his whole life had led up to that point and he had not been found wanting. Don't look at the fires, bollocks! He pushed hard against the Perspex watching HIS Messerschmitt rocket earthwards. Below the city was burning over a wide area and the fighter was going to land somewhere among it. George swivelled his turret as far as it would go so that he could look over his shoulder and down behind Freddy to keep his kill in sight as long as possible.

Suddenly there was a horrendous bang and George fell backwards out of his turret. The ice-cold wind took his breath away and tore at his clothes. He was stunned and had no idea what had happened to him. His feet were caught in the turret controls and holding him in, while his body was buffeted around in the slipstream. He thought Freddy must have been hit and he had to try and get back inside to his parachute before the Lancaster went out of control. Reaching down his legs he managed to get hold of the sides of the turret doors and ease himself back into the turret. The slipstream pulled against his efforts, reluctant to let him go. He could feel his burnt and bruised feet starting to slip from wherever they had got wedged. If he wasn't quick he was going to fall, God he wished he wore a seat parachute. Desperation gave extra strength to his powerful arms and after what seemed an age he got back into the turret. His intercom lead had come out and he still had no idea what had happened as he reached behind himself and slid the turret doors shut and rotated the turret rearwards so he could climb out into the fuselage and get his parachute. As he centred the turret with one hand he located his intercom lead with the other and once his other hand was free he reconnected it. He had expected to hear lots of frantic orders but there was nothing except static. It had to be broken. He turned on his microphone switch.

"Is everybody alright?"
"Yes, he didn't get a shot at us," Doug replied.
"Photoflash fired, let's go home," said Bob.
"All bombs gone, no hang ups and the bomb doors are fully closed," reported Harry.
"What about the armed delayed action?" asked Bob.
"Funnily enough I checked that one first," replied Harry sarcastically.

What the hell had happened, thought George? Then he realized. When he had strained to see his falling fighter he had raised himself up in his seat and his parachute harness straps must have caught on the turret door release handles. With the turret turned fully to one side the slipstream had ripped the doors open and sucked him out of the turret. He started to shake with shock and he was sweating all over. He had jarred his feet and knees, which were both sore and aching. After a couple of deep breaths he tried to slow down his breathing and checked his oxygen was still connected and the tube free of ice. Get back to your job, he thought over the pounding of his heart.

The return route was a series of short legs with small course changes to keep them clear of the defended German towns. Every now and then George would see a cluster of searchlights away to one side or another. It took him a long time to calm down after his fright, so for most of the trip back across Germany he didn't feel cold. But as the adrenalin drained from his system the numbing cold started to seep back through his layers of clothing, chilling the sweat that had wet the clothes next to his skin. He had only recently managed to stop himself shaking from shock and now he was starting to shake from shivering. Reluctantly he turned on his heated suit again and was pleasantly surprised to find the feet didn't heat up quickly this time. In fact they didn't heat up at all; the wires had been snapped while he struggled to get back inside the aeroplane. This didn't bother George, he could cope with the cold on his feet better than the intense heat and now he could leave the suit on to warm his body up a bit. Even with the suit on it was still cold, but now at least it wasn't so cold that it hurt and George felt far more comfortable.

Over the intercom Doug and Ron were discussing increasing their speed to get home more quickly. Doug wanted to put them into a shallow dive and run quickly to the coast but Ron was against it because of the changing wind as they descended. One by one others in the crew added their comments. Not surprisingly they all wanted to get out of Germany as quickly as possible and Ron gave in. In a slight dive Freddy was soon doing 300 mph and the noise of the slipstream around George's turret increased remarkably. No other bombers were likely to come roaring out of the darkness at them at this speed. In fact anything that was catching up to them now was almost certainly enemy.

"Coast ahead," called Bob.

The dark line of the land gave way to the silvery reflection of the sea below them. Then the dark patches of the East Frisian Islands just off the mainland came into view. Sporadic bursts of flak twinkled well behind them. We're going faster than you thought, thought George. Some light flak hosed upward from one of the islands, the green tracer weaving around in the dark sky behind them and they were clear. We're not safe yet, George cautioned himself, thinking about the night fighter that had shot them into the sea, and he continued his search.

"10,000 feet everybody, you can come off oxygen now," said Doug.

George felt for the clip of his oxygen mask with his heavily gloved hands and fumbled with it until he eventually freed it and the mask fell away from his face. It was always good to get off oxygen and breathe real air. While the air in the turret was cold the oxygen had a chill to it that seemed to take the cold to your very core. It was also very dry and made you thirsty and dehydrated. Elsewhere in

Freddy people would be drinking hot coffee, which did more to thaw out a frozen body than anything else and was another reason crews liked to get below 10,000 feet as soon as possible. Lucky bastards, thought George, who like Alex, had no room for coffee in his turret. One and a quarter hours to the English coast, George remembered from the briefing, then he could relax a bit. His mind started to turn to thoughts of whiskey-laced coffee and a large corned beef sandwich. He also realized he was desperate for a cigarette; he hadn't thought about it until now but he really needed a fag. He found that while he quartered the sky he could think of nothing except how good it would be to stand beside Freddy's tail with Alex, Bob, Harry and Jimmy and have a good long smoke. With the thought of cigarettes on his mind the long leg across the North Sea seemed endless, especially as George always dreaded flying over water anyway.

After what seemed like an eternity Bob spotted the English coast. Ron had got a good GEE fix and they were heading direct to Metheringham. George couldn't get on the ground soon enough; he was chilled to the bone and his legs were so cramped he could hardly bear to move them. His feet still felt very sore, his body was numb and tingling from the waist down because of the hard seat and his back was one long line of agony that no amount of stretching could relieve. God, he felt hollow inside, he needed a cigarette and something to eat, in that order. They crossed the coast into Lincolnshire and George breathed a sigh of relief; once again he wouldn't drown. A red light flashed out its Morse letters to George's right, Spilsby, another Lancaster base, about 6 miles to East Kirkby, 57 and 630 Squadrons, both Lancasters. Then 7 miles to Woodhall Spa, 617 Squadron, more Lancasters and then Metheringham. George tried to get some feeling back into his legs so that it wouldn't be too painful getting out of the turret. Freddy's engines were throttled back and they were in a long slow descent when Bob spotted Metheringham's beacon. Doug called them on RT and got clearance to land immediately on runway two zero. They must be one of the first back, overtaking the others in their long fast dive out of Germany, thought George.

Doug flew them into the overhead and down the length of Metheringham's main runway, turning slowly to the left into the circuit. George watched the dull white lights of the runway fall away behind and appear to swivel in the darkness as Freddy manoeuvred downwind, flying back parallel to the runway about a mile to one side. Over the intercom Doug and Jimmy were running through the pre-landing checks and he could feel the slight dips, bumps and vibrations as wheels and flaps came down. Then they were turning back towards the lights and George lost sight of them. The Merlins gave short bursts of power as Doug made slight adjustments to their approach. He could see the ground clearly now, not far below them and a bit unreal in the monochrome starlight. Then the runway lights were below him and Freddy's engines cut. There was that moment of floating and then, with a brief screech, the wheels touched and they were home. Gently Doug lowered Freddy's tail and the tailwheel rumbled below George while he let out a long breath. Op five over, a sixth of the way through their tour.

A dark shape caught his eye, high in Freddy's 5 o'clock. There was another aircraft in the circuit, but they hadn't heard it call flying control, it must have a radio problem. It was lining up to land and George checked the tail-light was on. They were only halfway down the runway and he didn't want it to run into the back of them. At the same time he reached for his facemask hanging from the left side of his helmet to tell Doug. At that moment he realized the dark shape only had two engines, its wheels were up and it was closing in fast. He dropped his mask and grabbed at his gun controls. Simultaneously Alex yelled the warning,

"Intruder, 6 o'clock high!"

George's guns were too low and he twisted the controls to give full elevation and pulled and held the triggers, but he knew he was too late and the nose of the Junkers 88 lit up in a blaze of yellow flashes.

Sally was sitting in her wagon parked at Freddy's dispersal watching the red and green navigation lights slowly approach and touch down. Sergeant Green and the rest of Freddy's ground crew were standing by her cab, glad that Freddy was first back and they could get their checks done and go straight to bed. Sergeant Green heard the second set of engines first as Freddy's engines cut over the runway threshold. Instantly he knew they were not bomber engines and he searched the dark sky across the airfield. The first indication Sally had that all was not well was when George and the Junkers simultaneously opened fire. The red tracer from Freddy's tail flew into the air passing under the fighter and continuing out into the night, while the green tracer from the fighter flashed down at the helpless bomber erupting in large yellow tongues of flame on the runway behind the Lancaster. The clattering of the guns reached out across the airfield and Sally's world seemed to go into slow motion as Freddy's mid-upper turret started firing too. But it was going high and all the while the yellow explosions were getting closer until there were flashes on Freddy's fuselage and wings. Complete horror filled her and she felt totally helpless and sick as Freddy careered down the runway and the fighter disappeared into the night.

"Get in the wagon!" yelled Sergeant Green from beside her ear, so loud she almost jumped out of her skin. There was the clatter of boots and thumps as bodies fell over the tailboard and Sergeant Green jumped into the passenger seat.

"Drive!"

Alex's warning and the rattle of guns had stopped Doug's heart and frozen him to the spot for a fraction of a second. He had no idea what to do; should he open the throttles and take off or slam on the brakes and take a chance? If he took off he would be low and slow and a sitting target. He decided he would stay on the ground and get everybody out as quickly as possible. At that instant the decision was made for him as Freddy quivered with the hit of cannon shells and a shadow passed low over the top of the cockpit. With the throttles fully closed he held the control column fully back into the pit of his stomach and squeezed the brakes hard… Nothing happened.

"We've no brakes!"

Jimmy checked the triple pneumatic pressure gauge on the bottom right of the instrument panel.

"We've lost the pneumatics!"

The end of the runway was close and approaching at 50 mph, the red lights just in front of the nose showed the end of the runway. Then the outside world went black. Doug jumped at the suddenness of it, then realized that flying control had turned the runway lights off so that the intruder couldn't find them again in the dark. The completeness of the darkness shocked Doug, until he realized that it meant they couldn't be on fire and it would be very difficult for the intruder to make another pass at them. With no pneumatics there would be no brakes and while there was a system to keep a reserve for the brakes this must have been hit in the attack. They were going to crash and there was nothing he could do about it.

"Brace! Brace! Brace!"

"Fuel booster pumps off!" yelled Jimmy, jolting Doug back into action. There were still things that could be done to minimise the damage of the coming crash.

"Master engine fuel cocks off!"

"Master fuel cocks off!" echoed Jimmy.

"Ignition off!"

Jimmy flicked the switches. "Ignition off!"

"Get behind my seat, Jimmy!"

"Turn the lights off!" instructed Jimmy as he left, and Doug flicked them off.

Then they went off the end of the runway with a thump and started to bounce and bump over the uneven grass. The wheels rumbled and all the internal fitting rattled and shook. Doug prayed the wheels would take the strain. It couldn't be far now to the boundary fence and the Martin village road. If they ran into that the wheels would snap like matchwood. Jimmy had swivelled behind the pilot's seat and Doug felt alone as Freddy rumbled on into the darkness. He pulled his straps tight until they hurt, to try and prevent the black eyes he had received during the ditching. Then suddenly, everything went quiet… They had stopped. They were still on their wheels and they were safe. Doug took a deep breath and slumped down in his seat as outside the hot engines hissed.

"He's comin' in again!" yelled Alex.

Doug was again spurred into action.

"Everybody out! Quick!"

He pulled the pin from his harness straps and turned the quick release box of his parachute, hitting it to free the locking pins. Sliding out of his seat he raced after Jimmy who was already clambering over the main spar. The dark tunnel of the fuselage smelt of acrid cordite from the exploded cannon shells and Freddy's own guns. He was hard on Jimmy's heels now over the second spar and jumping down off the bomb bay to duck under Alex's turret as the mid-uppers twin Brownings rattled again with a long burst. With Freddy's engines shut down Alex had to be rotating his turret manually which was slow and far from accurate. He reached up and grabbed Alex's leg.

"Get out!" he yelled up at the young Scot.

"He's not going for us, he's going for a truck!" Alex replied.

Sally had her foot hard down as she raced to where she had seen Freddy leave the runway, just before the lights had gone out. The truck's taped-over headlights barely illuminated the perimeter track through the thin slits and she was very aware that she was charging at full speed into complete blackness and would not see anything until it was far too late. Ahead her crew were off the runway in a crashed Lancaster and every second could count. At least there was no fire. She had seen a Lancaster burn and the thought of it still sent shivers down her spine. Don't burn, don't burn, she thought, her eyes glued to the thin strip of dimly lit concrete directly in front of the snowplough. She was nearing the end of the runway now and she lifted her foot from the accelerator and searched the darkness for Freddy. A dark silhouette with two indigo glows was heading towards her from above flying control on the other side of the airfield.

"Lights!" yelled Sergeant Green. "Turn the lights out!"

Sally flicked the lights off and as the shadow swooped down at them she threw the wheel to the left and a burst of red tracer rose into the air from her left, which had to come from Freddy. Then the shadow's nose blazed yellow and explosions erupted everywhere.

Doug jumped out of Freddy's rear door just as a heavy thump, thump, thump started from the airfield's 40 mm Bofors anti-aircraft guns of 2756 RAF Regiment Flight and bright red balls of tracer raced after the departing Junkers. The danger past, he walked slowly around Freddy's tail and saw a truck on fire about 100 yards away. He could see figures against the flames and not being able to see his crew anywhere near realized that it must be them. As he walked towards the fire Alex caught him up. He nodded towards the truck.

"It was beltin' round the peri track towards us when the Jerry clobbered it. They must a bin comin' to help us."

There weren't many trucks on this side of the airfield at night, thought Doug and he started to worry and he looked more closely at the outline of the flames. Then he started to run. Alex wondered what was going on and then it dawned.

"Oh shit!" And he too started to run.

As they got closer Doug started to count the figures against the flames but they kept moving in and out of the shadows. There were at least six, so if five were his crew someone had got out of the wagon. Sirens wailed behind him as the fire trucks and ambulance race towards the fire.

"Is everybody alright?" gasped Doug, when he got to the crowd of people and recognised Bob, Harry and Jimmy, who were helping others to the edge of the perimeter track.

"There's a few wounded. It's our ground crew and Sally," replied Bob.

"Is Sally alright?"

"She's been hit, I don't know how badly. She's over there." He pointed to the edge of the track.

Sally was lying on the edge of the perimeter track with Sergeant Green supporting her shoulders.

"Bastards, bastards, bastards," she said over and over under her breath. She saw Doug in the firelight and stared at him. "Look what the bastards have done to my truck!"

He knelt down beside her. "Are you okay?"

She sniffed. "Yes."

"Well, don't worry about the truck, so long as you're alright." He smiled down at her.

"She's been hit in the side," said Sergeant Green. "The snowplough blade took most of the splinters and we both ducked as the windscreen came in. Some of the lads in the back got hit as well. If Sally hadn't swerved we would have been blown to bits. Can you take over here, sir, while I go and see to my lads?"

Doug slid up Sally's left side and supported her head with his right arm.

"Put pressure on here," said Sergeant Green, indicating where he was holding a cloth against Sally's right side. Doug put his left hand on the cloth and blood oozed out of it over his hand. The bullet had gone into her side just above her belt and the sergeant had opened her greatcoat and pulled her other clothes up to expose the wound. Doug cupped his hand tightly around it and felt the warm sticky liquid sliding through his fingers. He looked up at Sergeant Green. The sergeant stared back at him.

"I have to go and see to my lads," he said, and he was gone.

"You just relax," said Doug. "The ambulance is on its way."

"I'm alright," replied Sally. "It doesn't hurt."

"Well, just lie still until the doc's seen you."

"Funny isn't it? I thought that being shot must really hurt but I can't feel a thing. I'm just very cold." Doug pulled her close and tried to wrap as much of her greatcoat back around her as he could. "This is cosy," she teased.

Doug could feel a lump rising in his throat and he swallowed it back down. He was surprised how strongly he felt about her and it had come as a shock to him. He had liked her from their first meeting but he suddenly realised how lovely she was. Thank God she was going to be alright.

"Are all your crew alright?"

"Yes," he said, although he wasn't really sure.

"Good. I would have hated all this to have been for nothing." The fire reflected in her eyes as they scanned the burning truck and surrounding figures. Then their eyes met and they stared for a second that seemed like a lifetime and both knew.

"Some people say I'm psychic and can see the future, and I do sometimes know things are going to happen before they do, but I didn't see this."

"I've just realised."

"I've thought about it, but didn't think anything would ever happen."

"Why not?"

"You're an officer." They continued to stare at each other. "Well, are you going to kiss me then?" she eventually asked. He leaned down and gently kissed her, then they continued to stare. "It's very cold on this concrete." Doug tried to pull her closer and moved to adjust her greatcoat. Then he saw the dark puddle she was lying in spreading out over the perimeter track. Panic rose inside him and he noticed her multiple layers of clothes down the right side of her body were soaking wet. "I'm very tired."

"Well, you can't go to sleep just yet!" said Doug quickly. "You have to wait until you're in the hospital!"

"Oh, I do like it when you're masterful," she teased and he started to blush in the darkness, but she could see the worry on his face. "What is it?"

"Nothing, just lie still. Everything's going to be fine." He forced a smile at her and she shivered violently.

"I'm so cold."

"Just hang on. It'll be nice and warm in the ambulance." He turned and yelled over his shoulder, "Where the hell is the ambulance?" his panic rising to the surface. She heard the panic in his voice and he felt her body tense up. "It's okay," he soothed. "We'll soon have you fixed up."

Sally yawned. "It will be nice to be warm. It's always so cold here, I can hardly remember what summer is like."

"Well, you'll be driving your truck again in no time."

"Not my truck," said Sally sadly. "The Jerries blew it up." Her eyes left his and looked at the burning truck.

Behind Doug there was a screech of brakes and the ambulance bell stopped.

"Look at me," ordered Doug, but Sally didn't seem to hear. "Look at me!" Sally's eyes returned to his. "It's alright, the ambulance is here now, just stay with me."

Men were jumping out of the ambulance and grabbing stretchers from the back.

"Over here!" yelled Doug. "Quick!"

Sally's eyes now looked sleepy and she was no longer taking in what was happening around her.

"Yes, it will be warm in the ambulance and everything will be alright. Will you come with me?" she asked, her voice now distant.

"Yes, of course." Two ambulance men put a stretcher down beside her and started to lift her on. Suddenly, as she was laid on the stretcher she turned to Doug.

"No, you can't come with me yet, you have to look after your crew."

Doug was walking by the stretcher now.

"They'll be alright."

"No! You don't understand. You must listen." She was fully conscious now and desperate to be understood as she was lifted into the ambulance. The medical orderlies tried to restrain her but she fought them off with weakening arms, then a look of resignation came over her face.

"You have to stay here. Your crew need you!"

"Alright," agreed Doug reluctantly, not understanding what she was talking about and desperate to stay with her, but feeling tears well up in his eyes, which he didn't want her to see.

"I'll see you soon," she said, as the stretcher was slid into the ambulance where a doctor looked down at her and put a hand to her neck. Then he took his stethoscope and put it to her chest. He paused and moved it around a few times while staring at the ambulance wall in front of him. Finally he put his hand to her neck again and stared into her face.

After what seemed like a lifetime he said in a voice that could have been announcing the mail had just arrived, "She's dead, where are the others?" He flipped the rough service issue blanket up over her face and barged past Doug and into the darkness.

Doug stared at the blanketed shape on the stretcher and couldn't believe she had gone.

"But I was just talking to her."

"She had massive internal bleeding," the doctor called back over his shoulder. "Even if it had happened in an operating theatre we couldn't have saved her. But I don't suppose she felt much."

Doug was numb and could feel the colour draining from his face while tears started to run down his cheeks.

"How's Sally?" asked Bob, from behind him. Doug didn't need to turn around, he recognised the accent.

"She's dead."

"Oh, Jesus, no!"

"What?" asked Harry.

"Sally's dead."

"Christ."

There was a long pause before Bob tapped Doug on the shoulder and offered him a cigarette. He took it and drew in a deep lungful of smoke. Then he took one last look at the blanket that covered what had once been Sally and walked back towards Freddy. He could hear the rest of the crew following him, but he didn't turn because he didn't want them to see his tears. Nobody spoke, and then suddenly Alex asked, "Where's George?" They had a quick look around but George wasn't there and nobody had seen him since they took off.

"Oh God, not George too," thought Doug as they all started to run back to Freddy. The dying flames of Sally's truck reflected off the rear turret, which was traversed as far right as it would go, and the guns hung down lifelessly. Bob and Harry got to the turret first and raced around the other side to the turret doors.

"It's empty!" exclaimed Harry.

"Well, where the hell is he?" asked Alex. "He wid nae miss the burnin' truck."

"Maybe he's inside," said Jimmy.

"George!" called Bob. "Where the hell are yer?" There was no reply.

"He must have fallen out," said Ron.

"He fired at the intruder," said Alex. "So he was still in the turret when we landed."

Thank God for that, thought Doug, at least he hadn't fallen to his death.

"What's that?" asked Harry, looking back up towards the runway.

A small red light was moving slowly towards them down the runway, swinging from side to side. Slowly out of the darkness a ball-like figure with a cigarette in its hand limped into view.

"You stupid short-arsed little bastard!" yelled Bob. "You scared the shit out of us!"

"Fancy falling out of your turret," said Harry.

"I didn't fall out," said George. "It was pretty obvious that you dozy bastards were going to crash so I jumped." It was an option some rear gunners recommended, jumping out of an aeroplane before it crashed to make sure you were clear of the explosion or flames. The rear turret was turned fully to the side; the rear doors opened and the gunner did a backward roll out of the turret curled up into a ball. With all the layers of clothing acting as padding the gunner tended to skid along without doing himself any real harm, unless they hit something solid, which wasn't likely in the middle of an airfield.

"We were doing over 50 mph," said Doug.

"I thought I rolled a long way," was George's only reply.

15

Voices penetrated Harry's head and brought him slowly closer to consciousness, but still he tried desperately to cling to sleep. He had always loved sleeping and his mother often despaired at trying to get him up in the mornings. Harry knew he was fighting a losing battle and he would have to stir himself eventually, but he would put it off as long as he could. Soon, the guard that had been sent in to wake them would get to his bed and shake him awake. After a few minutes the shake didn't come and he became curious, so he tuned his ears into the voices. It was Bob, Alex, George and occasionally Jimmy, but nobody else and the rest of the billet was unusually quiet and still. Rolling over he sat up and the cold air immediately got under the blankets and made him shiver. He looked around the dim billet and saw that only their five beds had been slept in.

"Where's Digger and his crew?" he asked, knowing what the answer must be.

"Don't know," replied George. "Probably diverted somewhere else with the rest of the Squadron. We were the only ones to get back in here last night remember. Then the intruder shot up the field."

"Oh yeah," said Harry, rising to full consciousness. "And Sally…"

"Yeah, Sally," said Bob, cutting him short.

"Aye, it's a real shame, she was a bonny lass," Alex chipped in.

"I wish I'd stayed in me turret," said George. "Maybe the two of us could have clobbered him before he got his shot in."

"You can't live your life on ifs, buts and maybes," said Bob.

"Or anybody else's," said Harry, thinking about Sally's blanket-covered body.

"It wouldna ha made any difference, George. Doug cut the engines afore we went off the end of the runway. A was using ma turret manually and it was painful slow."

They all fell silent and the stillness that descended was total and unreal. After what seemed like ages Harry could stand the silence no longer.

"Still it was a bit like a rat leaving a sinking ship," he said, staring at George with a glint in his eye. Bob looked at him and understood straight away.

"Yeah, they should do you for desertion, jumping out and leaving us like that."

"I didn't jump out and leave you," protested George. "You stayed behind and left me!"

"I doubt a court martial would see it that way," said Harry. "The aircraft captain did not give the order to abandon the aircraft. It was cowardice, that's what it was."

"It didn't feel very cowardly when I was skiddin' down the runway on me arse!"

Jimmy forced a smile at the protective shield of banter and eased the blackout curtain over the window by his bed to one side.

"Christ!"

"What?" asked four other voices in unison.

"We're snowed in." There was two feet of snow outside and in places it had drifted against the sides of buildings to between three and four feet.

"No wonder nobody else is back yet," said Harry. "What time is it?"

"Eleven o'clock," said Jimmy.

"As late as that," said Bob.

"Well, they can't have wanted us or they would have sent somebody," replied George. "But I suppose we'd better show willing and go down to the Squadron Office and see what's going on."

With greatcoats pulled tightly around them against the cold they trudged through the snow to the mess for an early lunch, enjoying being the only crew on the station and not having to queue. Then they went straight to the Squadron Office where Nigel was, as usual, sitting behind his desk with his pipe hanging from the corner of his mouth.

"There you are. I was just going to send for you. The Station Commander has declared it's all hands on deck to clear the snow from the runways and taxiways so the Squadron can get back in here as soon as possible. They're scattered over half the country at the moment and it's not at all military."

"Is everybody accounted for?" asked George.

"It looks like P for Peter's bought it. Nobody's heard anything. Apparently the Halifaxes took a real pasting. There's talk that it may be the end of them on long range Ops."

None of the sergeants knew anyone from P for Peter so it had no effect on them and they reported, as Nigel had instructed, to the MT yard, where the Station Warrant Officer issued them with shovels and detailed them to a working party. In the corner of the yard a tarpaulin didn't quite succeed in hiding a fire-blackened truck, but nobody mentioned it.

The snowploughs concentrated on clearing the runways and taxiways while the gangs of men with shovels cleared the dispersals. Harry and the rest had been dropped off at Freddy's dispersal, where Sergeant Green was climbing out of the Lancaster.

"How are your lads?" asked George.

"Well, young Frank got a bullet through his arm and he'll be gone for a while but he should make a full recovery. Bob got some shell splinters in his leg but he should be back in a couple of days. All in all it could have been a lot worse."

"What about Freddy?" said Harry.

"Funnily enough he's hardly touched. There's one or two bullet holes but none anywhere vital and two cannon shell hits. One in the right wing and one in the mid section. That's why you lost your brakes, it shattered the pneumatic reservoir. It's made a right mess but it won't take long to fix." He cupped his mittened hands and blew on them to try and warm up. "They've got you on snow clearing duties then?"

"Yeah," replied Harry unenthusiastically.

"Well, at least it will keep you warm." He smiled. "When you've finished the dispersal we'll have a brew." He nodded towards the ground crew shack and climbed back into Freddy.

They formed a line at one side of the dispersal and were just about to start when another truck pulled up and Doug and Ron jumped out with their shovels.

"My God!" exclaimed Harry. "They've even got the landed gentry out."

"We've just come to experience how you peasants live," replied Doug. "Our role will be purely supervisory."

"So why have ya both got shovels?" asked Alex.

"Because we couldn't find whips." Doug was getting the hang of banter and found he was quite good at it.

With the grey sky threatening to undo all their good work they shovelled the snow for two hours. Working from the edge of the dispersal was easy because the snow could be dumped on the grass beside them, but the further they got from the grass the further they had to carry the snow before they could dump it. Now they were all tired. The banter and chat had been replaced with grunting and heavy breathing.

"Fancy a brew?" asked Sergeant Green as he and two other ground crew climbed out of Freddy.

"Damn right!" said Harry, dropping his shovel and making a beeline for the hut. Inside the hut steam started to rise off their clothes in the cold air while the primus stove roared away under the tin kettle.

"We're a couple of mugs short so two of you will have to share!" called one of the ground crew through the mass of bodies.

"No problem!" Bob called back; he couldn't believe how hot his body was but how cold his fingers, toes and face felt.

Harry was inspecting a couple of large blisters on his hands.

"Look at that!" said George, pointing to Harry's hands. "You've got a bairn's hands! They've never done a hard day's work in their lives."

"We electricians are skilled tradesmen. We do not lower ourselves to the levels of you manual labourers," scoffed Harry in an upper class voice.

"Mollycoddled that's what you are."

"Brains before brawn."

"Oh, shut up and get this down you," interrupted Sergeant Green with two mugs of tea.

"How's the work on Freddy coming along?" asked Doug.

"Pretty good. Most of it's finished. Just the patching up to do and we'll finish that off tomorrow morning. It should be ready for Ops tomorrow night if needs be."

"Will there be Ops tomorrow night?" asked Jimmy quickly.

"No idea," said the older sergeant. "That sort of thing's not my department."

The crew all looked at each other without knowing that they were all thinking the same thing, Sally would have known. With hands wrapped around warm mugs and tea warming their innards Bob, George and two of the ground crew went outside to leave more space inside for the rest. Harry could feel the warn glow starting to spread over him and knew he would soon drift off to sleep if he was allowed to. He had no idea how long he had been drifting in and out of consciousness as he snuggled down into the old damp sofa the ground crew had acquired for their hut when he was suddenly roused by a shout.

"Alex! Alex! Come out here a minute!"

It was Bob's voice and everyone else in the hut followed Alex outside to see what was going on. Harry paused not wanting to move, then his curiosity got the better of him and with a sigh he pulled himself up and strolled out.

"Alex," said Bob. "Tim here," he motioned to one of the ground crew, "says that that over there is a scarecrow and I say it's a farmer. You've got the best eyes, what do you say?"

Alex stared at the black figure, which stood out stark against the white snow. It was at least half a mile away and the brightness of the snow forced everyone to squint.

"I'm not sure but I think it's a scarecrow."

"Bollocks!" roared Bob. "If it was a scarecrow it would be covered with snow."

"But it's nae movin'."

"So he's standing still."

"Why would he stand still all this time?" asked George.

"I don't know but I still say it's a farmer."

"Well, I think Tim and Alex are right and it's a scarecrow. So you owe Tim a beer."

Harry now understood; it had been one of Bob's many bets and it looked like he had lost.

"No I don't," said Bob defiantly. "He'll move eventually."

"We've been watching him now for five minutes," said George.

"He'll move."

"We'll bloody freeze to death first," replied George.

"Put a time limit on it," said Doug. "If he hasn't moved in a minute it's a scarecrow."

"Alright," said Bob, as George looked at his watch.

Half a minute later the black figure was still motionless.

"You'll have to pay up on this one," goaded Harry.

"We'll see," replied Bob turning and jogging over to Freddy.

"What the hell is he up to now?" asked George.

"There aren't any binoculars aboard are there?" inquired Doug.

"There shouldn't be," said Ron.

Bob appeared in Freddy's nose and a few seconds later the front turret started to be slowly manually cranked round.

"He's not!" said George his voice full of surprise.

"He is!" chuckled Harry.

"Bob! Don't you dare!" yelled Doug. But it was too late and a short sharp burst of machine gun fire thundered out over the flat silent Lincolnshire countryside. The tracer, strangely dull in the bright light, whizzed over the fields and flashed over the scarecrow's head before disappearing into the empty landscape. The effect was startling; the scarecrow took off across the field like a hare and disappeared over a gate in a single bound.

"Told you it was a farmer," said Bob smugly, as he strolled back towards the open-mouthed and stunned group.

"You'll be strung up for that!" cried Harry.

"I was just testing my turret and I must have forgotten the safety catches."

"They'll never believe that," said George.

"They don't have to, but they can't prove anything."

"Alright," said Doug, a bit flushed and not knowing what to do. If he told the truth Bob would be court-martialled and they would lose him from the crew. If he backed up Bob's story and got caught out they would all be in trouble and there were an awful lot of witnesses. "We all stick to the same story. Bob was testing the guns and they went off, okay?" He looked at Ron. They all nodded. Doug turned to Sergeant Green. "Is that okay with you?"

"Yes, fine, sir." The sergeant was grinning from ear to ear. "Anything to break up the boredom out here. And my lads won't say anything. Will you?" He flashed them a quick glance and they shook their heads.

It was four o'clock when they finished the snow clearing. A Warrant Officer from the station armoury had phoned Sergeant Green to find out what the shooting was and then he had come out to the dispersal to investigate. But he seemed to have been satisfied and left. Now Doug just hoped everyone would keep their mouths shut and the farmer wouldn't make an official complaint. As a truck picked them up to take them back to the technical site the first of the Squadron Lancasters started to return and soon the station was back to full operational readiness.

Although Metheringham was ready, many of the other stations in Bomber Command weren't and the weather for the next few days kept the bombers on the ground. Harry quickly got bored with reading books during the long cold days and volunteered to do a signals course in the station signals section. It wasn't purely out of professionalism however; the best looking WAAFs traditionally were found in the signals sections. Alex had already discovered this and was going out with two of them. He therefore always avoided the signal section in case he met them both at the same time.

By the end of the week Harry was friendly with all of the WAAF signallers but particularly friendly with one called Florence. Alex had given him the tip that the best place to take a WAAF after a night at the pictures in Woodhall Spa or one of the local pubs was the window store. In that small building the bundles of window were piled high. As soft as a large mattress and because the window had to be kept warm and dry it had to rank among the most comfortable of locations on the camp. But all good things come to an end and by the start of the following week the weather had improved so that it was obvious that it wouldn't be long before Ops were back on.

The only other significant event of their enforced time off Ops was Sally's funeral. She was buried in the small graveyard of Timberland village church, just over the fields from the airfield. There was a large turnout for the funeral and the church was full, with standing room only at the back. Harry and the others managed to get the last seats. Her parents were the only family at the service and they were all surprised to find her father was a Wing Commander pilot.

"Why on earth wasn't she an officer?" asked Harry. "She was clever enough and she had the background."

"Don't know," whispered George. "But she seemed happy enough just driving around in her truck."

"What a waste."

"It's all a bloody waste, mate."

Outside in the churchyard the last fall of snow had left the ground a fresh even white, which only went to emphasize the dark scar of the grave. A slight wind blew the one or two remaining snowflakes around the mourners as Sally's coffin covered with a Union Jack was carried slowly out to the grave by six of her fellow drivers. Freddy's crew stood out of the way to one side; there weren't many aircrews there. The crews only spent a relatively short time on a station and they were wrapped up in their own little worlds. Their crew, their ground crew, their driver and a few Ops personnel who briefed them. Everyone else tended to be outside their worlds and they never seemed to get the time to meet them. Sally's job on the other hand took her everywhere and there were few people who didn't know her. With the coffin lying next to the grave the padre read the service, which floated on the slight breeze over the silent flat landscape. Harry looked around at the other mourners. Most of the WAAFs were quietly crying and one or two of the men's eyes looked full. His own throat had a lump in it, which he tried repeatedly to swallow but it wouldn't go. He looked down the line of his crew. Beside him George stood straight, his blue eyes staring straight ahead and looking brighter than usual in the reflected brightness of the snow. On the other side of George was Doug, who was also looking straight ahead but was shuffling uneasily from foot to foot and looking down at the ground a lot. Poor bugger, thought Harry. Sally had practically died in his arms and it had been pretty obvious to anyone who ever saw her look at him that she had fancied him. I wonder if he ever realized. If he did he never showed it. Of course he liked her, but everybody liked Sally. His thoughts were interrupted by two of the pallbearers removing the flag from the coffin and folding it up. The other four pallbearers lifted the two ropes under the coffin and guided it over the grave, then slowly started to lower it. Sally's mother, who had been silent throughout, now let out a loud wail and sobbed uncontrollably, while Sally's father held her in his arms. Harry could hear some other quiet sobs behind him, where there was another group of WAAFs. The lump in his throat now seemed to stretch from ear to ear and his nose had started to run. Around him all the men were sniffing, shuffling and avoiding eye contact and he realized he was not alone in the way he was feeling.

"Earth to earth. Ashes to ashes. Dust to dust." The padre's voice rose clearly above the sobs and was carried by the breeze out across the silent white land.

Something shook Harry's foot and he woke up. "Ops are on, report to the Squadron office at 0900!" shouted the duty guard.

Around the cold billet men were stirring, reluctant to leave the semi-warmth of their beds.

"Thank Christ for that!" said Harry. "This hanging around was driving me up the wall. Let's get on with the war." Jimmy looked over at him with less than enthusiastic eyes. "Cheer up, Jimmy! It'll all be over by Christmas!"

"What the hell's got into him?" asked George. "He's usually half dead in the morning."

"Boredom," replied Harry. "We've got to get on with it. Live fast, die young and leave a good looking corpse."

"Mad bastard," muttered Digger, strolling out to the ablutions.

"I'll give the dying young bit a miss if you don't mind," replied George.

"Too bloody late for you to die young anyway," retorted Harry.

Wrapped in their greatcoats the sergeants waited outside the Squadron office while Doug and Ron went inside to see the Adj. It was a frosty winter's day with a bright cloudless blue sky. Being winter, the sun was still low in the sky, but its watery heatless light reflected off the snow, which around the station buildings was now a dirty off white colour. Soon Doug and Ron emerged.

"Ops are on," Doug announced needlessly. "1500 main briefing, 1400 specialist briefings, Freddy hasn't flown for a few days so we'll take him up for a quick air test now, okay? Is our transport here?"

"I think that might be it there," said George, nodding towards one of the wagons with a very young WAAF driver sitting in it looking lost.

"Right, we'll get our kit on, we should only be up about half an hour so don't bother with all your woollies."

By the time they had changed all the other crews had gone and theirs was the only wagon left. As they walked over to it the WAAF got out and walked around the front to face them before banging up a very smart salute.

"Are you Pilot Officer Jackson, sir?" she asked, in a distinct but soft Irish accent.

"Yes, that's right," replied Doug as Ron, being the senior officer, acknowledged the salute.

The one officer replying and a different officer saluting on top of their ranks being hidden under their leather flying jackets confused the girl and she glanced nervously between them.

"Oh thank goodness, sir. I thought I might be in the wrong place. I only got here the day before yesterday and I'm still finding my way around." She was barely five foot tall and skinny. Her nervous face was plain and freckly, but not unattractive, while the hair that was visible under her hat was bright red. But the thing that struck everyone about her was her bright green eyes.

"That's alright, bonny lass, I can show ya around later," offered Alex.

"Down boy," said George, dragging Alex away to the back of the truck by his collar.

"Don't mind the chaps," said Doug, while the rest of the crew clambered aboard the truck. "We'll be taking Freddy up for an air test for about half an hour, then if all's well coming straight back here. Is that alright?"

"Er, yes, sir." The girl looked confused again and she was starting to shiver in the cold. "Who's Freddy, sir?"

Doug smiled. "F for Freddy, our Lancaster. Are you alright?"

"Yes, sir, just cold."

"Yes, everywhere is cold around here, put plenty of layers of clothes on under your greatcoat. Especially tonight, or you'll freeze."

"Yes, sir," she replied, as they climbed into the truck. Starting the engine she ground the gears and there was a chorus of jeers from the back. "Sorry, sir."

"Don't worry about it."

"Which way do I go, sir?"

"Have you not been shown around yet?"

"No, sir." She looked close to tears.

"No problem, it's not your fault. Just go straight down here and turn right onto the peri track and I'll tell you when we get to Freddy."

She let the clutch out and the wagon jerked forward. There were a couple of loud thumps and some swearing from the back.

"Sorry, sir. We didn't have any wagons like this in training."

"Don't worry about it, it serves them right. What's your name?"

"Aircraft woman two O'Hannlan, sir."

"And your first name?"

She looked a bit surprised that an officer should want to know her first name.

"Caitlin, sir."

"Well, Caitlin, you're out of training now so you don't need to say sir quite as often and don't worry so much. There's a lot for you to find out over the next few days but you'll soon get into the routine. The main thing around here is to try and keep warm." He smiled at her. "When we get to Freddy you wait out of the way by the edge of the dispersal until we've gone. Then go and see Sergeant Green in the ground crew hut. He's always got some tea on and that will warm you up. But remember; tonight put as many clothes on as you can. Our last driver used to look like an over-stuffed Teddy bear." He went quiet as he thought of Sally.

"Thank you, sir." The rest of the drive to Freddy passed in silence, except for the rough gear changes, with each one making Caitlin more nervous.

When he got out at the dispersal Doug looked back at Caitlin.

"Remember, after we've gone see Sergeant Green for a brew. I'll tell him to expect guests and don't worry so much, we all have to learn, you know." He winked and left.

"Who the hell taught her to drive?" asked Bob.

"Douglas Bader," said Harry.

"He has nae got any legs," replied Alex.

"That's the problem!"

"Give her a chance," said Doug. "She's straight out of training, she just needs some practice."

"A'll gi' her some practice, skipper," said Alex.

"She's just a bairn and you've already got two WAAFs on the go," said George.

"Aye but did ya see her eyes?"

"Yeah, as bloody green as she is," replied Bob climbing up the ladder into Freddy.

Harry followed him with both his parachute pack and flight bag in one hand and steadying himself with the other. Inside, Freddy was like a fridge. With no sunlight getting in, the fuselage never got the chance to warm up and as Harry groped his way forward everything he touched was covered with frozen water droplets. Stepping up onto the bomb bay and squeezing over the rear spar he reached over the front spar and put his flight bag on his seat. Then, placing his parachute pack in its stowage on the right side of the fuselage, just behind the main spar, he strapped it in. Next he straddled over the main spar and lifting his bag onto his desk he slid sideways into his seat on the left side of the fuselage. Rummaging through his bag he pulled out the Very pistol cartridges with the colours of the day in them and stowed them in their racks along either side of the fuselage. Pulling out his flying helmet he slid it on, plugged it into the connection lead on his left and turned on the intercom. The crackle of static filled his ears and he plugged in and checked his oxygen. All was well and Doug and Jimmy were squeezing past him, so they would soon be starting engines.

"Skipper, I'd like to check the calibration of the Fishpond so could you call the heights every hundred feet as we climb away."

"Okay, Harry, I'll get Ron to do it." That was what Harry wanted, but he knew if he asked Ron directly he would say no. Doug would be busy enough during the climb while Ron on a local air test would have his own kit to check, but the navigation would be no problem.

With Ron outmanoeuvred he turned his attention to the large square black T1154 radio transmitter sitting in front of him, with its two vertical rows of three knobs down either side. The knobs were bright yellow, red and blue and each had a series of letters on them. These set the frequency for the HF transmitter and he checked they were all set correctly. Then he turned the aerial selector to the left of the T1154 from the earth or off position to the normal setting. The set would now transmit using the wire aerial stretching from the top of the mast above the set to the top of one of the tail fins. Now he would set the receiver. The T1155 receiver sat below the T1154 and was the same width but only half as high. This had a large central knob with a horseshoe shaped Perspex arc around it. Behind the Perspex were multiple arced lines with frequencies on them and turning the large knob moved a pointer to the appropriate frequency. To the left of the central knob was a volume control and below that a switch to select the correct frequency band. This would determine which frequency arc to use when tuning the receiver. The transmitter and receiver being completely separate meant you could transmit on one frequency and receive on a different frequency.

Doug had already checked everyone was ready for engine start and the starboard inner suddenly turned over and fired into life. The vibration went straight along the main spar, which formed the back of Harry's seat, and into his spine. One by one the other engines fired until all were rumbling away at low revs and Doug and Jimmy started one by one checking them over. Both of Freddy's generators were now on line so Harry could continue his checks. Checking again that he was set up on the 5 Group HF frequency, he unplugged his headset lead from the aircraft intercom and plugged it into the radio. Now he was cut off from anything that was said by the rest of the crew and it always made him feel isolated. Next he put his hand on the Morse key fixed to the right-hand side of his desk and tapped out a short test transmission. Although three of Freddy's engines were throttled back the fourth was being run at high revs and the noise was deafening. Harry pressed both his hands to his earphones forcing them tight onto his ears to try and cut out the noise. It was typical that the radio operator's position was probably the noisiest part of a Lancaster, thought Harry. After a few seconds he heard the distinct stuttering bleeps of the answering message coming back from 5 Group HQ. They were loud and clear both ways. When they got airborne he would try again using the trailing aerial, which would give far better long-range reception.

Swapping his headset plug back to the Lancaster's intercom he switched on his Fishpond screen. This little box was to the left of the T1155 and angled slightly to make the small green six-inch screen easier to see. It seemed to take a long time to warm up but eventually the rotating green trace line appeared and Harry adjusted the brightness and contrast until he was happy with it. Ever since their first trip he had put a lot of faith in that little box and whenever it didn't work he was not happy. Now the picture looked good, but he would not be able to check it properly until they were airborne and then that depended on Ron cooperating. Even now Ron was changing range scales on the H2S, which, as it used the same antenna as the Fishpond also changed Harry's range scales. Harry gritted his teeth. Ron really irritated him and he would do almost anything to get rid of him.

"Check in front to back with any problems," crackled Doug. As usual with Freddy, there were none and after a pause they taxied out onto the taxiway. Harry stowed any kit he didn't need immediately in his flight bag and pushed it under his desk while Bob passed him to sit behind the spar for takeoff. Normally Harry would join him but on this flight he wanted to calibrate the Fishpond so he needed to be in his seat. Bob wasn't on intercom so when Doug asked if everyone was ready for takeoff Harry looked around at him and put his thumb up, Bob replied with another thumbs up.

"Radio operator and bomb aimer ready for take-off. Don't forget the height calls every hundred feet, please."

"I won't," replied Ron sharply and Freddy set off down the runway.

The empty bomber seemed to rocket down the runway and leap into the air in no time at all. Harry recognised the sounds of the undercarriage being retracted and it seemed they would hardly be fully retracted when Ron called 100 feet. Bob squeezed past him and disappeared towards the nose while he checked the Fishpond screen. At this height ground echoes swamped the little screen but as they got higher these would reduce until the screen was clear. At 300 feet a ring clear of green ground returns appeared near the centre of the screen and by 1,500 feet nearly the whole screen was clear.

"Fishpond fully serviceable and calibrated," he reported. Now he got out of his seat and kneeling on the floor crawled under his desk to get at the trailing aerial handle. Why it had been put in such an inaccessible place he had no idea but he started to unwind it, letting the long lead-weighted aerial slide out behind the bomber. By the time he had finished he was out of breath and sweating. It was one of the radio operators' great secrets that the radio operator's position in a

Lancaster was the warmest place to be. The hot air vents for the fuselage were next to the radio operator and as he got the full benefit, Harry never wore the woollen sweaters the rest of the crew found essential. Once back in his seat he selected the trailing aerial and smiling to himself tuned the T1154 and T1155 to Metheringham's WT frequency. Standing up, he put one foot on his seat and holding the green vertical pole that stretched from floor to ceiling in the middle of the fuselage beside his radio equipment he raised himself up so that his head entered the circular Perspex astrodome, which formed the roof of his compartment. Most people didn't need the aid of the seat, but Harry didn't mind being short, it just meant he didn't bang his head on as many things. The view from the astrodome was breathtaking. The brilliant blue sky above them and the dazzling white snow below. Harry reckoned they were more than halfway to the coast and screwing up his eyes against the glare he scanned the sky for other aircraft, but there were none to be seen. He could see the sea ahead of them and so they would be far enough away from Metheringham to test the trailing aerial. Back in his seat he sent the short test message and the reply quickly came back. All Morse operators have their own style and with practice an operator can tell one from another. Harry immediately recognised Florence's style and smiling he sent a quick, "Back soon."

When they reached the coast they turned and followed it north. Now Harry could check the calibration of the DF direction finding aerial.

"Can you hold her straight and level for a DF bearing check, skipper?"

"Okay, Harry, steady on north."

Harry smiled, good old Doug. The DF aerial scale read bearings relative to the aircraft heading and had to be converted into a true bearing. But as they were heading north they would both be the same, saving Harry from having to work out the difference. Since the introduction of GEE and H2S many people thought homing and position fixing by radio was out of date, inaccurate and old-fashioned. But while it wasn't as fast or accurate as GEE and the accuracy fell off drastically if you were further away than 100 miles from the transmitting station Harry thought it was still a good system and far better than nothing. Switching his headset lead to the radio he tuned his receiver to Metheringham's DF frequency and selected the direction finding loop aerial above the fuselage just forward of his position and under the Perspex cockpit fairing. Listening to the continuous tone in his earphones he reached above the T1154 set and turned the DF aerial rotating gear slowly, while keeping his eyes fixed on the visual tuning indicator on the top right of the T1155. When the tuning indicator showed minimum signal strength and the aural tune all but disappeared the aerial was at 90 degrees to the transmitter. Now by reading the graduated scale on the DF aerial rotating gear he could find the bearing. Two six four degrees to Metheringham, or it could be zero eight four degrees, the direct opposite of two six four. In most cases it was obvious which was correct, as in this case. They had flown east so Metheringham must be to their west, but just to check the equipment Harry turned the aerial to the left and watched the tuning indicator. It moved to the right showing the aerial was right. If it had moved left it would have meant he was 180 degrees out and zero eight four was the correct bearing.

"Metheringham bearing two six four degrees true," he announced after swapping his headset lead back to intercom.

"I make it two six one," said Ron.

Harry gritted his teeth. Ron seemed to like finding fault and criticising everything anyone else did. A 3-degree error over a distance of 30 miles would get them within one and a half miles of Metheringham and even that small error was probably due to the delay while he switched his headset lead over. Well sod him, he thought, that was as accurate a bearing as anyone was ever going to get and he was happy that Freddy was on top line. Now he stood in the astrodome and watched Skegness slide past down their left side as Doug turned them back towards Metheringham.

"Will we be needed for anything after we land, skipper?"

"I won't need you for anything, Harry, but I don't know if the Adj might need us for something. Why?" Doug knew why but he thought he might have a bit of fun at Harry's expense.

"No reason, skipper."

"He's got a hot date, skipper," chipped in Alex, as Doug knew he would.

"Yeah, skip, Harry doesn't have any time for his old mates now he's got a sheila."

"That's right, Bob, there was a time when Harry was always there to stand his round but now we hardly ever see him," said George. "I think it's bad for the harmony of the crew."

"Bollocks!" said Harry.

"You never were one for the more complex reasoned argument, were you Harry?" retorted Bob.

"Never you mind, Harry," said Alex. "They're only jealous, you gi' her one from me."

"You've got two on the go already, you'll wear it out if you're not careful," called George.

"She's not like that," interrupted Harry.

"Oh, it's no love is it?" asked Alex. "Medic, quick!"

"You're all better off without them!" said Ron, his voice full of venom. "They're fine so long as you give them everything they want whenever they want it. But as soon as they want something you can't give them they turn on you!"

The outburst silenced the intercom and after a few seconds Doug felt the need to fill the void.

"Metheringham ahead, prepare for landing."

Harry rushed into the main briefing room with the rest of the radio operators, just ahead of the Station and Squadron Commanders and took his usual seat between Alex and Ron, four rows from the front of the room. Florence had taken an early lunch and he had met her outside the large dining room. She didn't need to go back to work for over an hour so, wrapped up against the cold, they walked up the lane towards Metheringham village. The lane had been cleared of snow and slush and now it was almost dry in the winter sun. When they got to the north side of the airfield they cut over the fields heading east. They had talked happily and freely about anything and everything. The subject didn't matter so much as the learning of the other's opinion on it. Their world consisted of two people in a brilliant white landscape and they were happy with that. Then they reached the bomb dump, with the tractors pulling bomb trains from the dump to the waiting bombers and their world changed. Florence had gone very quiet and they walked almost in silence to Blankney wood, before turning south along the perimeter track, past the bombers being bombed and fuelled up. Eventually she had asked how long he thought the war would last and what he was going to do then. It had struck him that he had never thought about it before, because it had always seemed so far away. He had always assumed he would go back to being an electrician and it still seemed the logical thing to do, but he had never thought about it. Planning ahead had never been something Harry did; he just went along with what life brought him and in the present situation that seemed to be the best thing to do.

At that time bomber crews lasted on average seven missions and that night would be their sixth Op. So as far as Harry knew he might only have a few hours of future left. It was the first time he had thought of it like that and it scared him. The faces of people whom you didn't really know but who suddenly weren't there anymore; they hadn't moved on to somewhere else, they were dead. His attitude had always been if it's going to happen it will happen and there's nothing you can do about it, so why worry. But now, in the middle of a flat snow-covered Lincolnshire landscape, alone with Florence, it suddenly struck him that he was happy, he enjoyed life and didn't want to die. He had said he thought the war would last another couple of years and he would go back to being an electrician. But now, as he listened to Florence talk about her plans, he was thinking about what his chances were of seeing the end of the war. They had called into the NAAFI on the communal site for a mug of tea before Florence had to go back to work. This was their first goodbye before an Op and the silent tension in the air was oppressive. Both felt they were bursting with things they wanted to say, but dared not. If they never saw each other again they would regret their silence for the rest of their lives, but to say those things was almost like admitting this meeting would be their last. Eventually it could be postponed no longer and they hugged and kissed and went their separate ways, with all the things left unsaid and trying to believe that it was just another everyday parting. Harry had swallowed the lump from his throat, forced himself to think of what he needed to do for the Op and headed to the sergeants' mess. Florence had calmly walked out of sight, then dried her eyes, blown her nose and gone to work.

The radio operators' specialist briefing had consisted of the lists of frequencies to be use for wind finding, 5 Group command frequency, emergencies, Master Bomber and fixing and homing. The colours of the day: these were the correct colour flares, which could be fired to identify an aircraft as friendly to searchlights, ships or flak batteries. They were changed every few hours, so more than one set of flares was carried and it was important to have the right ones ready when needed. Codes for the night were issued and stowed carefully away. Finally the German colours of the day were issued. This information always came in late and nobody knew how it ever got into British hands, but it was obviously very useful to have and some people had gone to a lot of trouble to get it.

The main briefing followed the usual pattern. Tonight would be a trip to Schweinfurt and Harry checked his information and made any extra notes he thought might be useful. Then he followed everyone else out to the crew room to kit up. As he sat in the back of the truck, lurching through its gear changes around the airfield to Freddy, Harry watched the sun getting lower in the sky. Up until now he had felt nothing but excitement at this moment. Setting off on another great adventure, but now, while he wasn't exactly scared, it all suddenly seemed to have a finality about it. With a squeak of brakes and a lurch the truck stopped.

"Well, that's the most dangerous bit of the Op over," said George, climbing over the tailboard.

Harry smiled. Nothing seemed to bother George, and he wished he were like that. Or was George like that because he didn't have anything in his life he would really miss, he wondered. That was it, Jimmy was as attached as any married man and it was obvious Ops scared him to death. Ron was the same, but George didn't have anyone in his life and Ops didn't seem to bother him. Now it had happened to Harry, he had a girlfriend and he had more of a reason to want to come back. Well, there's nothing you can do about it, if it's going to happen it's going to happen, he thought to himself as he followed George over the tailboard and along the side of the wagon. It's all just one big exciting adventure and life goes on.

George pulled a large envelope full of letters out of one of his pockets and tapped on the driver's window.

"Same routine... Er... I mean, could you look after these for us?"

The large green eyes looked back puzzled.

"What do you want me to do with them, sergeant?"

"Just hold onto them for us, but if anything happens to us give it to the Squadron Adjutant. He'll know what to do with them."

Caitlin suddenly understood and she looked horrified.

"Yes, sergeant, of course."

Sometimes life doesn't go on, thought Harry.

16

They were well out over the southern North Sea now; level at 20,000 feet somewhere near the front of the bomber stream. Outside the night was dark but cloudless. Standing in the astrodome Harry scanned the sky but could only see a dozen or so stars. His headset was plugged into the radio and he was monitoring the Group frequency in case there were any recall orders cancelling the raid. It was vital any recall message wasn't missed, but he hated not being in contact with the rest of the crew, even if nothing was being said; at least he knew he wasn't missing anything. Lowering himself into his seat he pushed his headset leads and oxygen tube out of the way. Reaching for the small Anglepoise lamp to the left of his desk he shone it on his watch. The bulb was dulled with several layers of paper to protect his night vision. It was nearly time to receive the first of the Group winds. The Group wind finders would transmit their wind speed and direction estimations back to Group headquarters every half hour. Group would average them and retransmit that average for all the Group aircraft on the Group frequency fifteen minutes later. It was now nearly quarter past the hour so the new wind should come through any time. On cue the distinct stuttering of Morse pierced the static in Harry's headset. Grabbing his signal log he scribbled down the letters. The transmission ended, then after a pause started to repeat itself. Harry now took his codebook and transcribed the jumble of meaningless letters he had just copied down into an estimation of the current wind speed and direction. He wrote it down on a note pad and passed it around his radio equipment to Ron, who he guessed would probably ignore it and use whatever wind speed and direction he had found for himself.

With a sigh he switched his headset lead to intercom to see if there was anything going on among the crew, but all was quiet. He decided he would stay on intercom for a minute or two, because it was unlikely that any recall message would be passed immediately after a Group wind and strangely, he always felt safer when he was on intercom. To his left, by the radio equipment, the Fishpond screen glowed a dull green as the trace revolved. There were half a dozen contacts on it and he gave them a quick check but they were all obviously other bombers. Still, it proved the equipment was working and reluctantly he switched his headset back to WT. Then he stood on his seat again, with his head in the astrodome and continued his lookout.

Five minutes later Bob spotted the Belgian coast and reported it to Ron, but Harry on WT couldn't hear it and it was five minutes after that, when they actually crossed the coast, that Harry spotted it for himself. At the same time as he spotted the coast they were greeted by the usual sporadic coastal flak, which, while not as intense as the flak over a target, was nonetheless unsettling. The dull red flashes were nowhere near them and far below a string of red tennis balls arced slowly upwards as a light flak gunner also tried his luck. You'll be lucky, thought Harry, knowing they were well above the ceiling of any light flak. As he thought it the string of red balls curved in mid air and started their downward journey. He hated being so cut off from the rest of the crew; anything could be happening. He had talked to other radio operators and they felt the same. But most of them had navigators who would nudge or even kick them to get their attention, and then shout what was going on, write it down or repeat it once the radio operator had plugged into the intercom. But there would be none of that from Ron, unless it was absolutely necessary. Harry scowled to himself; still at least this was a comparatively short Op. Although Schweinfurt was over 150 miles inside Germany it was nowhere near as long a trip as to Berlin and back. Now they were over Belgium Doug was weaving and Harry swapped the flare in the Very pistol from the allied to the German colours of the day and alternated between scanning the sky from the astrodome and checking the Fishpond screen. Searchlights waved around the sky to the north, which must be Brussels and to the south, which must be Charleroi. Another Group wind came in and Harry decoded it and passed it to Ron. They must be near the German border by now, thought Harry. This line on the map scared most aircrew. The very thought that they were now over the Third Reich was a psychological hurdle to them, but to Harry it was the opposite. Once over Germany it was unlikely there would be any recall message and he could stop listening to WT except at the scheduled Group wind transmission times and would feel part of the crew again. As Harry passed the Group wind to Ron he swapped to intercom and breathed a silent sigh of relief. A few moments later they crossed into Germany and although nothing had been said on the intercom Harry was much happier.

"Bomber going down, 7 o'clock about two miles," said Alex. Harry twisted around in the astrodome but couldn't see it.

"Roger, one hour to the target," replied Ron.

Only an hour to the target. If only all the missions were this short, thought Harry as he sat down and looked at the Fishpond screen. Still plenty of contacts but none very close and all of them following their own independent weaving courses rather than steadily closing in on Freddy which would give them away as a night fighter. Twenty minutes later Ron ordered a course change to take them south of Koblenz but north of Frankfurt. The route would keep them out of the Koblenz flak zone, which seemed to be getting bigger all the time and the large Frankfurt Mannheim flak zone. Should be getting near the Rhein, thought Harry as he looked again at the Fishpond. Nothing again, he was just about to get back up when he looked again at a blip at maximum range. It was only just starting to appear and he had no idea what had made it catch his eye but he decided to watch it. It was dead astern but as they were weaving it looked to be at any time up to 20 degrees either side of their 6 o'clock. It was moving slightly faster than Freddy and appeared to be on a straight course. Either it was a fast but lazy bomber, which couldn't be bothered to weave, maybe a Mosquito. But a Mosquito would be faster than this contact, which was only catching them up very slowly.

"Possible Fishpond contact!"

"Where, Harry?" asked George. "I can't see anything.

"Dead astern, low, over 500 yards."

"Still no contact."

"Do you want me to corkscrew?" asked Doug.

"Not yet, we need to see him before we can call which way to go," replied George. "Where is he, Harry?"

"5 o'clock low 400 yards!"

George and Alex swivelled their turrets. "Can't see anything," said George.

"4 o'clock low 350 yards…Now 5 o'clock 350 yards closing slowly… Dead astern low and still closing…"

"A've got something 7 o'clock low, A cannae make it out," said Alex.

"That's him," exclaimed Harry. "300 yards."

"He's turning in!" yelled Alex.

"Corkscrew port skipper!" shouted George.

Freddy leapt to port and dived, the Merlins' rumble rising to a scream punctuated by a short burst of fire from Alex's guns.

"Junkers 88 6 o'clock high!" cried Alex. With Freddy's wings vertical Doug let the bomber's nose drop rapidly and heard a long rattle from George's turret as the fighter passed behind their tail.

"Reverse starboard and climb, skipper!" shouted George. Doug had been waiting for this. The fighter had overshot and now by turning tightly back towards him he would either end up in front of them or have to break away to avoid a collision. They had practised it enough during fighter affiliation. "Lost him! Last seen 6 o'clock low!"

"A had him 3 o'clock but he's gone now," said Alex.

"Have you got him, Harry?" asked Doug.

"No, skipper, but I'll keep looking."

"Roger, steadying back on course. Is there any damage?"

"Doubt it, skipper. A dinnae think he got a shot in."

"Okay, check everything anyway and good work."

"Yeah, nice one, Harry," echoed George.

Harry's legs were shaking, he was breathing heavily and he was sure the sweat had little to do with the hot air vent beside his seat. He took a few deep breaths of the cold oxygen and looked closely at every blip on the Fishpond screen until he was certain they were all bombers.

"Ten minutes to target," announced Ron.

Harry slid out of his seat and, lying on his front on the ice-cold floor, he crawled under his table to get at the handle to wind in the trailing aerial. If he didn't wind it in it could be ripped off by one of their bombs. As he lay on the floor, struggling with the winding handle, his intercom leads and oxygen tube seemed determined to tie him in knots. Several times he had to stop to straighten his oxygen tube so that he could breathe properly. By the time he had finished he was very out of breath and they were only five minutes from the target. He had a quick look at Fishpond and then looked out of the astrodome to see the searchlights dead ahead of them.

"Bomb doors open, master switch on, bombs fused and selected, skipper," said Bob. Doug repeated the instructions and Harry heard and felt the bomb bay doors directly below his compartment open. Now he would have to check they were fully open. If they weren't, in theory the electrical current that would release the bombs should not be allowed to go to the bomb carriers and the bombs would not fall. Worse still, if the bombs did fall into half open doors they would smash them. Reaching behind his seat he got hold of a portable oxygen bottle and, taking a deep breath, he disconnected his oxygen tube from the aircraft's oxygen supply and plugged it into the bottle. Now he could move around carrying his own bottled supply. Disconnecting his intercom leads he clambered over the main spar behind his seat and shone his torch on the floor between the main and rear spar. Here there was a small inspection hatch, which looked into the bomb bay. As he lifted the hatch, a blast of wind hit him square in the face and he squinted to see against it. He tilted his head from side to side to see between the bombs and incendiary containers. The bomb doors looked fully open and there were no signs of ice or anything else that could prevent the doors from having opened fully. Replacing the hatch he returned to his seat, plugged his oxygen back into the aircraft's supply and reconnected his intercom leads.

"Bomb doors fully open."

"Roger," replied Bob.

Freddy suddenly jumped and Harry heard a woof above the noise of the engines. They were entering the flak barrage so he stood in the astrodome to watch the display. Lots of people preferred not to look, but the flashes, coloured flares and burning city fascinated Harry. He wasn't really scared over the target. There was nothing he could do about it and with flak it was pure bad luck if it hit you, so it was better to just not think about it and enjoy the view. Although they were near the front of the bomber stream there were quite a few large fires burning in Schweinfurt and the red glow reflected off the curved Perspex of the astrodome. It was not the best of positions to observe the attack because the astrodome was designed to give good vision upwards. He could see the yellow and red bursts of flak and the weaving searchlights but anything below them was difficult to spot. To the front the Perspex of the cockpit canopy got in the way and to the sides the curve of the fuselage and the wings interrupted the view. Looking to the rear he could see the glow reflecting off Alex's turret, the shapes changing as the turret revolved. What must the view be like for Bob, he thought, a glimpse into hell? Bob's instructions were getting quicker, a sure sign they were near the release point and then with a "Bombs gone! Hold her steady for the photoflash!" Freddy shot upwards as the bombs fell away and a few seconds later he heard the hydraulic actuating jacks close the bomb doors.

Again he reached for and connected his portable oxygen bottle and scrambled back over the main spar to check the bomb bay. This time he was not greeted by an ice-cold blast of air so it looked as if the bomb bay doors had shut properly. He shone his torch into the now empty bomb bay. The inspection hatch was halfway down the thirty-three-foot long bomb bay and to see the full length he had to get right down on the floor and put his head through the hatch. With what space was left in the small hatchway he angled his torch beam around the dark recesses of the bay.

"Shit!"

Halfway between the hatch and the front of the bay there was an evil-looking squat cylinder. Standing up he reconnected his intercom leads. "Skipper, it's Harry, we've got a hung up 1,000 pounder."

"Which station is it on?" asked Bob.

"I don't know, it's towards the front of the bay."

"Well, all my switches are set correctly."

"I'm not saying it's your fault, I'm just saying we've got a hang up."

"Alright," interrupted Doug. "What should we do about it?"

"We're still heading east, how about we get out of the target area and on our way home first," said Ron sarcastically.

"Roger," said Bob. "The photoflash has fired."

"New heading one eight zero degrees compass," said Ron. The return route took them south before turning west.

"One eight zero degrees compass," repeated Doug. "Is it a delayed action?"

"All the 1,000 pounders were three or six-hour delayed actions," replied Bob.

"Well, could it be armed?"

"Was the fusing link still in, Harry?" asked Bob.

"I couldn't see. It's right forward. I'll have to go to the forward inspection hatch."

While Harry was making his way forward Doug asked Bob how they should get rid of the bomb.

"Well, I reckon we should find out which station it's on, open the bomb doors then dive and pull up quickly while I try the release again."

"And if that doesn't work?"

"We've got a length of quarter inch thick wire with a hook on the end and we try and pull the carriers apart with that."

"Will that work?"

"I have no idea, but we can't take it back. It may be just a three-hour delayed action and the delays are only approximate."

Doug didn't like the thought of landing with a hung up bomb on board, never mind one that had very little of its delayed action fuse left to run. There was no knowing how tightly the bomb was attached; maybe the smallest jolt would dislodge it.

"It's on number two station," cut in Harry from the forward inspection hatch.

"Roger. Number two station selected and armed. Bomb doors open, skipper, master arming switch on."

"Bomb doors open, master arming switch on," repeated Doug.

"Dive whenever you're ready, skipper." Doug eased the control column forward and let the speed build up. Harry had closed the inspection hatch before the bomb doors were opened and now he just lay on the floor while Freddy accelerated and started to buck and bounce.

"Pull up when you're ready, skipper," called Bob and Harry immediately felt himself get heavier as the G force increased pushing him hard down onto the cold floor. Freddy was now in a slight climb using the extra speed to regain some of the lost height.

"Has it gone?" asked Bob.

Harry took a quick look. "Has it bollocks."

"I'll get the wire," said Jimmy, disappearing down the dark tunnel of the fuselage and reappearing a few moments later.

With Harry's head through the hatch there wasn't much room for him to manoeuvre the five-foot length of wire and even less for Jimmy to shine the torch so that Harry could see what he was doing. The slipstream whipped a 200 mph wind around his head and upside down above him a blacked out Germany slid past. After a couple of attempts Harry managed to hook the wire around one arm of the bomb carrier and pulled, but it wouldn't budge. He straightened up and braced himself against the side of the fuselage and tried again; still nothing. It was hard work at 20,000 feet and straightening up he leaned back against the side of the fuselage for a rest.

"Give me a go!" yelled Jimmy off intercom, above the noise of the engines. They changed places and Jimmy pulled at the wire. For a second there was no movement, then the wire slipped off the carrier and Jimmy fell back against the fuselage wall. Undeterred he looked through the hatch while Harry shone the torch for him and on the third attempt reattached the wire. This time he braced himself tight and gave a massive heave. Again nothing, until all at once the wire gave and Freddy bounced up slightly. Jimmy had overbalanced again so Harry checked the bomb bay. The reluctant bomb was gone.

"Done it, skipper, it's gone you can close the bomb doors now," he panted.

"Roger, well done."

"Well, that's one bomb that won't do anybody any harm. We're over open country," said Bob, his voice full of disappointment.

"It's probably got as much chance as any other bomb you've ever dropped," teased George. They were heading southwest now aiming to pass between Karlsruhe and Stuttgart and they were still near the front of the bomber stream.

Ten miles from Karlsruhe, on the outskirts of the town of Baden-Baden, Feldwebel Willy Herget opened the door of the control room, which was really just a wooden hut with a telephone in it, and stepped out into the cold night. He was eighteen with bright red hair and a face full of freckles, which did nothing to stop him looking even younger. His detachment commander, an Oberfeldwebel, had just taken a telephone call from their area controller telling them that tonight's raid was approaching their area. He had immediately given his first orders and now to Willy's left a generator coughed and roared to life. In the darkness he could see shadows running to their stations. Most of them were the same age as Willy, or even younger. To his right, standing out against the sky, was the wire dish shaped aerial of the detachment's Wurzburg radar and to his front, with figures moving around it, was the squat shape of their two-metre searchlight in its sandbagged revetment. The detachment commander would be standing near the searchlight, wearing a headset connecting him to the radar operator in the Wurzburg cabin. The radar operator would tell him when he was locked onto a target and the searchlight would automatically follow the directions of the radar. The detachment commander would then give the order to "expose" and the brilliant beam would reach up into the sky. Willy's job was to man the unit telephone and pass on any instructions from higher command. He should be sitting by the phone now, but it was stuffy in the office and he needed some fresh air. If the phone rang he would still hear it from outside the door. This was a new site and they had only been there a few days. The hut smelt of freshly cut wood and the site was rutted and muddy from all the truck movements bringing in the equipment. They were the latest part of the extension of the Karlsruhe defences and in the area around the searchlight site there were four batteries of heavy flak guns, some light flak guns and four other searchlights, although theirs was the only one with radar guidance.

Above the noise of the generator he could hear barked orders but, barely audible, over that there was a low-pitched drone coming from the east. To the north a far-off air raid siren wailed. Suddenly the Wurzburg antenna swivelled to point east, the suddenness of the sound of the metal bearings making Willy jump. The drone was louder now and the radar aerial started to make small jerky movements as it searched for its prey, then it was still. Willy stared at the scanner and could just tell that it was moving very slowly; it had acquired a target and was tracking its every movement. Now the searchlight started to rotate and elevate, aligning itself with the radar. They had already been given clearance to expose their light as soon as they acquired a target so any second now the world would be lit up. The searchlight stopped its rapid movement and now slowly followed the guidance of the radar. A loud guttural order was barked from beside the light and with a sharp click the site was suddenly lit up with a brilliant white light, which painted Willy's world a stark black and white. The intense beam reached into the heavens.

Harry was in the astrodome giving the sky a quick once over before going back to his Fishpond screen when his eyes were suddenly seared by the brightest light he had ever experienced. It was like looking directly at the sun and he instinctively screwed his eyes tight shut and sought sanctuary in the depths of his compartment. Even back in his seat when he opened his eyes the normally dark space was lit brighter than the brightest day and the unnaturally intense light seemed to penetrate everywhere.

In the cockpit Doug and Jimmy were in a worse position than Harry because for them there was no escape.

"I can't see!" screamed Doug, as he tried to force his eyes open, but the light was so bright it hurt.

"Duck down and fly on instruments," suggested Jimmy.

"No! We have to break free quickly before other lights fasten onto us! Where's the light coming from?"

"1 o'clock, I think, skipper," yelled Bob, whose nose compartment was also dazzlingly bright.

"Okay, I'm going to dive directly towards the beam then veer away at high speed. Jimmy, I might need your help to pull out of the dive!" While he spoke Doug turned right and pushed the nose down towards the light. As he did so the first of the flak, which always followed searchlights, arrived and Freddy shook and bounced in the turbulent air.

"Call the speeds and height, Ron!" yelled Doug, remembering that behind his curtain Ron might be the only person in the crew who could still see.

"200 mph 20,000 feet," reported Ron, confirming he could still see. Doug kept Freddy's throttles where they were and let the speed rapidly build up in the dive. Flak burst around them, he could feel the bumps and the occasional rattle of shrapnel, but he could see nothing except the white glare.

"250 mph 18,000 feet!"

Doug knew the ground was somewhere in front of him but through the windscreen there was nothing but white. The controls were getting heavy as the speed increased and he thought about closing the throttles, but going fast was the whole point and he would need all the speed he could get when he tried to break away from the beam.

"300 mph 16,000 feet!"

Freddy kicked sideways and the left rudder hit the bottom of Doug's boot hard. Doug's eyes were now streaming with looking into the light and tears were running down his cheeks. They worked their way under his oxygen mast to leave their salty taste on his dry lips.

"350 mph 14,000 feet!"

Doug had never flown this fast before. The maximum diving speed of a Lancaster, according to the pilot's notes, was 360 mph and that gave a true air speed of about 450 mph, an incredible speed for a bomber. As the speed increased the controls got heavier and Freddy became more and more nose heavy. Now it was taking all of Doug's strength to stop the bomber dipping into an even steeper dive, from which there could be no recovery.

"360 mph 12,000 feet!"

Doug reached down quickly with his right hand and took a quick turn of nose up elevator trim to ease the pressure on his arms, which were holding back the control column to keep Freddy's nose from pitching down. Now was the time to break away, but as he was about to make his move a massive jolt lifted Freddy's tail and pitched the nose down. Curses and yells filled his ears as the crew were thrown around, but Doug was more concerned with getting them out of the dive which was now very steep, maybe too steep?

"380 mph 10,000 feet!"

Too fast, too fast, thought Doug, 20 mph too fast. The control column was solid when he tried to roll right and pull the nose up, but even standing on the rudder pedals and heaving for all he was worth he couldn't bring Freddy's nose up.

"Use the elevator trim! But for God's sake be gentle with it!" yelled Jimmy. A small amount of elevator trim should bring the nose up, but too much at this speed would rip Freddy's wings off. Quickly Doug reached down and eased on the tiniest amount of nose up trim. Then he jumped as two huge arms suddenly appeared either side of him and grabbed the control column above his own hands and he felt it move very slightly back.

"390 mph 8,000 feet!" Ron's voice sounded desperate and it was hardly surprising. Jimmy's oxygen mask had slipped off and Doug could feel his hot breath on the back of his neck as he breathed hard, straining at the controls. Ahead everything was still a blinding light and there was no way of seeing if the nose was coming up.

"390 mph 6,000 feet!"

It was working, the nose must be coming up if the speed wasn't increasing, but would it be quickly enough? How high was the ground around this area? Doug knew in some areas around this part of Germany the ground was over 2,000 feet and the damned light was still locked tightly to them. How could it have followed them through that dive? His instructors had always told him to dive towards searchlights and break away at high speed. Charlie had told him the same thing, but this light was stuck like glue.

"390 mph 5,000 feet!" Ron's voice now seemed to have a touch of pleading to it. Suddenly there was a hard deafening rattle right in front of him, which made him jump. What the hell was happening now? There was a brief pause then the rattle started again and Doug realised Bob had managed to scramble his way into the front turret and was now spraying machine gun fire into the glare.

"390 mph and level at 4,000 feet!" yelled Ron his voice now full of relief. Doug eased the nose up slightly, trading speed for height, his eyes still squinting through the glare and then suddenly all was darkness again.

Willy stared up the piercing blue white beam and saw the bomber caught in its brilliance, like a white moth impaled on a silver lance. Within seconds the other four searchlights in the area had also lit up and weaved around uncertainly, homing in on the bomber. It was turning now but one of the other beams also held it and the rest weren't far away. The flak batteries opened fire from the woods around him and their red and yellow muzzle flashes gave contrast to Willy's stark black and white world.

Willy was not a Nazi, he had been forced to join the Hitler Youth and now he was more than happy to help defend his country, but he hated the war and wished it were over. That said, he hated the terror bombers and what they were doing to Germany's cities. He had seen the devastation and knew how many women and children they killed and he willed the bomber in the searchlights to burn. It was diving now and at first he thought it had been hit, but it appeared to be under control. The other searchlights had found it and the first of the flak was bursting around it in yellow flashes at the apex of their pyramid. Soon it will fall, he thought. It had turned towards them and it looked smaller head on, but the flak was putting up a terrific barrage and the roar of the guns echoed around the woods in a continuous rumble. Why wouldn't it burn? One of the other searchlights lost the bomber and fumbled around trying to reacquire it. Then another flew wide,

"Don't lose it!" he yelled to the world in general, as his frustration rose. The bomber was still heading straight at them and approaching at a terrific speed; he could see it getting bigger all the time. If the guns weren't quick they would lose it and he urged them on. The flak was still thick and on target, but now there was only their light still on the bomber and it was getting very close. The bomber almost filled the searchlight beam and now it was below the effective height of the heavy flak batteries. From somewhere behind him a rhythmical thump, thump, thump announced the fire of a light flak gun, probably 40mm, thought Willy, as the red balls of fire passed over his head and seemed to rise slowly towards the rapidly approaching bomber. Now it was pulling out of its dive and the radar-guided light followed it unerringly. Willy saw half a dozen streaks of red fly out of the night in front of him and disappear over his head, followed a second later by a whipping sound and a series of sharp cracks.

Up until now the bomber had just been a target to be destroyed, but Willy suddenly realised it was a weapon of war and capable of fighting back and they were under fire. He started to move to his left where there was a slit trench, but he couldn't take his eyes off the bomber, which was now almost on them. It was a Lancaster, the wings and what he could see of the fuselage from the head on aspect were black, but the nose and cockpit were white in the reflected light. More streaks of red flashed out of the edge of the searchlight beam and headed towards them. One cracked close behind him and with a loud bang smashed through the wooden wall of the hut where he had just been standing. Another hit the ground three feet to his right with a thump that sent a shower of earth up over him making him raise his arms to protect himself. More rained down towards the light striking the ring of sandbags around its base. A man wearing a headset was lifted off his feet and flung backwards through the air like a doll. Then there was the crash of breaking glass and the world was plunged into darkness.

Doug blinked, stared and rubbed at his watering eyes, but they would not adjust to the darkness and he could not make out the instruments. He was happy that Freddy was in a steady climb, which was trading their excess speed back into height. The controls felt sluggish, but were all responding correctly and the engines all sounded okay. He turned up the instrument lighting to full, so that he could see it, he steadied his breathing, took a deep breath and asked, "Is everybody alright? Check in front to back with any damage."

"Bomb aimer okay and no signs of any damage here."

"Flight engineer alright and the engines and fuel tanks are okay. I'm still checking the other systems."

"Navigator, I'm alright, but a massive chunk of flak came through the roof and smashed the GEE box and the H2S isn't working anymore either."

"Radio operator okay and the radio seems fine, but the Fishpond's knackered."

"Mid-upper A'm fine, skipper, but A've got a few holes in ma turret and the tail and fins look like a sieve."

After a pause Doug asked, "George…George, are you okay?" But there was no reply.

"Alex here, skipper, most of the flak was behind us, they didnae expect us tae be goin' so fast in the dive, but oor tail got peppered."

"Roger, Harry, go and see if George is alright."

"Okay, skipper, how high are we?"

"I'll stay below 10,000 feet, you can all come off oxygen."

Harry pulled his oxygen mask off and breathed deeply. He was shaking slightly as he unplugged his headset and climbed over the main spar. He felt a little dizzy and his breathing was rapid and shallow. He had been very scared during the dive and now, stepping down from the bomb bay, he wondered what was waiting for him in the rear turret. Alex's turret swung from side to side above him while the gunner kept up his usual good lookout, but from the mid upper turret back the fuselage was full of small holes. A 200 mph wind came through the holes chilling the clammy sweat, which soaked Harry's body. Harry switched on his torch and shone it around the rear of the fuselage. It had been known for a crewman to fall through a flak hole in the floor of a damaged bomber and the thought of falling through blackness to eternity made Harry shiver all the more. At the tailplane carry through Harry stopped. The Elsan chemical toilet had received a direct hit from a large piece of flak and the contents were splattered around the walls and running along the floor, before draining away through the flak holes. Crawling onto the tailplane carry through he turned out his torch and slowly moved forward, feeling his way. The wind whistled through the holes and some were big enough for him to see stars through. Opening the fuselage rear doors he could see the rear of George's turret. It wasn't moving and there were a lot of shrapnel holes on the fuselage floor. Harry took a deep breath and, steeling himself for what might be waiting for him, he pulled the catch to release the rear doors of the turret.

George's body fell backwards out of the remains of the shattered turret, landing directly under Harry's face. Harry screamed in shock and George screamed in pain. The wind from the smashed turret whipped around the inside of the fuselage.

"Are you alright?" yelled Harry, above the gale.

"A bloody Jerry shell went off right under me bloody turret and I've got half a bloody ton of bloody shrapnel in me bloody arse! Of course I'm not bloody alright, you bloody idiot!"

"Just bloody asking!" replied Harry. "Does the intercom work?"

"Could you hear me screaming?"

"No!"

"Then it's buggered and the turret's buggered an all!"

"How hurt are you? Can you move?"

"I don't know. A lot of stuff came through the turret floor and seat and I can feel me legs and arse are wet, but some of that is hydraulic fluid from the turret!"

"Roll over and let me see!"

George gritted his teeth against the pain and rolled onto his front. George's bulky buoyancy and electrical suits had been shredded and Harry could immediately see George had collected a large amount of German shell about the posterior and legs. However, miraculously, the pieces all seemed small. From the waist down George was soaked and in the dark Harry wasn't sure if it was blood or hydraulic fluid and wasn't very keen on finding out.

"Can you move?"

"I just did!"

"Can you move up the fuselage to the rest bunk?"

"You have to be bloody kiddin'!"

"Okay, you wait here and I'll go and get some help!"

"Well, as I can't bloody move I may as well!"

"I wish you'd been shot in the mouth!" yelled Harry, leaving to make his way back up the fuselage. Scrambling back the way he had come, he eventually came to the rear spar and breathlessly plugged his headset into a fuselage intercom lead.

"Skipper, George is wounded and the turret's smashed..." he panted. "I need some help to get him out of the turret."

"Jimmy, go and give Harry a hand."

"On my way."

Back at the rear turret George was starting to shiver. "Alright, George mate, Jimmy's coming to help me move you up to the rest bunk."

"Great," replied George, without much enthusiasm.

When Jimmy arrived he took George's arms and dragged him forward towards the front of the tailplane carry through. Harry took George's legs, ready to lift them when they got off the tailplane. As they got to the front of the tail Jimmy dragged George through the remains of the Elsan.

"This just gets better and bloody better!" moaned George. Once off the tail, they carried George face down up the fuselage, crouching under the mid-upper turret. "Better get them to reset the DF compass after carrying this much metal past it!" called George, through gritted teeth.

"They're just pinheads," said Harry.

"Well, when they're in your arse those pinheads make it feel like your arse is on fire!" After much panting and heaving they got George over the rear spar and onto the rest bunk.

"We need to get this off," said Harry, looking at George's suit. Jimmy eased George onto his side, undid and removed his parachute harness. Then he produced a clasp knife and while Harry held a torch Jimmy cut away George's suit. As George suspected, from the waist down he was covered in blood. But the wounds were small and in the ice cold fuselage the blood congealed quickly. Already most of the wounds had stopped bleeding altogether.

"How bad is it?" he asked.

"Well it's not pretty," said Jimmy.

"Christ! That wouldn't be pretty at the best of times," said Harry, pointing at George's backside.

"Just tell me how bad it is!"

"Well, there are a lot of small wounds and most have bits of shrapnel in them. But they don't look too deep and most of the bleeding has stopped," said Jimmy.

"Never mind that! What about me bollocks?" Jimmy and Harry burst out laughing. "It's not bloody funny!"

"Yeah, they're alright," said Harry. "The Jerries can't shoot that well."

"You'd get a good clip if I could move."

"Yeah, well, you can't, so hold still while we clean you up a bit."

"What about a shot of morphine?" asked Jimmy.

"No thanks," said Harry. "I think I'll be able to manage without it."

"Yes, A would like some morphine, ta very much, and some people would say it might ha been a good idea to give uz it before you moved uz!"

"Has anyone ever told you your accent gets broader when you're angry?" asked Harry.

Jimmy took a phial of morphine from the First Aid kit and removed the protective cover over the needle. "Where should I put it?"

"Are you saying the target area isn't big enough?" asked Harry, and they both sniggered. "Maybe we should get Bob up here to do it," giggled Jimmy.

"Just hurry up and do it!" yelled George.

Jimmy took aim then jabbed the needle into George's right buttock and squeezed the morphine in. George gritted his teeth and Harry yelled,

"One hundred and eighty!"

Using one of the bomber's First Aid kits they cleaned off most of the dried blood, while trying not to disturb the congealed blood around the many wounds. Then they bandaged the wounds, which didn't appear to have any shrapnel in them as best they could. When they had done all they thought they could do, they covered George with a blanket, plugged his headset into the intercom so he could hear what was going on and went back to their stations.

Harry plugged in just in time to hear Ron announce they were 100 miles from the Belgian coast. The Fishpond was still broken and from the number of holes in the rear fuselage Harry guessed the antenna was smashed to pieces.

"There's a bank of low cloud ahead," said Bob. "We'll lose sight of the ground in a few minutes."

"Roger," replied Ron. "We're still on track and a little ahead of schedule."

Harry checked his watch; it was nearly time to receive the Group forecast winds. They had missed the last one while he was looking after George and now with both GEE and H2S unserviceable and low cloud closing in they would need all the navigation aids they could get. He swapped his headset to WT and stood in the astrodome scanning the sky. Above them the sky was clear and there were lots of stars out. Although there was no moon the night looked unnervingly bright. Looking to the front he strained to see the cloud Bob had reported and either side of the nose he could see the white rolling blanket stretching out into the distance. It was a layer of stratus, well below them at about 5,000 feet. It probably wasn't very thick, but it was continuous and they would be unable to see the ground through it. Worse still, with the bright sky above them they would be silhouetted against the cloud to any fighter flying above them, like a large black fly walking over a white tablecloth.

Harry had calmed down after the dive into the searchlights and his hands had stopped shaking, but now his nervous sweat had started to freeze. He would have loved to sit at his radio with the warm air vent beside it and warm up. But with the Fishpond out of action, the rear turret smashed and George injured they would need as many pairs of eyes on lookout as possible. His teeth started to chatter and he started to wish he had worn warmer clothes, instead of relying on the warm air. He was glad when the Morse of the Group winds started in his headset and he had an excuse to sit down at his radio and take down the message. After decoding the figures he passed them to Ron, reconnected to the intercom and took his place back in the astrodome. By now the ground was obscured by cloud in all directions and Ron would be navigating on dead reckoning alone, which was fine, so long as he was using accurate wind figures. If he wasn't, they could end up miles off course.

"The Belgian coast should be 10 miles ahead now," said Ron.

"We're still above ten tenths cloud," replied Bob.

"When we're clear of the coastal flak we'll descend below the cloud while we're over the sea," said Doug. "Let me know when we're 10 miles off the coast, Ron."

Slowly the minutes dragged past and Harry started to shiver again. The clear sky still looked empty and they were probably one of the lead bombers in the stream, but there was no telling where the night fighters would be hunting.

"Crossing the coast now," announced Ron, with far more certainty than he felt. Harry felt he knew Ron well enough now to know when he was bullshitting and he was certain that now was one of those times. Flying 50 miles on dead reckoning was no problem, but there were another 75 miles to the English coast and a one degree error over 120 miles would mean 2 miles off track. 10-degree errors were not uncommon and once you were 20 miles out of position it could take a lot of work to find yourself again. Harry knew that unless they could fix their position when they crossed the English coast there would be little to help them once inland over the blacked out countryside. With this in mind he planned ahead working out what he would do once they were safely out to sea and below the cloud.

"10 miles off the coast now."

"Roger, we'll start the descent now and I'll level out when we're in the clear below."

Doug left the throttles where they were and lowered the nose to give them a rate of descent of 500 feet per minute. He knew he should keep the speed constant, but he liked the idea of getting away from the enemy coast as quickly as possible. Freddy's speed rose slowly and Ron didn't notice the change, but it had thrown out his calculations. They were at 10,000 feet and the cloud would probably go down to about 3,000 feet, so a descent of 7,000 feet at 500 feet per minute would take them fourteen minutes. At their current estimated ground speed of 200 mph they would cover 47 miles in that time, so they should come out of the clouds about 20 miles off the English coast and that should set them up nicely to pinpoint their position as they crossed the coast. Unfortunately for Ron, Doug not sticking to his speed, and a change in the wind speed and direction during the descent, plus the cloud going down to 2,000 feet instead of 3,000 feet all compounded to mean Freddy travelled nearly 65 miles before breaking out of the clouds.

The descent through the clouds seemed like a lifetime to Doug and he was starting to get nervous when they were still in cloud at 2,000 feet. He knew there was no ground that high over southern England and they should still be over the sea anyway, but some of the east coast ports had barrage balloon defences and all aircrew had a very healthy respect for those. Suddenly they broke out of the cloud into a dark winter's night sky with poor visibility.

"We're over land!" exclaimed Bob.

"What?" asked Ron. "We can't be!"

"Well, we are."

"Are you sure?"

"Well, I just saw a railway line, that usually means you're over land." Bob was sick of Ron questioning his observations.

"How the hell did that happen? We should still be 20 miles off the coast!"

"Never mind, Ron, do you know where we are?" asked Doug, who realised what had happened and felt guilty, but hoped his mistake wouldn't be discovered. If they quickly found themselves he would say nothing, but if they were very lost he would admit his error and hope it would help Ron to find them again.

"A think A can just make out the coast behind us," said Alex.

Ron was now in a panic. They could be anywhere. It wasn't unusual for a compass to wander unnoticed and an aircraft to fly off in completely the wrong direction. Quite a few aircraft had got so lost they had landed in the wrong country and been captured. Now he was so confused, with his mind in a panic, he was not sure what country he was flying over. They had not seen the sea, so who was to say they had crossed the English Channel at all. They could still be over enemy territory and maybe flying further away from safety all the time.

While Ron was fighting his rising panic and trying to get his numbed brain to concentrate so he could go back over his calculations and check his instruments, Harry was tuning his receiver to the RAF Manston DF station. He switched his headset to intercom.

"Can you fly straight and level for a DF bearing, skipper?"

"Wilco."

Switching back, Harry listened to the strong signal, showing they were not very far from the transmitter, and he turned the loop aerial to its null point, one nine five degrees relative to Freddy's heading, so if they were flying northwest Manston was to their southeast. He made a quick check that it wasn't a reciprocal bearing, which would put Manston northwest of them and mean they were still over enemy territory. It wasn't a reciprocal and he wrote down on a piece of note pad, Manston 195 degrees relative, and passed it around the radio to Ron. Ron took the note and Harry thought he felt Ron's hand shaking. Ron stared at the note for a second before he grasped its significance. Then he applied one nine five degrees relative to Freddy's heading of three four zero degrees to give one five five degrees to Manston. He found Manston on his map and drew a line the reciprocal of one five five, three three five degrees on the map. They were somewhere along that line. He breathed deeply and started to relax. They were over East Anglia and safe, thank God for Harry and his DF bearings. Then he thought, what if it's a reciprocal bearing, that would put them over northern France. He reached for his intercom switch to ask and then changed his mind. Harry wouldn't make that mistake. Looking back over all their flights together as a crew Ron couldn't think of a time when Harry had made a significant mistake. Harry irritated him at times but there was no doubt about it, he knew his job.

"Can you get me bearings from Wyton and West Raynham?"

"No problem." Ron being civil, thought Harry, whatever next?

The other bearings fixed their position fairly accurately north of Colchester and fifteen minutes later half a dozen searchlights suddenly lit up a few miles ahead of them, which would probably be the defences around Cambridge. Harry had already changed the flare cartridge to the correct British colours of the day and as the searchlights swept closer Doug ordered him to fire them. Harry reached up and back behind his head to the flare pistol fitted into the roof of the Lancaster, above the main spar, and pulled the trigger. Then looking through the astrodome he saw the two red and yellow balls of the recognition flare fall rapidly away behind them. Immediately the searchlights all stopped sweeping the sky and all except one went out. The remaining light stood vertically, marking a briefed point 2 miles north of Cambridge and they were now certain of their position.

Five minutes later they were in RT range of Metheringham and Doug called them to say they had wounded aboard and to have an ambulance waiting. Soon Bob spotted Metheringham's beacon and made his way back to the main spar. Now was the time when Harry always started to get frightened. As far as he was concerned it was potentially the most dangerous part of the flight. Lots of bombers flying around in circles in a relatively small piece of sky and perhaps some Jerry intruders thrown in. Their last flight had proved how disaster could strike so close to home and it always got to him. He always thought it a particularly poignant tragedy when a bomber crashed close to its base, so near and yet so far.

Suddenly he remembered an aircraft landing with wounded aboard should fire a red flare and he started to search for one. As they flew downwind, having been given priority to land because of their wounded, Harry found a flare, snapped it into the Very pistol and fired it. Then he steadied George on the rest bunk against the jolt of landing. Freddy's engines cut back and the bomber started to sink towards the friendly earth, then at twenty feet there was a loud thump.

"What was that?" asked Doug, while everyone wondered how badly damaged Freddy was and what had broken off. Then Harry realised and started to blush.

"Sorry, skipper, I forgot to wind the trailing aerial in. We must have lost it."

Freddy's wheels touched the runway with a screech and ran on smoothly until the speed was under control and Doug turned onto the perimeter track back to their dispersal.

"Thank God that was only the trailing aerial. I thought a part of the tail had fallen off. There's an ambulance at the dispersal. How's George?"

"Numb," replied George, as Freddy came to a stop.

Before Doug and Jimmy could stop Freddy's engines a doctor and two stretcher-bearers were aboard and scrambling up the fuselage. The doctor got to the rear spar and asked, "Who's wounded?"

"The one lying on the bunk," said Harry flatly.

The doctor took a quick look.

"Christ, why did you get wounded there?"

George twisted around and looked him in the face.

"Because you don't get a bloody choice!"

17

"I wonder how George is," said Harry as the four sergeants cycled from the mess to the Squadron Office the next morning.

"He wasn't badly hurt," replied Bob. "But he won't be fit to sit in a turret for a while."

"He win nae be fit tae sit anywhere for a while," said Alex.

"Will they keep him on the station or send him to hospital?" asked Jimmy.

"I don't think he was bad enough to be sent to hospital, but he'll probably be stuck in sick quarters for a few days," said Harry.

"Jammy bastard," laughed Alex. "There are some bonny nurses in there. We should go an visit him."

"Well, I can't see that we'll have anything else to do. We can't fly without a rear gunner," said Jimmy, trying not to sound too relieved.

"We might not have an aeroplane for a few days," said Harry. "Freddy was like a sieve down the back."

As they rode up to the Squadron Office Doug and Ron were already there with another two officers whom the sergeants had seen talking to Doug before. With the usual round of greetings they all trooped into the office which, as usual, was warm and very stuffy. From near the back of the group Alex heard the Squadron Adjutant call good morning, but couldn't see him sitting at his desk because of all the people in front of him.

"Special job for you, Charlie, as it's your last Op," the adjutant continued. "We're to provide five aircraft for a gardening trip."

Alex knew gardening was the Bomber Command term for a mining Op. The mines were vegetables and the areas the mines were to be dropped were plots. Each plot was named after a type of vegetable: carrot, potato, artichoke etc. At one time mining Ops had been popular because they were short and, depending on the plot, relatively easy trips. Then Bomber Command had changed the policy for mining trips and most mining Ops now only counted as a third of an Op, so to complete a tour purely on mining trips would now take ninety missions. The exceptions to these rules were if the mining Op took place east of the 6-degree east line of longitude, or were inside some of the heavily defended French harbours.

"The boss says you can run this show and have your pick of the other four crews. The intelligence bods have all the target details, maps, photographs and the like. But I'll need to know the other four crews you want as soon as possible."

"I can't pick the other crews until I know more about the Op, old boy," replied Charlie.

"Well, it will be low level and I would think it will be a split second timing affair. Where's your crew by the way?"

"Oh, they're already out at the kite. Low and split second timing, eh?" Charlie paused to think. Alex moved to get a better view. This was out of the ordinary and he wanted to see the young pilot who had made it to the end of a tour and the Squadron Commander thought good enough to run his own Op. "What's your low flying like, Doug?" Charlie suddenly asked.

"Average I suppose."

"Well, you're always one of the first back, so you must dive out of the target area and you've brought back some beaten-up kites and pulled off a ditching. Ron here must know east from west or you wouldn't beat us back, so how do you fancy a spot of gardening?"

"How far east is the target?" interrupted Ron.

"You'll get a full Op out of it," said the Adjutant icily.

"Well, I'm up for it, but my rear gunner's off Ops wounded and Freddy took a bit of a beating last night. I don't know if my ground crew will be able to fix it in time."

As usual, the Adjutant was well ahead of Doug.

"I have a spare gunner lined up for you. He'll be here in an hour and Sergeant Green says your Lancaster will be ready for an air test this afternoon. It's late takeoffs tonight because of the moon so there won't be any problems with you being ready in time." The moon was almost a quarter of the way through its cycle and between a quarter and half full. Worse still it didn't set until the early hours of the morning, leaving the bombers to run the gauntlet of the moonlight.

"Okay, Charlie, we're in."

"Good," said the Adjutant. "You need to plan the Op." He nodded to Charlie. "And you just need to sort out your aircraft," he said to Doug. "Your briefing will be at 21.00 before the main Squadron briefing. You'll probably need the moonlight to see the target and it will help you with the low flying. Your gunner will be here when you get back from your kite and your drivers should be outside. Anything else… No… Good."

Caitlin was waiting outside in the truck and while they jerked around the perimeter track to Freddy Alex stared out at the grey sky and rapidly melting snow that was slushy and dirty over the grass and making the roads wet.

"I don't like flying without George," said Harry. "It's unlucky."

"Aye, it wi' nae be the same without him takin' the piss."

"Oh, we can take the piss out of you, Alex, if it'll make you feel any better," offered Bob.

"Ock, when it comes ta takin' the piss you Aussies are pretty good, but you're not in the same league as a genuine Geordie twat," insulted Alex.

A squeal of brakes sent them all grabbing for support as the truck stopped.

"We must be there," said Harry, getting up. Freddy had ground crew crawling all over him as they walked over. The rear turret, both rudders and the H2S were missing and the ground crew were busy patching all the holes in the fuselage.

Sergeant Green met them halfway across the dispersal; his eyes were red and sunken with dark bags underneath.

"We won't be ready for you for at least another four hours, sir."

"That's okay, sarge," said Doug. "We just came over to see how things are going. You look done in."

The sergeant smiled.

"Well, we've all been up all night, it was all a bit of a mess. We've patched most of the fuselage holes and removed the H2S, rear turret and rudders; you'll need new ones of all of those. You've got a new GEE box as well, but it's not been tested yet. We're waiting for the new parts now; they should be over any time. It's surprising really that considering the number of holes there wasn't more damage to the control lines. But providing we don't hit any snags we should be ready for you to air test it about 15.00."

"Well, we're going to be doing a spot of gardening and it's a late takeoff so there should still be plenty of time. There's no point in us hanging around here getting in your way so we'll come back for an air test at 15.00."

Back at the Squadron Office a small sergeant stood up as Doug walked in.

"This is your replacement gunner for tonight," said the Adjutant.

The sergeant was in his early twenties, stood not much over five foot tall and his oil-stained battledress looked two sizes too big for his thin body. His black hair was Brylcreemed back and there were deep wrinkles around the corners of his eyes.

"Hello, sarge," said Doug, reaching out to shake the sergeant's hand. "I'm Doug Jackson and these are the rest of my crew. I don't know what you've been told but we're on a gardening Op tonight and we're a gunner down, so we're glad to have you with us."

"Sammy Sampson, sir. Is your gunner likely to be unfit for long?"

"Don't know yet, we're going to see him now. You can come along if you like."

"Thanks, sir, it's just I've only got five more Ops to do, but without a crew I could be here quite a while if I have to do them all as a spare bod."

Doug smiled; spare crewmembers who had lost the rest of their crew were always desperate to get teamed up with another crew. By themselves they could end up flying with anyone and they cut very lonely and isolated figures on the Squadron.

"Well, let's go and see, but I wouldn't want to raise your hopes. George is as tough as a boot and I doubt he'll be grounded for long."

At the station hospital Doug and his crew were confronted by a very stern-looking nurse.

"You can't come in. Visiting hours are in the evening. The times are published in Station Routine Orders."

"But we're flying tonight," protested Doug.

"I can't help that. We don't run this hospital for your convenience you know."

"I thought that's exactly why they ran this hospital," said Harry, immediately retreating from the hard stare of the nurse.

Alex stepped forward. "We only want tae see oor mate 'afor' we fly taenite. We've never flown wi' oot him yer see, an he'll be orfa upset if we dinae see him 'afor' we go." Alex's dark brown eyes were large and pleading as he stared the young nurse in the face so that she squirmed a little and he knew he'd won.

"Well, you shouldn't be in the ward during the day."

"We'll no be long, bonny lass, and nobody a'll ever know." He pulled a bar of chocolate from his pocket.

"Five minutes and not a second more. If Sister catches me she'll skin me alive," she said, taking the chocolate.

"Well, you'll be in the right place," said Harry rushing past.

"She'd get it," said Alex, from the safety of the ward. "An you all owe me a bar of chocolate. A've only got one left and A need that this afternoon."

George was lying on his side in a bed at the near end of the ward; in the bed opposite was another gunner with frostbite. At the far end of the ward were two other patients with flu.

"Hello, you malingering little git!" said Harry. "Christ, you whiff a bit."

"Yeah, two soft buggers dragged me through the remains of Freddy's Elsan, didn't they?"

"Oh yeah," sniggered Harry.

"Don't they have baths here?" asked Bob.

"Oh aye, but with half the Jerry armaments industry in me arse I only get a rub over with a damp cloth."

"By that nurse oot there?" asked Alex.

"Yeah."

"You jammy sod. She's up for it, she is."

"Possibly, but you may have noticed that I'm not exactly match fit."

"How are you feeling?" asked Doug.

"As sore as hell, but they've got all the bits out, so I should be okay in a couple of days."

"Will you be fit to fly then?"

"Well, that's down to the doc, but I reckon so. Sorry to keep ya off Ops like this, but it should be a nice little holiday for ya."

"No such luck, mate," said Harry. "We've got a replacement and we're flying tonight."

"What?" George was alarmed and suddenly saw Sammy. "But I'm ya rear gunner, boss." He looked at Doug as if he had been betrayed.

"It's alright, George, it's only for tonight. You'll be back with us as soon as you're fit."

"But I'll be a trip behind," he protested.

"I'm afraid it can't be helped George," said Doug, who was shocked at how strongly George felt. "But it's just the one trip."

"But…" George started to protest but realized it was hopeless and turned to Sammy. "How many trips have you done?"

"Twenty-five."

"See, we're in good hands," said Doug, who was now feeling guilty about flying without George.

"And what happened to ya crew?" asked George, ignoring Doug.

Sammy shifted uncomfortably. "A couple of months ago I got flu and the doc grounded me for a week. My crew went flying with a replacement gunner and got chopped."

George stared at Doug and said nothing.

"I'm sorry, George, but it's only one trip," repeated Doug.

"Yeah, mate, and it's a short hop too," said Bob.

"Aye, just a spot o gardening," offered Alex.

"Mining! Low level? Where?"

"It's low level, but we don't know the target yet," replied Doug.

"Christ, man, some o them mining targets are riddled wi' light flak!"

"Don't panic, George, we'll be careful. It'll just be a quick in and out before they know we're there." Doug hadn't really thought about the Op until that point.

"Look, skipper, I was talkin' to one of the old hand gunners on his second tour a couple of weeks ago. He told us about gardening along the Kiel Canal. The Jerries have flak guns along both banks and any Lanc flying down the canal is a sitting duck. Apparently yer only chance is to only fly along the canal for the bomb run and go flat out as low as yer can."

"Okay, but we don't know what the target is yet."

"Another tip is to put Harry in the front turret to shoot at the flak gunners and put them off their aim."

"That's a good idea," said Harry, relishing the chance to get a better view and be able to hit back. "And what do you mean, put them off their aim! They'll have more to worry about than being put off their aim with me in a turret!"

"Ock, listen to the wee man. A sniff o a gun an he's Billy the Kid."

"And you need to have yer turret facing forward an all! One turret shoots at the flak on the right, the other at the flak on the left!"

"Alright! You'll all have to leave now, Sister's coming!" said the stern nurse, who was now looking decidedly nervous.

"Okay, George, you take it easy," said Doug, as he left.

"Yeah, don't strain anything!" added Alex, nodding at the nurse.

"Get her to kiss it better!" called Harry.

Sammy was the last out of the ward.

"Hoy!" George shouted so that Sammy turned. "They're my crew and I want them back!" Sammy nodded and left. A lump rose in George's throat and his eyes filled. It was more from frustration than anything else, but he couldn't help but think that he might never see them again.

At three that afternoon they gave Freddy a quick air test and everything worked well. The newly painted repairs stood out against the duller faded paint on the rest of the fuselage and the smell of paint inside was alien and strange. Alex wasn't happy, things didn't seem right. He couldn't explain it so he said nothing but he felt uneasy and nervous. When they landed the six mines were sitting on their bomb trolleys by the side of Freddy's dispersal. They were ten feet long and eighteen inches in diameter. Each weighed 1,400 pounds, of which 650 pounds was explosive. One end of the black cylinder was cut off at a 45-degree angle so the mine would lie horizontal on the seabed. The other end had a drab brown drogue chute attached to it, which would slow the mine's descent and ensure it entered the water vertically. The mine would then sink to the bottom and wait for a metal ship to go over it and trigger its magnetic fuse. 650 pounds of explosives going off under a ship would be enough to break most ships' backs and any tough enough not to be broken would be severely damaged, especially in shallow water. It was the first time Alex had seen an aerial mine and he decided straight away he didn't like them. Bombs didn't affect him, they were just cylinders of explosive that went off when they hit the ground. But the mine was different; it waited for its victim to come to it. To Alex it was like the mine had some sort of intelligence and although he knew it was irrational he didn't like it. With the hair bristling on his neck he was only too pleased to leave the mines behind and try to relax in the sergeants' mess.

As usual before an Op the mess was full of other sergeants, all trying to do the same thing and as usual everyone was far from relaxed. Some tried to read, others played cards, some chatted, but no matter what they did their minds were all elsewhere and they were all trying to hide it. Alex had his own way of forgetting about an impending Op. He had already phoned the signal section and arranged to meet Sue, one of his two regular girlfriends, in the station window store at 20.00. By coincidence his other regular girlfriend also worked in the signal section but on the opposite shift. So one girlfriend was always available and while one was off duty the other was on. This also meant that there was far less chance of them ever finding out about each other. Metheringham's window store was a medium sized hut that had to be kept warm and dry to stop the strips of metalled paper getting damp and sticking together. By 20.00 all the window needed for the night's Op would have been loaded into the Squadron's Lancasters and they would have the place to themselves. Strangely, Sue had seemed reluctant to meet him, which was unusual, because she was usually keener than he was, but this time he had needed to talk her around. It hadn't taken much, he had mentioned the chocolate, but had also played the "I'm going on a special Op and we might never see each other again" card. He had also claimed he didn't feel lucky if they didn't "meet" before a trip. She had soon given in, but he was left feeling unhappy that he had needed to talk her into seeing him. Still, she loved sex and she would soon change her tune when he got his hands on her.

As usual the time before an Op dragged, but soon it was time to meet Sue and Harry and Bob nodded and winked at him as he left, knowing full well what he was up to. Sue arrived just after him and without much conversation they selected a suitable pile of soft packages of window for a mattress and got down to it. It occurred to Alex that she didn't seem to have her heart in it and was doing it because she felt she should. But what the hell, a shag's a shag, he thought. Afterwards she made an excuse and quickly left, which was strange. But he had got what he wanted so he was happy, although not as happy as he thought he would be and that worried him a bit.

"Another notch up!" said Harry, when Alex entered the billet.

"Yeah."

"Give us the details then," said Bob. "Was it that randy Sue again?"

"Aye."

"You're being a bit cagey, mate, were you a bit off your stroke, so to speak?" sniggered Harry.

"Well, you'd know aboot that. Nae, she just had some things tae do so a couldn't gi' her the usual full treatment."

"There's a novelty, the woman finishing prematurely!" laughed Harry.

They were all pulling on their wool sweaters and thick socks in preparation for their briefing and fifteen minutes later they were in their usual seats in the briefing room. Charlie was on the stage with Taffy, his navigator, making the last adjustments to his briefing when they entered with the other four crews.

"Couple of minutes yet, chaps, the Wingco wants to be in on the briefing."

Alex looked around the room. It was unusual for it to be so empty and they were by far the most junior crew there. Charlie's crew, as he had heard the Adjutant say, were on their thirtieth and last Op. Digger's crew were there, and they had twenty-seven Ops behind them. The other two crews Alex didn't know except by sight but they had both had the air of experienced crews when Alex had first arrived.

"Attention!" called Charlie, as the Wing Commander walked in.

"Sit down chaps," he called, striding to the front of the room. "This is Flight Lieutenant Clarke's show, so I won't steal his thunder. I just want to say this will be a new sort of Op for most of you. But you've been handpicked for the job and it's the sort of thing that can do a lot of damage to Jerry. So press home the attack and hit them hard. I'm flying on the main Op so I can't stay for the briefing but I know the plan and I'm sure it will work well. Good luck." With that the crews stood up again and he left.

When the door shut Charlie pulled the curtain covering the briefing map to one side and announced, "Our target, gentlemen, is Aalburg." There were two ribbons on the map, a red ribbon going to Essen and obviously the target for the rest of the Squadron, who would be briefed later, off the same map. The Squadron's later takeoff would get them to Essen as the moon set and they could come home in complete darkness. The other ribbon, a blue one, was what interested everyone currently in the room. It led across the North Sea in a northeasterly direction to the north of Denmark.

"Aalburg," Charlie continued, "is one of the main ports in the north of Denmark and a vital port for Jerry to supply his troops in Norway. We are going to mine the harbour at Aalburg. This will give Jerry a major headache, but it's not an easy target. There's a lot of flak around the harbour and there will probably be some warships there too who will try and take a shot at us. On top of this there's a Jerry airfield just outside the town and they have day and night fighters stationed there. Taffy will pass out all the course and routing details to the navigators, but the gist of things is we will fly out individually at 10,000 feet until we're 150 miles off the coast. Then we descend to low level and fly to the holding points allocated to you. From the Danish coast you can adjust the route to your holding points as you see fit. But you are to leave the holding points at the exact time specified on Taffy's route plans and at exactly 240 mph, which is just about flat out at that height. The route then takes you to this point."

He flipped a cloth off a blackboard and easel to reveal a large grainy blown up photograph of a couple of bridges over a river. The picture had been taken from a low flying aircraft, probably a photo recce Spitfire, and showed the bridges as they would be seen from the Lancasters approaching them. In the foreground was a railway bridge, low on the water with an iron girder structure above the rail bed; the centre section looked like it could be opened to let ships through. About half a mile behind this was a bigger road bridge. This was much higher and sloped upwards from the town on either bank to an apex in the middle of the river. It looked to be made of concrete and again the middle could be lifted up to let the masts of large ships through. A small cabin, like a railway signal box, sat in the middle of the bridge and was obviously the control room for raising and lowering the bridge.

"The initial point for your run in to the target is the centre of the railway bridge," said Charlie. "From there you turn straight for the road bridge and fly over it as low as you dare. The harbour is on the other side. I'll fly directly over the centre of the control box, which will line me up with the centre of the harbour and drop my veg at three-second intervals down the middle of the harbour. Doug, you line up with the bridge pillar to the right of centre. This will take you along the right side of the harbour. Sid, you line up on the pillar left of centre and do the left side of the harbour. You're both to release your mines as you go over the bridge at three-second intervals, which should spread your mines over about a mile of harbour front. Digger, you also take the right pillar and Stu, you take the left but drop your mines one and a half seconds after you cross the bridge, again at three-second intervals.

"The key to success on this Op is speed! We need to get in and out as fast as possible. If we take them by surprise they won't know what's hit them and our best chance of that is to go in as low as possible so they don't get any warning of us coming. If you all leave your holding points on time at the right speed you'll be five seconds apart at the initial point over the railway bridge."

Digger whistled.

"Yes, I know it's a bit close, but that will get us all through in twenty seconds and the time from the first Lanc over the target to the last leaving will be thirty-five seconds, which won't give the flak gunners much of a shot at us. Which brings me to another point. Any flak will need to be put off its aim. I suggest you have your front turrets manned over the target. It will mean someone's feet hanging down in front of your bomb aimer's face but all he has to do is hit the release on time; the lining things up will be up to the pilot. All gunners, you can have a bloody good go at any flak or searchlights in the area, but remember, Aalburg harbour is in the middle of Aalburg city and the Danes are on our side, so don't just squirt your bullets anywhere! Any questions?"

Taffy passed out the route plans and large scale detailed maps of the target area. These showed the run-in from the holding point to the railway bridge and on over the harbour.

"Once we're through the target we turn north and then west to the coast, staying low until we're 100 miles off shore. Then we climb back up to 10,000 feet and fly home direct. Now, work your way through your individual planning and if there are no questions takeoff will be at 22.30 hours."

Doug took a long close look at the large-scale map of the target. Aalburg wasn't like most harbours because it was inland rather than on the coast. It was reached along a long narrow inlet, which Doug supposed was technically a fiord, but as Denmark was very flat it was nothing like the classical Norwegian fiords and looked more like a wide river. The harbour itself was just a stretch of the fiord about half a mile wide where it passed through Aalburg city. The city spread along both banks with what looked to be factories and warehouses next to the quaysides. They would be running into the target from the west and the fiord to the west of Aalburg got rapidly wider with a low island in the middle, making it look like a fork in a river. West of the island the fiord was over 4 miles wide and well to the west it opened into a lake 10 miles square. Freddy's holding point was a collection of windmills on the edge of a village by the south shore of the 4 mile wide section of fiord. From there it was 8 miles, or two minutes, to the railway bridge, following the fiord around the south side of the island.

Alex also took a good look at the map. Normally there was little he could do to help with the navigation but at low level every pair of eyes helped. He committed the holding point and the run into the target to memory and then kept out of the way while Ron and the others checked the finer points of the route. There weren't many questions for Charlie to answer and at 21.30 Charlie cautioned them to stay as low as they could and not fly along the banks of the fiord for any longer than necessary. Then picking up their bags they left for the crew room. Alex scrambled into his electric suit then helped Sammy into his, but it didn't feel right without George being there and the banter was stilted and forced. George for all his cutting comments never seemed to be fazed before an Op and it had a calming effect on everyone. Now that veneer of calming, cutting banter was missing and Alex had inherited George's job of carrying the envelope holding the crew's last letters and he didn't like that job either.

Caitlin sat waiting outside for them and Alex passed the envelope to her.

"Just in case," he started to say.

"Yes, sergeant, it will be alright with me."

Alex would have normally taken this opportunity to chat her up but he didn't feel like it at the moment, which wasn't like him at all. Even Harry was strangely quiet during the drive out to Freddy. As they walked over to the Lancaster the moon was high in a crisp clear winter's night sky and its light reflected off the last of the snow. In almost total silence they lit a last cigarette by the rear door, while Bob, Jimmy and Doug signed the form 700. Ron had climbed straight inside leaving Alex, Harry and Sammy outside. Normally this would have led to a vicious round of banter, usually concerning each other's professional capabilities, followed by George taking a leak against the tailwheel while the others climbed aboard. It just wasn't right without George. Aircrew need their routines to get them through the time between Ops and if that routine is disturbed it can badly affect their state of mind at the very moment they need to be completely focused. Alex threw his parachute pack through the door and hauled himself up the ladder, casting a quick look at the dry tailwheel before ducking inside.

As usual, the fuselage was cold, damp and dark. He located the recess on the right side of the fuselage forward of the rear door and slid his parachute pack into it, securing it with a bungee cord. Then ducking under the bottom of his turret he stood to one side to let Harry pass, then facing the rear of the aircraft he released the clip that held the stirrup, which folded down to give him a foothold so he could climb up into his turret. With his left foot on the stirrup, he reached up and pulled himself forward and upwards into the turret. The forward edge of the turret scraped down the back of his neck and the top of his shoulders. But his right foot was now on the floor of the turret and squatting down on his haunches he reached under himself to find the sling seat. After a second's fumbling, he pulled the seat under him and locating the metal bar on the end of the seat he slipped it over the hooks on the side of the turret and lowered himself onto the thinly padded cushion. He took a quick look around the inside of the turret to make sure all was well then connected his suit heating and intercom leads into the turret directly in front of him. Underneath him he heard Jimmy and Doug moving up the fuselage. Jimmy would stow the stirrup back against the wall and Alex would now be without a foothold to get back out of the turret. He had once asked another gunner, who had baled out of a Lancaster, how he had got out of the turret. "I turned the turret to face forwards, released the seat and fell out backwards!" he'd said. Alex hadn't been impressed because it was a six-foot fall to the metal fuselage floor.

Static crackled in his earphones and a few moments later the first of Freddy's engines fired. Alex reached for the vertical crank handle directly in front of him and turned it rapidly round and round anticlockwise to manually rotate the turret to face the right wing. The starboard inner engine was running smoothly and the propeller of the starboard outer was starting to turn jerkily, then, with a belch of smoke, it too fired and settled down into a fast tick over. This was the engine that powered Alex's turret, so now he moved his hands to his turret control handles and twisted the handles to the right. The turret swung smoothly and effortlessly to the right. He checked the speed of rotation and the elevation of the guns, then left the turret facing the left wing to watch the port engines start. When they were all running smoothly he plugged in his oxygen and turned it on. He checked the small gauge close to his chest and holding his mask to his face he breathed deeply. All was well. Above the oxygen gauge was a panel with three switches on it and he turned them all on. His gun sight lit up and he turned the knurled knob to adjust the brightness so that it was barely visible. Then he checked the two vertical knobs either side of his reflector sight; they were set to fifty feet and 400 yards, so when a fighter with a fifty-foot wingspan filled the circle of the sight it would be at 400 yards range. By now he could feel his electric suit starting to warm up and lifting the ammunition belts out of the breeches of his Browning he tested the triggers. Satisfied, he reloaded them and his checks were complete.

When everybody had checked in as ready they sat for about two minutes before a green flare arced into the air and they started to taxi. The two boys were missing from the gate because it was too late for them to be out. Too many things were different and Alex didn't like it. As they lined up on the runway Alex thought he could make out the shape of Caitlin's truck, but he wasn't sure. Sally would have been there, he thought, too many changes, it's not lucky. Then they were off and Lincolnshire fell away below them.

In RAF Metheringham's medical centre George listened to the five aircrafts' engines fade into the night knowing one of them was Freddy and wishing he was with them. A lump came to his throat and he gritted his teeth and swallowed it down.

They were level at 10,000 feet long before they crossed the coast at Spurn Head and set course across the silvery-black North Sea, which sparkled in the moonlight. At 10,000 feet it was relatively warm at a balmy minus 5 degrees and inside his heavy suit Alex was quite comfortable. His scanning of the black sky was now, after long hours of Ops, automatic and he settled down into the routine easily. He was thinking about the target. He should get a good view of things, but they would be very close to the flak guns and he hoped they would take the gunners by surprise.

The turret's sling seat was just starting to get uncomfortable and he stood to ease the pins and needles in his buttocks. Then Ron announced they were 150 miles from the Danish coast and they started to descend to low level.

Freddy slid slowly down until it seemed the water was brushing the bottom of the fuselage. Alex concentrated on searching the sky above and behind them, but out of the corner of his eye he could see the black sea flashing past just below them giving an impression of speed he wasn't used to.

"Enemy coast ahead," announced Bob. Alex waited a minute then rotated his turret quickly forward to take a look ahead. The coast was a mere dark line where the sparkling of the moon on the water stopped. His curiosity satisfied he spun himself back around and continued his search above and behind. From what he had memorised from the route, he remembered they should cross the Danish coast at the north end of a narrow strip of land separating the North Sea from a lake or bay.

"Crossing the coast … now," said Bob. "Looks like we're on track."

"Fifty-six seconds ahead of schedule," said Ron.

The dark strip of land flashed below Alex and thirty seconds later was again replaced by water as they crossed the lake.

"Do you want me to adjust the speed?" asked Doug.

"No, we'll just hold for a minute before we run in on the target," replied Ron.

"About to cross to land again," said Bob.

Alex had never had this impression of speed before in a Lancaster and certainly never at night. Everything seemed to be happening a lot faster than usual.

"Over land … now."

"Roger, still one minute ahead of schedule."

At this height there was very little chance of the German night fighters being able to detect them. Their radars would be swamped by echoes from the ground just below them.

"Crossing a road, there's a village to our right, railway just ahead, over the railway now. I can see water about 2 miles ahead." Bob's commentary continued unabated while Ron checked the features against his charts. Alex didn't see any of the ground features until they were past them and then only out of the corner of his eye as they sped past. "We're over water now, land about a mile ahead." The moon and clear sky made the visibility perfect and the monochrome landscape flashed by in varying shades of grey. "We've just flown over a village... there's a road ahead and I can see water behind that."

"That should be the Limfjorden," said Ron. That was the 10 mile square fiord Alex had seen on the map. "There should be an island off to our right."

"I see it," said Bob. "We'll pass close to the north of it."

"Next time we go over land we'll pass just south of the town of Logstor. Then we're looking for an inlet and we follow the coast north until we see the windmills and that's our holding point," briefed Ron.

"Roger." Bob was enjoying himself. There was no chore of dropping chaff at this height and he could be a real help with the navigating at low level. "Over land now. I can see the town to the north, road ahead." Bob's eyes peered into the darkness glancing between the moonlit panorama and the map he had spread in front of him where he lay in Freddy's nose. Only briefly did it occur to him that they were very low, probably about 100 feet, and the slightest mistake by Doug would smash him into the ground at well over 200 mph. But he was too busy to think of such things and he looked for the next feature. It should be a railway, there it was, a flash of silver in the moonlight, the twin parallel lines stretching out either side of him.

"Crossing railway now." He glanced at the map, next feature should be a road, they were harder to see at night and it would be close under the nose by the time he saw it. He screwed his eyes up and strained to penetrate the darkness. A shape materialized to his right, he wasn't expecting anything there and he wasn't sure what it was. It didn't look solid but it was tall, reaching up to their height, and would pass down their right side. As they got rapidly closer he could make out the crisscross girder structure and then a second tower appeared to their left.

"CABLES, SKIPPER! PULL UP!" The pylons were right on top of them and Freddy lurched up as Doug pulled back, forcing Bob down onto the floor, but they were too close and there was no way they would ever clear the top of the cables. Then Bob was lifted off the floor and floated in space as Freddy fell away from him. The ground rushed up towards him and his arms flailed wildly to grab hold of something to stop him floating upwards. Bob gritted his teeth for the impact that would bring oblivion. Then he was flung bodily downwards onto the padded bomb aimer's cushion forcing the air out of him. He had a brief glimpse of the high tension wires flashing past above his head and they were climbing slowly back to 100 feet. "Bloody hell, skipper! I've been higher when I've travelled by train!"

Bob's cry of cables had given Alex just enough time for his heart to stop and feel Freddy jump then dive and the next thing he saw were the wires flash just over his head and disappear into the darkness while his heart accelerated to make up for lost time.

"You can gladly have your own gunner back after this trip," said Sammy. "You're all bloody mad!"

"Oh, this is nothing! You should see us when we really get started," said Harry.

"I can see the inlet in our 2 o'clock," called Bob.

"I see it," echoed Doug.

"Fly down the inlet and you should see the windmills on the eastern bank," instructed Ron. Once out over the water again Doug waited until the far bank approached then, putting on a little bank, he turned slowly to the left to follow the coast. He was very aware that a Lancaster had a wingspan of 105 feet and when flying at about 100 feet above the ground a tight, steeply banked turn would put the down going wing a lot closer to the ground. Altimeters were useless at this height and he was judging Freddy's height purely by eye. During the day this was relatively easy. One of his flying instructors had once told him that if you could see the legs on a cow you were at 250 feet and if you could see the legs on a sheep you were at about 100 feet. But at night it was far more difficult to judge distance and the moonlight was very deceptive, especially over water. It would be very easy to fly straight into the sea if he lost concentration for just a second.

"There's a town to our left, 2 o'clock," said Bob.

"That will be Nibe, the windmills are 2 miles ahead," replied Ron, confidently. Alex glanced over at the town and saw one or two brief flashes of light as people ignored the blackout and opened doors or curtains to try and see the low-flying aircraft. German aero engines sounded very different to Merlins and after years of occupation most Danes could tell the difference.

"I see the windmills. Come right, skipper, and I'll fly them down our left side so you can keep them in sight."

Freddy eased to the right.

"I see them, Bob. How long to the start of the run in, Ron?"

"One minute thirty-two seconds."

"Roger, up you come to the front turret, Harry. I'll open the bomb doors as we start our run."

Freddy started a wide slow left hand turn around the windmills, Doug glancing from the windmills to the ground in front of and along the left side of the nose to maintain his height and keep in position orbiting the holding point. Suddenly he saw a flash to his left from near one of the windmills. The white light went out as suddenly as it appeared but immediately came back, stuttering in the darkness.

"Someone's signalling."

"Where?" asked Bob.

"By the windmill."

Jimmy had grabbed Harry as he made his way forward off intercom and pointed him at the light. After a few seconds Harry appeared by Doug's side and shouted into his ear.

"He says good luck!"

"He's wishing us good luck," Doug repeated over the intercom for the rest of the crew.

"Good on him! Give him a flash of the lights, skipper," said Bob.

Doug reached down between his knees and flicked the navigation lights' switch twice. He knew it was a needless risk to show any lights over enemy territory but it was far less of a risk than the Dane had taken.

"Heading for initial point zero six zero degrees compass, fifteen seconds to the start of the run," cut in Ron.

Doug set the heading on his compass. "Are you ready yet, Harry?"

"I was born ready, skipper," came the reply from the front turret.

"Well, get your bloody feet out of my face then!" said Bob, as Harry's feet hung down in front of him.

"Five seconds to start of run... Two. One. Go!"

Doug pushed the throttles fully forward at the five seconds call and straightened on the run-in heading exactly on the word go. Now he glanced between the airspeed indicator, the compass and the ground flashing past just below them, and juggled the controls to keep everything where he wanted it.

"Bomb doors open, master switch on, bombs... mines fused and selected, skipper," Bob corrected himself.

Doug reached gingerly round his left side, while flying Freddy with his right hand and moved the lever to open the bomb doors.

"Bomb doors open, master switch on, mines fused and selected."

"One minute to initial point," reported Ron.

"Aalburg in our 1 o'clock," said Bob.

"I see it," replied Doug. The houses were only just visible in the moonlight but light grey smoke haze rose from factory chimneys and the pollution hung in the air lowering the visibility of the otherwise crystal clear night. "I can see the island now."

"I've got the railway bridge!" called Bob.

"I can't see it," answered Doug.

"Just right of the nose. Come right... Right... Right... Steady... Dead ahead now."

"Thirty seconds," said Ron.

"Gunners, stand by, but don't shoot unless they do."

"Lancaster 10 o'clock, well clear," said Harry.

Alex had his turret facing forwards now with his guns aimed down the right side of the fuselage, just clear of the cockpit and above the starboard propellers. The city raced toward him and he could see Charlie's Lancaster out of the corner of his eye, cutting across in front of them at a shallow angle, heading for the centre of the railway bridge, which he couldn't see because of Freddy's raised cockpit. He estimated they would be about 500 yards behind Charlie's Lancaster at the initial point, perfect. The railway bridge shot below them and Alex saw the higher road bridge right ahead and above them. Freddy started a slight climb as the other Lancaster reached the road bridge and as it raced low over the road a stream of green tracer rose up from somewhere ahead of it. The Lancaster disappeared when it dived down on the other side of the bridge and more tracer arced into the air from three different points ahead of them on the other side of the bridge.

Then they were over the bridge and in a split second Alex took in the panoramic scene in front of him, while he was lifted out of his seat and his stomach was left behind as Doug pushed Freddy into a dive for the surface of the harbour. Down Freddy's right side was the quayside, with buildings set back from it. Two freighters were tied up to the quay and Freddy's wing tip was going to come within 20 yards of their sides. From their 2 o'clock 20 mm light flak curved towards them in a bent green line, like water from a garden hose when swung from side to side. From the left side of the harbour, where another two ships were tied up, more light flak reached towards them, moving painfully slowly until it was close, then suddenly accelerating to incredible speed and whipping past above them. Alex saw all of this in a second, while at the same time lining his turret up on the source of the nearest flak. Freddy suddenly jumped and Alex thought they were hit, but then realized it was the first of the mines dropping. Then he pulled his triggers and the turret shook. The yellow flashes from his guns' ejection ports reflected around his turret and the ejected cartridge cases tinkled down into the canvas bags between his knees which were used to collect them. His tracer sped towards the origin of the light flak and he saw yellow flashes in the darkness where his de Wilde incendiary bullets impacted. He kept firing in one long burst, constantly adjusting his aim until, when his turret was pointing towards Freddy's 3 o'clock, a freighter got between him and the flak gun as another mine fell. Harry was still firing so there was obviously more flak ahead and Freddy lurched again as the third mine fell away.

Looking back to the front Alex saw what Harry was firing at and his heart missed a beat. Moored ahead of the freighters was a German destroyer. Harry's guns were spreading a shower of flashes over the destroyer's quarterdeck, but 20 mm flak was arcing back from the port bridge wing and whizzing close over their heads; the Germans obviously couldn't believe how low they were flying. Alex adjusted his aim to target the destroyer's bridge, which was above Freddy's starboard propellers, and let fly with another long burst, which turned the superstructure into a mass of flashes, as they flew past at deck level. Another mine fell, while Alex watched the destroyer's bridge windows shatter under his fire and the shards of glass twinkle in the moonlight. The 20 mm fire was still going high and was now falling astern as the destroyer was left behind. Sammy was now also sending long bursts of fire into the destroyer, which amazingly seemed to be coming a poor second to Freddy in this gunfight, then four red tennis balls curved after them as the ship's heavier 40 mm flak belatedly came to life. Too late bonny lad, thought Alex as the balls fell behind them and another mine fell. Then the flak's attention shifted and Alex saw the next Lancaster appearing over the bridge, while the last mine fell and Doug threw Freddy into a tight turn which put their wing tip perilously close to the water as he broke away from the harbour and out over the flat countryside to the east of Aalburg.

"Christ! That was a bit hot!" said Bob, as they got well clear of the target.

"Did you see that Jerry destroyer?" asked Sammy.

"See it! I could have spat on it!" said Harry.

"Did yer see us kick its arse!" laughed Alex.

"We were lucky we caught them by surprise," said Doug.

"Shit!" exclaimed Sammy. "Aircraft on fire 6 o'clock, about a mile back."

Alex saw the yellow flames backlit by three searchlights that were now uselessly sweeping the sky above Aalburg. The flames slowly gained height but were falling further behind, while Alex tried to wish them out. Then they suddenly dropped out of the sky and there was a silent red and yellow flash on the ground.

"He's gone in," said Sammy quietly. "I doubt there'll be any survivors."

"He was under control for a while. Someone might a got out," said Alex.

"I don't think he got high enough for anyone to bale out," replied Sammy, "although that was obviously what he was trying to do."

"Course for the coast two eight zero compass," said Ron, bringing them back to the job in hand.

Freed of the weight of the mines Freddy was a lot livelier and Doug kept the speed up while they weaved their way towards the coast. Once more the ground flashed by just below them, but Alex wasn't worried; they had been through the target and were now on their way home. The route was planned to keep them well clear of flak sites and no night fighter could find them at this height. Still he kept scanning the sky, but he was exhilarated rather than scared; it felt like a ride on a roller coaster, exciting without really being dangerous.

"Coast ahead," called Bob, and a few seconds later the dark ground just below them was replaced by black shiny water.

"New course two six zero degrees compass."

"Two six zero degrees, let me know when we're 100 miles out and I'll start climbing back to 10,000, Ron."

"Wilco."

Alex watched the dark line of the Danish coast fade into the blackness behind them, took a deep breath and relaxed. He suddenly realised how numb his bottom was and how cramped his knees felt. It was always the same, he never felt uncomfortable until they were well on their way home. That was when all the aches and pains started and the landing back at Metheringham couldn't come soon enough.

Five red tennis balls shot over his head from behind and continued on into the night behind Freddy.

"Ships 2 o'clock!" yelled Jimmy.

Alex spun his turret rapidly to the left while Doug threw Freddy into a tight left turn. He strained to look down behind the trailing edge of the starboard wing to see the ships and got a brief glimpse of a small dark shape sitting on top of a large white bow wave. Yellow flashes pulsed from the bow and more red tennis balls curved towards them, getting faster as they closed and swerving in the air to pass close behind Freddy's tail. With Freddy banked over at such a steep angle Alex couldn't depress his guns enough to return the fire and all he could do was watch in terrified frustration as the 40 mm flak got closer. Having turned to put the danger in their 5 o'clock Doug straightened up and as the bank came off Alex's guns finally bore. Sammy was already firing at the dark shape sitting on top of the curved bow wave, showing that the E-boat was turning to put itself beam on to Freddy, so that its rear guns could also engage. Green tracer now flashed at them from the rear of the E-boat and white spray erupted short of the boat's side where Sammy's shots were reaching towards their target. Alex pulled both triggers with all his strength, as if the force would give added destruction to his bullets. Yellow flashes appeared on the E-boat where Sammy was getting his first hits and Alex saw his shots falling short and raising mountains of spray in front of the target. Doug was jinking Freddy around the sky to throw the Germans off their aim, but at the same time it was making it difficult for Alex to keep his guns on target. The best he could do was a few yellow flashes of hits before his fire was thrown off in a white curving arc of flying spray. But they were almost clear and the E boat was slowing down, so they had probably done some damage. Then out of the corner of his eye Alex saw the second E boat, bow on and flat out and as he saw it the string of red tennis balls started. These were sent on their way with a lot of deflection and at first looked like they would pass ahead. But as always happens when looking at a moving object from another moving object they appeared to curve slowly in flight and accelerate towards them until one whizzed so close past the back of Alex's turret he involuntarily ducked. As he did there were two loud bangs and Alex saw a blue flash inside the fuselage. When he looked out again he couldn't see for stars caused by the flash, but there was no more flak so they had to be out of range.

"We've been hit! Jimmy, check the fuel and systems, the controls feel okay, everybody alright? Check in front to back," Doug gabbled in one quick breath.

"Bomb aimer okay."

"Flight engineer okay."

"Nav okay."

"I'm scared shitless, skipper, but I'm alright."

"Thanks for that, Harry. Alex?"

"A'm okay, skipper, and one of the hits was on the fuselage behind ma turret, but A canae see any damage."

"Roger, Sammy?... Sammy?...Shit! Go and take a look at Sammy, Harry."

"This is starting to get monotonous," said Harry, unplugging his intercom and making his way to the back of the aircraft. As he ducked under the mid-upper turret the smell of the cordite fumes was thick in the fuselage and seemed to stick in the back of Harry's throat. Freddy was still bouncing around quite a bit in the pockets of low-level turbulence and Harry clung on as he made his way slowly aft. He was dreading what he would find and wished Doug had given the job to someone else; after all he had done it the last time. God, was that really only last night? In front of the tailplane carry through there was a hole in the side of the fuselage big enough to get a football through and on the other side lots of small holes where the shrapnel had carried on out after the shell had exploded. Crawling over the tailplane Harry came to the fuselage rear doors, which had half a dozen small holes in them. Behind these Harry stared at the rear turret's doors and didn't want to go any further. Again there were half a dozen holes in the metal doors with vicious looking strips of jagged metal pointing outwards. One of the holes was near the top of the turret doors and the size of a fist. He knocked on the back of the turret, but there was no reply. Harry swallowed hard, took a deep breath and released the turret door catch, then slid the doors open. At first they didn't move, jammed in their runners by the damage.

Then, all at once, they flew open and the half of Sammy's head that was left hit Harry in the face as the corpse fell backwards out of the turret. Harry, on his hands and knees, sat up quickly in shock and banged his head hard on the roof of the fuselage. Sammy's body fell flat on its back in the rear fuselage and when Harry looked down he saw Sammy's right eye staring up at him. Where his left eye should have been was a dark red hole. The left side of his flying helmet was gone and from his nose left his cheek and jaw were missing. White bone and remains of teeth shone in the moonlight and a gory flap of muscle and skin hung down onto his neck. In horror, Harry suddenly realized that this was what was left of his tongue. Harry's stomach heaved and he quickly crawled backwards away from the gore before him. By the time he got forward of the tailplane he was sweating uncontrollably and was just in time to open the Elsan and vomit violently into it. After a moment of heavy breathing he spat and made his way shakily forward. He dropped heavily back into his seat and shakily reconnected his intercom. Steadying his breathing he flicked on his microphone.

"Sammy's dead, skipper, and the turret's smashed."

There was a pause.

"Are you sure he's dead?"

"Half his head's gone."

"Okay... We'll leave him where he is as the turret's smashed. There's nothing else we can do for him. How long until we're 100 miles off the coast, Ron?"

"Two minutes."

The rest of the flight back was in silence, while they all examined their own mortality. As they approached Metheringham Doug called in and reported their casualty. The ambulance was already waiting at the dispersal when Freddy taxied in and as the engines stopped the doctor and two medical orderlies climbed aboard.

"Where is he?" the doc asked Alex as he climbed backwards out of his turret.

"Rear turret."

"Right, we'll leave him there until after you're all off."

The crew all climbed stiffly out of the Lancaster, taking care to avoid looking at the rear turret. The ground crew also stayed well away from the rear of Freddy, finding lots to do at the front. After the usual quick chat to Sergeant Green Caitlin drove them to the interrogation room. Another Lancaster landed while they were driving in. The main body of the Squadron wouldn't be back for a while yet and Freddy was the first of the gardeners back. The interrogation went quickly and they were almost finished by the time the second crew walked in, but all the while it was hard not to keep looking at the empty seventh chair.

"Are you F for Freddy's crew?" asked the padre.

"Yes," said Doug.

"Could you phone the medical centre? Your gunner asked me to let him know when you got back, but as you lost one of your chaps..." The padre looked embarrassed. "Well, I thought it would probably be better coming from you."

"We'll call in on him on our way back to our billet," offered Harry.

"Aye," agreed Alex, thinking it was time he acquired a more willing girlfriend and where better than the station hospital? Just then one of the intelligence officers took Doug to one side to ask him some more questions and the sergeants took the opportunity to leave.

Five minutes later, their spirits high at still being alive, they burst through the doors to the medical centre and headed for the ward.

"You can't go in there!" yelled a little nurse on night duty.

"Don't worry, bonny lass! We're celebrating oor return from the dead," said Alex, picking her up and, squeezing her wriggling body against his, planted a smacker of a kiss full on her lips. With the nurse temporarily neutralised the other three sergeants rushed into the ward.

George was still lying awake.

"Christ, you have no idea how lucky you are mate!" exclaimed Harry.

As usual Doug and Ron cycled in silence back to their billet. Doug felt shaken by Sammy's death, but wondered how much worse it would have been if it had been George. Walking into the hut Doug felt with his right hand and turned on the light. A figure sat up in surprise in the fifth bed.

"Oh sorry," said Doug, "we didn't think anyone would be in."

The young looking fair-haired man in the bed screwed his eyes up against the light and rubbed his hand over his face. He had obviously only half unpacked his kit and most of it was spread around the floor under his bed.

"That's alright, I only got in yesterday evening. I'm John Baker. I won't get up if you don't mind. I've only just managed to get warm."

"No problem. Doug Jackson, and this is Ron Dune. Are you part of a new crew?" He walked over and shook John's hand.

"Yes, pilot, all my crew are sergeants. It's a bit awkward because I hardly ever see them away from flying."

"Yes, it is a bit strange," agreed Doug, as he and Ron started to get ready for bed.

"Have you just been on Ops?"

"Yes."

"What was it like?"

"It was a gardening Op, the first one we've done and it was a bit of a rough trip." Doug stopped short of telling John about Sammy, although he felt the need to talk to someone about it.

"How many trips have you done?"

"Seven."

"Almost a quarter of a tour."

"Yes." Doug hadn't realized this himself because he was starting to believe it was less and less likely he would see the end of a tour. "I suppose you have to see the Squadron Adj in the morning?"

"Yes, eight o'clock."

"Well, we won't be up until later than that so get Goddard to boil you a kettle of hot water to shave with and get shaved in the locker room so you can keep the light off in here."

"Alright, goodnight."

18

A bright light lit up everything around him and the glare made Doug screw up his eyes in pain. For a second he thought it was a searchlight, and then he heard a voice.

"I'm sorry, chaps, I can't find my shoes in the dark." Doug forced his eyes open to see John on his hands and knees under the bed.

"Christ," said Ron.

"I'm sorry," repeated John. "But I don't want to be late on my first day."

Doug relaxed a little after the initial shock.

"It's alright, but get your kit sorted out and move it into the locker room, then you can get dressed there without disturbing anyone in here." Doug's voice tailed away as he saw the two empty beds in the far corner of the room and he glanced across at Ron who had also seen them and was looking back at him. "What time is it?"

"Seven thirty, why?"

"Nothing," said Doug, rolling over and pretending to go back to sleep.

George opened the door to the billet quietly and walked in. It was dark inside with the blackout curtains still drawn and the soft sound of snoring was coming from Harry's bed. With his eyes unaccustomed to the dark George slowly felt his way to his bed. He moved slowly, partly not to wake anyone but also because he was still in quite a bit of pain. The station doctor had asked him how he felt and he had said never better, which was a complete lie, but he was determined he was not going to let his crew fly without him again. Reaching his bed he gingerly sat down, gritting his teeth against the pain as the weight went onto his lacerated backside. Suddenly Bob yawned and stretched, then sat up.

"Hello, George, are you back with us?"

"Well, I'm out of hospital, but the doc won't let me fly for another couple of days."

"What time is it?"

"Half twelve."

Bob threw his pillow at Harry.

"Wake up, you lazy bastard! George is back."

Jimmy and Alex woke up quickly and Harry started to stir.

"Hello, George, how are you feeling?"

"Bit sore but I'll live."

"Where's Digger's crew?" asked Alex.

"Don't know," said George, looking around, his eyes now adjusted to the dark.

"Did anyone hear them come in last night?" asked Jimmy. They all shook their heads.

"They were after us into the right side o the harbour last night. They must ha been the bomber we saw on fire."

"Shit, and they only had another couple of trips to do," said Harry, rubbing his eyes.

"Yeah, it's a shame," said Bob. "Let's go and eat."

After lunch they cycled over to the Squadron Office where the Adj told them there were to be no Ops that night and they were stood down until the morning. This relieved George because he hoped he would be fit again before they had to fly their next Op. That afternoon Bob, Jimmy, Harry and Alex took a bus into Lincoln to see the sights, which basically meant they were going to get drunk. George stayed behind and went to look at Freddy. The rear turret was removed and the ground crew were about to fit a new one. George took some measurements and then went to the crew room and made some enquiries before returning to Freddy after the turret had been fitted. There he made some adjustments to the turret, while trying to ignore the dried blood in the rear fuselage, which the ground crew hadn't quite managed to fully remove.

The next day at eight the sergeants met Doug and Ron in the Squadron Office only to be told that while there were Ops on that evening they were not on the flying programme. Doug decided to take Freddy for an air test and because George still wasn't declared fit to fly they would go without him and Alex would check his turret while George went back to the doctor hoping to be passed fit again.

George was back in the billet when they got back from the test flight.

"What the hell have you done tae the rear turret, you Geordie pratt?" asked Alex.

"I've taken the seat out."

"A can see that! It nearly crippled me while a was checking it. Why the hell did ya do it?"

"So I can fit a seat parachute in it."

"Why the hell wid ya want a seat parachute?"

"If a flak shell goes off under me turret again I'll be sittin' on six inches of tightly packed silk. So there won't be much chance of any shrapnel coming through an rippin' me bollocks off."

"He has a point," conceded Bob, who always felt a vital part of his anatomy was dangerously exposed when he lay on his stomach over a target.

"But Doug says his seat parachute is like sitting on concrete after a couple of hours. After a long flight he can hardly stand," added Jimmy.

"I don't care. I'd rather sit on concrete than get me balls blown off!"

"Well, it's your arse, but I wouldn't have thought the safety equipment bods would let you have a seat parachute anyway," said Harry.

"Already sorted that and there's no problem."

"So what did the doc say? When will you be back with us?" asked Bob.

"I am back. He says I'm fit to fly now."

"Good," said Alex.

"Did you miss me, darling?"

"No! But if we get the chop A want you there with us."

"What are we going to do tonight?" asked Jimmy, changing the subject. "Being as we've got a night off."

"A have plans," said Alex.

"You randy bastard," commented Bob.

"So have I," said Harry grinning.

"And you're getting as bad as him," replied Bob.

"One will do for me," countered Harry.

"Well I reckon us happy bachelors should have a couple of pints and go to the pictures," said George.

"What's on?" asked Bob.

"Dangerous Moonlight."

"Bloody appropriate! But I haven't seen it and with the rest of the Squadron flying we shouldn't have any problems getting in."

As it turned out the Op that night was cancelled because of fog and the cinema was packed.

Cycling to the Squadron Office the next morning the main topic of conversation was whether there would be any more major raids for a while. The moon was now half full and too bright for the bombers to travel across Germany without risking a severe mauling. Most people thought there might be a few small short-range raids but most of the crews might be able to get some leave. However, at the Squadron Office there was a disappointment in store.

"Maximum effort tonight, chaps. Yes, I know there's a half moon, it's not my decision, just get your kites ready. Specialist briefings 17.00, main briefing 19.00." Nigel wasn't happy about the raid either. He could sense trouble but he was just the Adj, what could he do?

"Right, chaps," said Doug. "We'll check Freddy and then the time's your own until specialist briefings." Freddy was fully serviceable, as usual, although Sergeant Green was as surprised as everyone else that there was to be a large raid this late in the moon cycle.

"They must be forecasting cloud cover," he observed to Doug while he signed the 700 after the ground test. "It's a full fuel load, so it's probably the big city again," he added pessimistically.

The afternoon passed the usual way. Alex went off to the window store with one of his girlfriends. Harry went for a long walk around the airfield with Florence. Jimmy, Bob and George played cards. Doug read a book and Ron lay on his bed and stared at the ceiling. Doug was getting very worried about Ron. He might have been a pain before, but he was a good navigator. Now there was no life in him and he hardly ever spoke. But whenever Doug asked him he always maintained there was nothing wrong.

Halfway through the afternoon George came back into the billet.

"The thieving colonial bastards!"

"What?" asked Bob.

"They ran out of coal for their stoves, so they've nicked every bloody toilet door on the camp and burnt them instead!"

"You're kidding," said Jimmy.

"Go and see for yourself! I've just had to sit there and wave at every bugger that passed! And you can stop laughin an all!" Bob was curled up on his bed convulsed in laughter. Like many RAF squadrons 106 Squadron had a large number of non-British personnel and in 106 Squadron's case most were Australians. They were well known for having little respect for what they regarded as stupid decisions, so when they ran out of coal they used their initiative to ward off the cold which they felt far more keenly than their British comrades.

At 18.55 the crew all met outside the main briefing room, having completed their specialist briefings. It was already dark and there was no cloud cover, so the moon cast dark shadows around the buildings. All the crews agreed it was very bright and tonight would probably be another scrub. The briefing room doors opened and the crews filed in. Doug's crew hurriedly finished their cigarettes and followed.

"Hey, skipper, look. They're sitting in our seats," said Harry. Four rows from the front on the left one of the new replacement crews were sitting in the seats Doug's crew always sat in.

Doug walked up to their captain.

"I'm sorry but these are our seats."

"I thought you could just sit anywhere."

"Well, you can, but most crews always sit in the same place."

"Well, we're here now, can't you just sit somewhere else."

The pilot was a sergeant and he obviously didn't know the significance of what he was asking. By now the crews were starting to get tense and Bob tried to appraise the new captain of the magnitude of what he wanted them to do.

"Look! Just bloody move, alright!"

The new captain was startled by the violence of the response while Doug held up his hand to try and calm the situation.

"Sorry, but it's a luck thing. You'll feel the same after a couple of Ops. Now we're asking politely, would you mind moving?"

The new captain sighed.

"Alright, come on, lads, we'll move." And they all shuffled out to a row of seats further back.

As everyone got seated the Station Commander and OC 106 Squadron walked in and everyone stood up. After the usual sit down chaps, and pep talk, the briefing was handed over to the briefing officers and the curtain pulled back.

"Gentlemen, your target for tonight is Nuremberg."

There was a large intake of breath and a "Jesus." Nuremberg was as far as Berlin but in southern Germany, so nearly all the flight had to be over hostile territory, whereas much of the flight against Berlin could be done over the North Sea. The route involved the bombers flying southeast over the southern North Sea to a rendezvous 30 miles off the Belgian coast, and then continuing on to a point south of Brussels. Then the route turned east, passing south of Liege and going through the gap between the Ruhr and Frankfurt defences. This leg was 265 miles long and took the bomber stream close to the Ruhr defences, two fighter beacons and a number of night fighter airfields, consequently it was not popular. At the end of this leg the route turned south for 79 miles to Nuremberg; all of this section of the route would have to be undertaken while the moon was up.

The briefers played heavily on two points. Firstly, although the eastern leg was long there was a strong tail wind and the total flying time from the Belgian coast to the target was only 100 minutes. So it was hoped the Germans would not be able to get their fighters into position before the bombers had sped past. The second point was there was expected to be high cloud to cover the moon, so the bombers could reach the target in total darkness. Zero hour for the main attack was 01.10, with the Pathfinders starting their marking five minutes before that. There was to be no Master Bomber for the raid but a new system of a flexible zero hour was to be used so that Bomber Command could broadcast a change to zero hour if it became obvious that the bombers were going to arrive early or late. A few weeks previously Bomber Command had suffered heavy losses on a raid on Leipzig, when the bombers arrived early. Then they had been forced to circle the target waiting for zero hour and the target marking to begin.

Shortly after reaching Nuremberg the moon was due to set, leaving the bombers to make a looping return flight over northern France and re-crossing the English Channel at Dieppe, with no threat of moonlight. Of course the return flight would be against the wind, so it would take about five hours to get back to Metheringham from the target and the total distance for the flight was almost 1,500 miles. Other details of the raid were pretty standard. The plan was to mark the target as a Newhaven with an emergency Waganui as back up, if the target was covered by cloud. The route out would be 21,000 feet for 106 Squadron although Number One Group were going to fly 4,000 feet lower to hopefully take more advantage of the forecast cloud cover.

The main briefing over, the crews started their individual planning, but the general feeling was not one of confidence and the older crews were still holding out for the Op being scrubbed. One by one the crews left for the crew room and struggled into their kit. Doug saw George pick up a seat parachute.

"What are you doing with that?"

"I've adjusted my turret so I can wear one of these in it."

"Why?"

"To protect me arse from shrapnel."

"You'll regret it. They're very uncomfortable."

"But it's better than a shell up yer arse."

Doug conceded that point, but still thought it was a mistake.

Caitlin drove them to Freddy; her driving did seem to be getting better, or perhaps they were getting more used to it. George gave her the envelope of six letters; Ron didn't leave a letter with him anymore. Then Harry appeared by her window.

"Florence says she'll meet you by the flying control tower."

"Alright, sarge, see you when you get back."

As usual Ron climbed straight aboard and Harry, Alex and George had a quick smoke while Doug and Jimmy checked the 700 and Bob signed for his bombs. The moon was high in the crisp clear sky to the north and visibility was excellent.

"It's too bloody bright," said George.

"Dinnae worry, it'll scrub, you'll see."

George looked over at Alex and smiled.

"I'm not so sure. Still best take a leak now." Alex smiled back and hauled himself up the ladder.

"We missed you and your filthy habits," said Harry, following Alex. The crew went slowly through their pre-flight checks because there was no hurry and they stopped short of starting the engines. Slowly the time ticked around to 22.00.

"It'll be a scrub," said Alex again, and then a green flare soared into the sky from the flying control tower and Doug and Jimmy started Freddy's number three engine. Soon Freddy had come to life and with the red and green navigation lights of the other bombers twinkling in the bright moonlight the dark shadows of the Lancasters started to move off.

They taxied slowly through the black and grey landscape in the procession of Lancasters queuing for takeoff.

"Too late for the lads at the gate again," said Alex, when they taxied slowly past. "A wonder what they'll remember o this when they're older?"

"I just hope they never have to do it themselves," replied George.

"It's exciting though, isn't it?" commented Bob.

"I could do without it," responded Jimmy, checking the brake pressures.

Then they were lining up and Harry, standing in the astrodome, looked over to the runway caravan to see Caitlin's truck with Caitlin and Florence standing beside it waving. Then there was the green light and they were away. Harry had just enough time to flash I.L.U back to Florence with his Aldis lamp, before he had to hold on as Freddy accelerated. Soon they were climbing away and turning onto a southeasterly heading to take them out over the North Sea at Southwold, where a vertical searchlight gave a last visual navigation fix.

"I've never seen visibility this good at night," said Bob.

"I can see fifteen other bombers back here," said George. The bombers had switched off their navigation lights at the coast, but were still all too visible in the moonlight.

"It'll be better when we get under the cloud cover over the continent," said Doug. "That should cut the visibility right down."

They tested guns and armed bombs and with the aid of the tailwind soon reached the assembly point. Not that there was anything different to see there because it was just a random point in space 51 degrees 50 minutes north 2 degrees and 30 minutes east. But each bomber had to reach that point at a specific height and time to slide itself into the right slot in the bomber stream. Tonight the 785 planned heavy bombers would form a stream 68 miles long. In the first 20 miles of the stream there were only ninety-seven aircraft. These were the initial Pathfinders consisting of twenty-four target illuminators and six visual markers, backed up by sixty-seven Lancasters from 8 and 5 Groups carrying high explosive loads to back up the Pathfinders by demolishing buildings ready for the mainly incendiary loads of the main force. It was hoped these aircraft would also block the streets with the debris from collapsed buildings, so that the fire fighters could not effectively fight the resulting fires. Then there were another five waves consisting of, on average, nine Pathfinder backers up, who would top up the target marking flares, five ABC jamming Lancasters, with their eighth German-speaking crewman, to try to confuse the German defences, seventy-eight ordinary Lancasters with a 4,000 pound high explosive Cookie and incendiary load and forty-six Halifaxes with an incendiary only load. All of these waves were joined together in one long stream of aircraft.

20 miles from the coast Bob started to drop window and Doug started to weave. There was still no sign of the forecast high level cloud and with the moon still high in the sky visibility was still far too good.

Crossing the Belgian coast at Knokke there was a light smattering of flak, which did no damage, and they were allowed to proceed into hostile territory unmolested. By now what few wisps of high cloud there had been had disappeared and the crews were getting very nervous; it was only a matter of time before the German fighters found them in the moonlight. But still there was no opposition and the bombers swept on turning over the Napoleonic battlefield at Ligny and starting the long easterly leg. After a few minutes Ron announced the forecast winds were wrong and they were getting blown north of track and he made a course correction to allow for this. Unfortunately, while Ron had H2S and had acquired considerable skill in its use, most Lancasters had yet to be fitted with it. With their GEE boxes jammed they failed to detect the change in the wind and the bomber stream started to get dispersed to the north of its planned route.

As they approached the German border Bob saw the first fire in the sky and soon after they crossed the frontier there was another. There was still no sign of the forecast cloud and now it was obvious there wasn't going to be any. But there was worse to come.

"Skipper, we're contrailing," announced George, as the white vapour trails started to appear behind Freddy. It was very unusual for condensation trails to form below 25,000 feet and while it was common to see the white lines in the sky behind the high flying American Flying Fortresses, it was very uncommon to see them at the heights the British bombers flew. But now, on a crystal clear night with visibility far too good to be healthy, fate dealt Bomber Command another bad card. Now each bomber was not only visible from many hundreds of yards but each bomber had a long white finger pointing at it.

Doug looked around him in dismay. Everywhere he could see bombers leaving arrow straight white lines in the sky, which no German could fail to see.

"This is no good," he said to the world in general. "We'll climb as high as we can and see if we can get above the contrail layer and if we can't hopefully the Jerries will go for the easier targets below us."

Coaxing everything he could from Freddy he managed to stagger up to 23,500 feet and as he reached it the condensation trails stopped. Below him the wide white road in the sky stretched out in front of him and now there were regular bursts of tracer in the night. These often ended with red and yellow comets plunging to the ground so that a trail of fires on the ground marked their progress.

Suddenly five white magnesium flares lit up the sky to the right and were rapidly left behind. The flares hung in their parachutes and could be seen from many miles.

"Junkers 88 3 o'clock high," yelled Alex.

"I see him," replied George. "He's just dropped those flares and now he's sitting there just out of range."

"It's an 88 bomber," said Alex. "The bastards just markin' the route for the fighters."

Further ahead more flares dropped under their parachutes. By now they were all very scared. Everything seemed to be conspiring against them. The night was too light, the visibility too clear, the condensation trails gave away their route and the German fighters had found the bomber stream in strength early in the raid. It all seemed like it was now just a matter of time before a fighter found them. All eyes except Ron's scanned the sky for shadows. Jimmy was almost frantic and he was convinced that at any moment he was about to be blown to smithereens. His hands were shaking and he knew if he had to he wouldn't be able to speak. Nothing could be as bad as this, just waiting to die. Another yellow flash marked where a bomber had exploded and Jimmy cringed down in the cockpit and pretended to check the fuel gauges. The Junker 88 dropped another row of five flares.

"Skipper, that bastard's pissing me right off. If we break towards it Alex might get a shot at it before he can run away and even if we don't get him it should scare him off."

"Alright, George, are you ready, Alex?"

"Aye, skipper, whenever you're ready."

Doug suddenly turned sharply to the right and headed straight for the German bomber. Alex gave a good amount of deflection and fired a two second burst at it. The red tracers soared up and over the Junkers appearing to slide backwards as they did so until they whipped close past his tail. But they had the desired effect. The startled pilot, who thought he was well out of harm's way, broke violently away and Doug resumed his original course with the Junkers lost well astern in the darkness.

So many bombers were seen going down Alex, George and Bob stopped reporting them and it was obvious Bomber Command was taking a hammering. The only consolation Doug's crew had was that most of the fires were to the north, where the main stream of bombers had been blown off course by the devious wind. Ron, for all he was a pain, had kept them safe again. With nerves stretched to breaking point they reached the end of the long easterly leg and turned south towards Nuremberg. The turn was not well marked because fighters were being sent to any ground markers dropped by Pathfinder aircraft to mark turns, so this method of marking turning points had been discontinued. There were no obvious ground features in this area, so most bombers, already off course because of the wind, turned well to the north and west of where they should have been. Ron, with the aid of his H2S, natural ability, and a little luck, was only 5 miles off course. Some of the others were 30 miles away from where they thought they were, with the majority being between 20 and 25 miles out; now there were 643 bombers left from the original planned total. Some had failed to get airborne because of technical problems, others had been forced to turn back because of mechanical failures, but sixty had been shot down.

By now the Pathfinders at the front of the bomber stream were approaching the target and preparations were underway for the attack. Bombsights were readied, the rate of windowing was increased to confuse the radar-guided searchlights and flak and a last radio message from Bomber Command informed them that the zero hour remained unchanged.

The plan for the marking was typical of that for most raids. Ten minutes before zero hour nine fast flying Mosquitoes would drop large quantities of window over the target to neutralise the radar-guided ground defences. Five minutes before zero hour twenty-four blind marker illuminator Lancasters would drop large numbers of parachute flares over the city, lighting up the ground below. These would be supported by sixty-two other Lancasters carrying purely high explosive bombs. The aim of these bombers was to give the defences more aircraft than just the illuminators to shoot at and to block the streets below with collapsed buildings. Finally, at three minutes to zero hour, six visual marker

Lancasters would fly over the neutralised target and in the light of the illuminators' flares visually spot and mark the aiming point with their bright red and green target indicators. In all, ninety-two Lancasters and nine Mosquitoes would mark the target with 120 parachute flares, 156 target indicators, twenty-four sky markers and 383 tons of explosives. And it would all be for nothing.

Earlier in the day, a single Mosquito of the RAF's Weather Reconnaissance Flight had flown high and fast over southern Germany, assessing the weather for the raid. It had seen a layer of cloud well to the south of Nuremberg, but the Meteorological Office had decided it wouldn't be a problem because it wouldn't move north. But it did.

Nuremberg was covered by a layer of low cloud over 10,000 feet thick, which meant all the illuminating flares and target indicators would be invisible below the thick layer of cloud. The Newhaven method of marking would be useless and it would have to be a Wanganui. Now the main force would have to rely on the twenty-four red and yellow sky markers as an aiming point for their bombs and these would be quickly blown away by the strong wind. From crossing the edge of the cloud front the Pathfinders had eight minutes before they reached the target. This was all the time they had to decide what to do and set up for the complicated and inaccurate Wanganui marking method. For most, it wasn't long enough. Tonight there was no Master Bomber to coordinate the attack and each crew had to do their best as individuals and hope they were doing the right thing.

At this point a vital mistake was made. A few of the Pathfinders, despite having the best navigators in Bomber Command, had not detected the change in the wind and were out of position. By pure bad luck, at their estimated time of arrival at Nuremberg, they arrived over the town of Lauf, 10 miles east of Nuremberg. Lauf was also under the thick layer of cloud and while it was much smaller than Nuremberg it had similar H2S radar features. It was on a river and was surrounded by woods, which on a grainy flickering green H2S screen were almost identical. Some of the Pathfinders spotted the difference and corrected their error, but others didn't. The result was two groups of sky markers; one over Nuremberg, one over Lauf and both groups of flares were being blown rapidly east, away from their targets.

At zero hour the main force should have arrived en masse and started to rain bombs down on Nuremberg at a rate of 160 tons a minute. But in the first five minutes after zero hour only thirty-three bombers arrived. Presented with the two groups of sky markers they were split between the two aiming points and all they could do was make educated guesses as to which one was correct. With no Master Bomber to guide them the split was about even between the right and wrong targets and as the markers blew further away from their drop points the bombing accuracy got worse and worse. As the Pathfinders flew away from the target area most of them were asking the same question. Where the hell was the main force?

There were two answers to this. Firstly, the Pathfinders had been lucky in that, because of the tailwind, they had passed the point where the fighters intercepted the bomber stream before the slaughter started and they had no idea about the carnage behind them. Secondly, the wind had blown most of the bombers further off course than the Pathfinders would have expected and this caused yet another problem. Flying over the blacked out countryside with few things on the ground to visually fix their position the navigators were forced to rely on the Group broadcast winds and dead reckoning. This would have been alright if the broadcast winds had been accurate, but they weren't, and with no prominent features at the turning point most of the bombers had to turn onto the next leg at their estimated time of arrival and hope for the best. Unfortunately this put them 25 miles northwest of where they should be and if they then flew one seven five degrees for Nuremberg from that position they would actually reach Schweinfurt. And Schweinfurt wasn't covered by clouds.

At zero hour minus ten a solitary Mosquito Pathfinder was lost. Its GEE equipment was jammed and its radio was playing up. Without any aids the navigator was doing his best using dead reckoning and guesswork. With so much depending on them the pressure on the Pathfinders was far greater than on the other main force crews and this Mosquito crew were well aware they were lost. Then, at the right estimated time, a large concentration of searchlights and flak appeared directly in front of them. They couldn't believe their luck; after 600 miles of enemy territory with no navigational fixes they had hit their target right on the nose.

Only it wasn't the target. The Schweinfurt defences put up a lively defence, but the Mosquito flew on through them to drop its load of three 500-pound bombs, bundles of window and one green target indicator. In the next few minutes seven Lancasters drawn by the lone green target indicator had also dropped their loads on Schweinfurt. This in itself would not have been a major disaster had fate, which had already conspired against Bomber Command from the very start of this raid, not once more stuck in the knife. Another Lancaster heading towards the marker and small fires of Schweinfurt already had company. A Messerschmitt 110 was already stalking it and just short of the town it struck. The Lancaster's port wing erupted in flames, which rapidly spread to the fuselage, and the big bomber spiralled out of control spewing a brilliant orange flame in a wide helix. This massive falling Catherine Wheel was held as it fell by the Schweinfurt searchlights, marking the area for all the main force bombers for miles around. When it hit the ground the fires lit up the town and from that moment on Schweinfurt was going to receive the attention of up to 100 bombers.

Freddy was steady on the new southerly course and thanks to Ron they were less than 5 miles off track. Most of the casualties had happened in the middle of the stream just in front of them and while they had had a ringside seat only a few bombers as far back in the stream as they were had been shot down. Because they were in the last quarter of the bomber stream they expected to see a well-lit target when they arrived. Although the moon was now low in the sky and the night less bright the visibility was still very good and they didn't expect any trouble locating and hitting the target.

"Target indicator 2 o'clock!" called Bob.

"I see it," replied Doug.

"I'm not expecting to see the target for a while yet and it should be dead ahead," said Ron, with unusual confidence, which he seemed to have acquired after their low-level mining Op. Freddy's H2S had been working well and Ron had got some good fixes, so he was sure he knew exactly where they were.

"Well, there's definitely bombing going on over there," said Bob. "Jesus, look at that!" A Lancaster was falling in flames over the target lighting up the countryside for miles around.

"We'll go over and have a closer look," decided Doug, altering course slightly. As they got closer they could see the town in the light of the burning bomber. Bombs were exploding among the houses and factories with brilliant orange flashes and sprinkles of white incendiaries bursting over a wide area.

"Looks like the target to me," said Bob.

"Well I think the target's 50 miles southeast of here," replied Ron.

"Well, you seem to be in a minority because plenty of other people are dropping their loads here." Bob wasn't positive that this was the right place, but it was an industrial town in Germany and other people seemed to think it was the right place.

Bob's belligerence immediately put Ron on the defensive and while a moment before he would have accepted a decision to bomb, whether it was the right place or not, now it was a matter of face and he wouldn't back down.

"Just because other people are bombing here doesn't make this the right place, sergeant! I say the target is 50 miles to the southeast."

"Alright," said Doug. "We'll take a look to the southeast. If we don't see anything after fifteen minutes we'll come back."

Ron gave them a course for Nuremberg and they set off. Now they were out of the bomber stream and they felt more exposed than ever. Not that being in the stream tonight had seemed like a good place to be, but being able to see other bombers had at least been moral support. Now they were alone in a bright and dangerous sky. After ten minutes of seeing nothing Ron's confidence was fading rapidly. He must have been wrong and having made such a big thing of it he would now be made to feel stupid. He could already see Bob's smug face grinning at him insolently. Why hadn't he just let them bomb wherever it was, he looked at his map, probably Schweinfurt, he thought. Now they were over cloud and even if he were right he wouldn't be able to prove it, because they would never be able to see Nuremberg. Or maybe that was Nuremberg they had seen and now they were heading miles off course into southern Germany. Why did he get himself into these situations? Why was he so stupid? Why was he always wrong?

"Aircraft on fire 9 o'clock," said Alex.

"Sky marker 11 o'clock," said Bob.

"I see it," echoed Doug. "There's a group of them. Looks like you were right, Ron, well done."

Thank God, thought Ron, whose confidence was at an all time low and his self-esteem even lower. When they got closer to the group of markers it turned into a line and a second group appeared further away. They had obviously been dropped in two different places and were being rapidly dispersed by the wind.

"How the hell am I supposed to aim at that?" asked Bob "They must be strung out over 20 miles."

"There seems to be a group further over," offered Jimmy.

"Yeah, but that's the way the wind's blowing. They've probably just been brought together by the wind and anyway they're probably all well out of position by now."

"Can you see anything on H2S, Ron?" asked Doug.

Ron was already looking. "There's a large town in our 1 o'clock at 8 miles."

"That's to the right of the sky markers," replied Doug.

"Yeah, skip, but the way the wind's blowing that would be right."

"Okay, Ron, steer us to the middle of the town and tell Bob when to drop."

"Roger, turn right 10 degrees, range to target 5 miles."

This was unlike anything they had ever seen before. The target area was empty. There was no flak, no searchlights, only the eerie yellow and red light of the last of the sky markers low over the tops of the clouds 10,000 feet below them. One by one the markers were being swallowed by the clouds making their tops glow briefly mustard or pink as they defused the light of the flare and soon they would all be gone.

"Bomb doors open, master switch on, bombs fused and selected," said Bob and Doug repeated it back while the bomb doors opened and the wind noise inside Freddy increased.

"Target on the nose 2 miles."

"Bomb doors fully open," reported Harry.

"Target still on the nose, standby... Drop." Bob hit the release and Freddy leapt upwards.

"Bombs gone skipper. Sod the photo flash, there's bugger all to see anyway, let's get out of here!"

Freddy swung away to the south and continued on the route of the main bomber stream. But now, because of the wind, the confusion over the target and the concentrated enemy action the bomber stream was so scattered it no longer really existed.

George glanced quickly to his left as green tracer streaked across the sky. Red tracer whizzed back, but there were no hits.

"There's a fight going on in our 5 o'clock," he reported. Another burst of green tracer shot forward and there was a yellow flash. Two more bursts of red tracer hosed into the night. Then a yellow light appeared in the sky and slowly got bigger. Someone had been hit but George couldn't tell if it was friend or foe. The yellow flame continued on the same course, parallel to Freddy, and grew bigger. By now it was obviously a bomber, but still flying and still under control. George stopped looking at it to preserve his night vision, but out of the corner of his eye he kept it in sight. After about five minutes the flame started to descend until it made a sudden rush at the clouds below them and disappeared. Well, at least they had plenty of time to bale out, he thought.

Now they turned to head west, towards the Rhine. They would fly south of Stuttgart, north of Strasbourg and out over northern France to the English Channel. The cloud below was still a continuous white carpet and while Doug would normally have dived for home to gain speed, to fly low over that cloud would have made Freddy visible to any night fighters flying above them. He could of course fly in the cloud, but he hated instrument flying so much he persuaded himself it would be risking icing Freddy up and it would be safer to stay high.

The other problem caused by the cloud was navigation. Ron hadn't had a good position fix for some time and now they were flying against a headwind and it would be a long drag home. He desperately needed a fix to check their progress and ensure that they would have enough fuel to get home. For this reason he was staring at the H2S screen desperate for some feature he could recognise. At last he saw it, a solid line right across their path. It could only be the Rhine and he turned to his map to start working out the actual wind and their estimated time at the coast.

Gunter Voss had just dispatched his third victim of the night. He had been forced to use his fighter's nose cannon, because the new Schrage Musik or slanting or jazz music cannon, which fired upwards through the Messerschmitt's long cockpit canopy, had jammed. He had used the Schrage Musik to dispatch his first two kills of the night and it had been easy. Since Gunter's last Commanding Officer had killed himself by flying into the ground one foggy night his new CO had made sure Gunter, as one of the most experienced and successful pilots, always had one of the squadron's best fighters. Tonight he had their latest aircraft, straight from the factory. Not only did it have the twin upward firing 30 mm cannon, it had the latest SN2 radar, which the British didn't yet know about and couldn't jam. This radar had an effective range of 4,000 metres, twice that of the Lichtenstein sets. It also had a new locating system called Naxos; this system homed in on the H2S radar emissions of the British bombers. It only gave a direction and it only worked if you were lower than the bomber, but it worked through 360 degrees whereas the radar could only see forward. Using the Naxos to point the fighter the right way and get into the bomber stream and then homing in on the individual targets with the radar it was easy to find victims. Once you could see them you no longer had to worry about the hated rear turret that had killed so many German night fighter crews. You just stayed very low or moved out to one side, keeping the bomber just within visual range and manoeuvred slowly until the bomber was right above you. Then you climbed slowly up directly beneath it, where the gunners couldn't see you. Once there you could take your time and line your Schrage Musik up on the wing fuel tanks. A very short burst of 30 mm cannon fire was enough to set the bomber on fire. Then you dived clear and watched the fire eat the bomber away until it fell apart or blew up. The only thing you had to be careful of was when the bombers were on their way to the target. Then, if you hit the bomb bay, the bomber was likely to explode and destroy you as well. The extra equipment also meant there was no space for a rear gunner and with the British sending an ever growing number of Mosquitoes and Beaufighter intruders along with their bombers that left him feeling a little exposed.

Gunter's last victim had flown along with a wing on fire for five minutes before falling out of control and breaking up, just before it entered the cloud below him. Gunter was happy about this; it gave the crews plenty of time to bale out. But even when there was plenty of time he rarely saw any parachutes. The British crews seemed very reluctant to abandon their aircraft until absolutely necessary and then it was often too late.

Karl, Gunter's radar operator, was now working on the Schrage Musik cannon to try and free the jam. Gunter could hear him banging at the breeches just behind his seat trying to clear them. After five minutes a breathless Karl announced that he thought the cannon would work now and he was back in his seat. Gunter, on the other hand, was cold, tired and had had a successful night and was prepared to call it a night and head for home and a hot coffee.

"Naxos contact left 60 degrees."

"Okay, Karl." He glanced at the fuel gauges. They had been airborne a long time and it was about time to head for home. But as long as this wasn't too long a chase it would be fine. "We'll have a look, but if it's a long way off we'll have to leave him."

"Roger, come left 50 degrees."

The fighter turned slowly onto the new course and steadied. Karl checked the new Naxos bearing; the signal was still left of the fighter's nose, but crossing slowly from left to right. He looked quickly across to the SN2 radar screen, but there was nothing there. The bomber was still beyond the SN2's range, which was a lot less than that of the Naxos. The rate of change in the bearing suggested the target was either very fast, possibly a Mosquito and therefore faster than the Messerschmitt and not worth the effort of even attempting to catch. Or a slower target quite close, but still just beyond radar range. He waited until the Naxos showed the target directly ahead and there was still no radar contact. The bomber could be a long way off and until they got radar contact they would have no idea of the target's range.

"Come right 20 degrees and increase speed."

This should cut the corner a little and close the range. Again the signal settled 20 degrees left of the Messerschmitt's nose, then slowly started to cross from left to right. Karl switched his attention quickly between the Naxos and the SN2 looking for a sign of the target appearing at the maximum radar range. Once again the signal from the Naxos worked its way to directly ahead of the fighter and, just as Karl was about to order another 20-degree right turn, to which Gunter was going to reply they were too short of fuel and to call it a night, a faint echo appeared on the SN2 screen and started to slide down the range scale.

"Radar contact dead ahead crossing slowly left to right." He paused until the contact was 10 degrees right of the nose.

"Come right 10 degrees." The bomber was now dead ahead and they were catching it up quickly.

"Dead ahead and slightly above, range 3,000 metres…2,500 metres." The range rapidly closed, this was no Mosquito. At 1,000 metres Karl slowed the rate of closure to prevent them overshooting.

"Speed back… 800 metres… Still ahead and slightly above… 600 metres." Karl felt the fighter twitch to a movement he hadn't ordered and knew from experience that Gunter could see the target. A few seconds passed. Gunter was getting closer to make sure he wouldn't lose the bomber in the dark, then he announced, "I see him, a Lancaster, dead ahead and slightly above."

The bomber was weaving from side to side, which would make this more difficult than some, which flew straight and level as if there was no need for any evasive action. With the white cloud below Gunter decided he would pull off to one side to make his approach then slide under the bomber from the side, where the gunners tended to be less vigilant. Holding the Lancaster at the limit of his visual range, which, now the moon had set and the night was much darker, was about 600 metres; he flew up the right side of the bomber keeping about 100 feet below it. The weaving made things tricky because at the far side of the weave the bomber was almost invisible, but at the near side it seemed alarmingly close. Soon he was in the bomber's low 3 o'clock and he started to slide over. This was the dangerous bit; until he was directly underneath it the gunners might see him. Slowly he got closer, descending as he did to try to stay at the limit of vision and prevent the gunners spotting him. Finally he was underneath. Now he was safe and he started to breathe more easily. After a few seconds to steady his breathing and never moving his eyes from the weaving Lancaster directly above him he started to climb until he was only fifty feet below it.

"Everything alright, Karl?"

"Everything's okay, we're clear behind and the cannon are set."

"Alright, here we go."

His left hand advanced the throttles an eighth of an inch while his right hand automatically kept the fighter fifty feet below the weaving target. This was not easy to do and involved throwing the heavy fighter quickly from left to right. Gunter knew he couldn't keep this up for long without tiring but he hung grimly onto his difficult target. There was a point at the end of each weave where the bomber stopped turning one way and started to turn the other and that was the moment he intended to fire. The sights, which were a simple cross on the Perspex roof of his cockpit canopy, were halfway up the bomber's fuselage and moving slowly forward. He had no idea at the moment if he was in a left or right turn; he was just concentrating on staying in the same place relative to the bomber. The sight was now under the centre of the bomber and he allowed the fighter to drift out to the left of the Lancaster so that he was below the left wing and at the same time he moved the throttles back so slightly the engine note hardly changed. Now for the bomber to stabilize before its next weave. His thumb rested gently on the firing button and as the cross steadied on the space between the two port engines and the bomber started to turn to the left, he fired.

19

Caitlin and Florence had watched Freddy accelerate down the runway and seen Harry's last flashed message. Then they'd listened to the drone of the Squadron's engines fade into the darkness, until it mingled with the drone of all the other squadrons taking off from their airfields all over Lincolnshire. By 22.30 all the bombers were long gone and the small group of people at the end of the runway slowly started to disperse. Caitlin and Florence drove to the NAAFI and had a hot cup of tea before going to bed. They both lived in the same WAAF billet and like most of the other occupants they would get up again to meet the bombers when they returned. The majority of the hut's occupants had duties to perform when the bombers got back but others just wanted to make sure boyfriends were safe. For those there was never a good night's sleep when there were Ops on, and unlike the crews they couldn't catch up on their sleep during the day. In lots of ways the strain on those left behind was greater than on those that flew.

But tonight was different to the others; tonight there would be no alarm clocks going off in the early hours to be quickly silenced, lest they wake others who were not going to see the bombers in. Tonight everybody would be awake.

At about two in the morning a force of about twenty-five German aircraft appeared on the British radar screens off the coast of Norfolk and Lincolnshire and night fighters were vectored to intercept them. The force split up and a few crossed the coast, but some slipped in at low level and started to hunt for the bombers' bases. At about three o'clock a howl of engines, a clatter of cannon and two loud explosions caused Caitlin and Florence, along with all the other WAAFs in the billet, to throw themselves out of bed onto the floor. The Junkers 88 intruder hurtled down the Metheringham runway at zero feet and dropped two bombs.

After the shocked shrieks had stopped and the Junkers' engines faded into the night they all quickly dressed and went outside to see what had happened. Soon a WAAF sergeant appeared and sent them to their places of duty, where they stayed for an hour until things calmed down and it was realised it was a lone intruder and he had gone. The damage was slight. Two bombs had been dropped on one of the runways, but they were being repaired. Everyone was stood down to their billets but few went. The Squadron was due back around six and there was little point going to bed now. Caitlin took Florence to flying control, where she knew there would be a pot of tea available and she knew one of the senior WAAFs who worked there. Jane had for some reason befriended her when she had first arrived and shown her the ropes. As they quietly entered the dark glass hut on the roof of the building Jane spotted them and came over.

"This is Flo, she's seeing the radio operator from my crew," said Caitlin.

"Hello," smiled Jane, who was probably a couple of years older than Caitlin and Florence. "None of our aircraft have checked in yet, but if you wait over there you'll see everything as it happens and there's a pot of tea on its way." Behind her a loud speaker crackled to life.

"Coffee Stall, Coffee Stall, this is Hadnone B for Baker, do you read me, over?"

That's the first of them now," smiled Jane. "Excuse me." And she went quickly back to her desk beside the flight lieutenant controller, who was now answering the bomber.

It was still dark outside and while the glass protected them from the wind there was no heating and it was very cold. One by one bomber after bomber checked in while other bombers droned slowly overhead, unseen in the darkness, heading for bases further north. Caitlin and Florence wrapped their hands around their mugs of hot tea and sipped at the rapidly cooling liquid to keep warm, while the flying control staff checked off each bomber that checked in by moving a large drawing pin marked with that aircraft's letter to different places on their control board. Now of the eighteen bombers the Squadron had despatched earlier that night the board showed twelve aircraft in the airborne section of the board and six in the checked-in section. Outside, the airfield lights were turned on, and a few minutes later a Lancaster's red and green navigation lights appeared. They got slowly closer until the black bomber screeched down on the runway and slid past the tower. A pin marked with a B was moved to the landed Metheringham section.

The flight lieutenant was talking constantly into the radio now, pointing and directing the actions of his WAAF assistants, who moved pins and made phone calls with smooth efficiency. After another half an hour ten pins were in the landed slot, three in the checked-in slot, five in the airborne slot and the work rate of the flying control staff had slowed considerably. Freddy's pin hadn't moved. The last three checked-in Lancasters landed and the activity in flying control stopped. Jane glanced nervously over, and then quickly busied herself with some other work. Florence was staring out of the window into the darkness, biting her lip and on the verge of tears. Caitlin stood beside her, but could say nothing to help her.

Suddenly the telephone rang and they both wheeled around, but the Flight Lieutenant was quicker still and the receiver was already to his ear.

"Yes… Yes, at Manston… Alright." He hung up. "Flying Officer Penman, M for Mike has crash-landed at Manston. All the crew are safe but the kite's a wreck."

He glanced from Florence to the other girls in the tower and one of them moved the M pin to the landed away slot. There were still four pins airborne. The atmosphere in the tower was very tense. While losing one or even two bombers wasn't uncommon, four was another matter.

"There's still time yet," he said positively. The minutes dragged until another half hour had passed in almost complete silence. The lights of the last trucks taking the crews for interrogation had long since disappeared from the airfield.

Florence suddenly turned to the officer and with full eyes, which were not yet crying, asked, "Sir, how long before their fuel runs out?"

The officer looked back with sad old eyes then looked at the flying control clock, which showed seven o'clock. He looked her straight in the eye and said, "With the engines leaned right back, a good crew could stay airborne another forty-five or so minutes." Florence nodded, bit her lip and turned back to look out across the airfield.

The sky in the east was a shade lighter and the trees on the far side of the field were more distinct. The static from the tower speaker and the ticking of the clock dragged the time out. Everyone checked the clock every couple of minutes until eventually it said 07.45. Florence stared at Flight Lieutenant Bill Fairclough who could feel her gaze but avoided eye contact and looked down at the control board in front of him.

"Get me Ops, Jane," he instructed. There was a pause then he took the receiver. "Is the Station Commander there? It's Flight Lieutenant Fairclough at flying control... Hello, sir, I'm afraid that's it, there's four missing." Without looking, he was aware of Florence staring at him with silent tears streaming down her face.

"Yes, sir, Flight Sergeant Hall's crew, O for Oboe, Pilot Officer Starkey's crew, S for Sugar, Pilot Officer Moxey's crew, T for Tore and Pilot Officer Jackson's crew, F for Freddy." With this Florence quietly sobbed and rushed from the tower with Caitlin close behind her. "Alright, sir... Yes, I'll just clear things up here, sir, goodbye." He hung up and sighed. The sky was a dull red in the east and the dawn was lighting up the field. "Well, that's it, girls. I'll wait for the day shift but you might as well go now."

The tower crew, sombre and quiet at the Squadron's loss, like the rest of the station would be when the word went around, picked up their kit and started to leave. Jane followed the other WAAFs to the tower door then looked back. Uncle Bill was standing silently staring out at the dawn. Jane knew he had been in the war from the start and seen too much of this. He was such a nice gentle man who would have felt very badly seeing Florence in so much pain. She would make sure no WAAFs with boyfriends on Ops ever came to the tower again. She had befriended Caitlin because she had been Sally's replacement and she and Sally had been together since basic training.

She closed the tower door and made her way down the tower steps. Above her a thrush started to sing in the early dawn light and another day started.

The first 30 mm shell hit Freddy's wing just behind the main spar and just inboard of the number one engine. There the heavy shell exploded with the force of a small hand grenade sending lumps of shrapnel outwards to smash into the side of the engine. The shrapnel wasn't heavy enough to shatter the engine block but it ripped several fuel pipes and high tension leads. A spark from one of these leads ignited a jet of fuel from one of the severed fuel lines and a jet of flame two feet long shot inboard from the engine. Other pieces of shrapnel lacerated the port number two fuel tank between the two port engines causing fuel to spill out into the interior of the wing. The second shell scored a direct hit on the same fuel tank and blew the tank wide open. Surprisingly the explosion didn't cause the fuel to ignite but a stream of fuel leaking from the bottom of the wing and vaporising in the slipstream was caught by the jet of flame from the number one engine and the petrol flared into a gigantic wall of yellow flame.

Gunter was holding his fighter steady underneath Freddy and letting the bomber move from right to left above him so that Freddy's left turn spread the cannon fire down the length of the wing. The next shell hit the rear of the number two engine and shattered the engine block, tearing apart the crankshaft and snapping connecting rods. The front half of the Merlin however was still intact and still tried to drive the engine, which thrust smashed pieces of the rear of the engine through the engine block as the 1,460 horse power engine ripped itself apart. The fourth shell exploded inches behind the main spar between the number two engine and the fuselage. It ripped a massive lump of metal from the spar and punched a large hole in the port number one fuel tank before continuing on into Freddy's fuselage between the spars. Harry, sitting just ahead of the spar was only saved from being cut in half by the bulk of the spar itself.

As Freddy had started to turn on its left-hand weave Doug had allowed the nose to drop slightly and Gunter, seeing this, had pushed his fighter's nose down slightly to maintain the distance between the aircraft. As a result of this the cannon shells were hitting slightly forward of where Gunter intended them to go. Freddy was also turning more quickly than Gunter had expected and the next shell missed ahead of the port wing, skimming the side of the fuselage. The sixth and final shell to hit punched through the bomb bay doors and exploded as it hit the underside of the fuselage floor, flinging a wall of shrapnel upwards through the fuselage. Four more shells missed ahead of Freddy's right wing as Gunter dived away, well aware that if Freddy had still had his bombs on board the shell exploding in the bomb bay would have blown Freddy and Gunter's fighter to eternity.

The impact of the exploding shells ran through Freddy with a rapid series of thuds. Doug felt the controls shudder in his hands and the left wing dipped rapidly so that he had to apply full right aileron to raise it. The inside of the cockpit was filled with a flickering yellow light as he got Freddy back on an even keel and looking out to his left the whole wing was a mass of flames. He could already feel the heat through the cockpit window, but the shock of one moment quietly flying back to Metheringham and the next second Freddy being a flying torch froze him and he just stared into the inferno.

Bob was lying in the nose looking through his bomb aimer's blister with a map in front of him and looking for an end to the layer of cloud below them. He was thinking of a hot coffee to warm himself up with when he felt a shudder through his stomach and Freddy dipped to the left. He instinctively looked to the left and saw the flash of the port wing fuel tanks igniting in a wall of flames, which rapidly hid the whole wing from view so that only the engines were visible sticking out of the front of the inferno. With his mouth open in shock he swivelled around to sit facing the rear of his compartment; he could see Doug's feet working hard on the rudder pedals to keep Freddy straight. He felt sick with shock and his heart was in his mouth. It was obvious Freddy was a goner and he quickly looked at his watch. By his reckoning they were still over Germany and could expect no help if they baled out, but the fire was well out of control and they had no choice. Why hadn't Doug given the order to bale out?

Then Doug recovered from his shock.

"Bale out! Bale out! Quick!"

Bob was already crawling towards the rear of his compartment, scrambling over the last of the bundles of window. His hands pushed them aside as he went, until he could reach behind the bombing computer. Here he fumbled in the darkness and grabbed the square canvas pack of his parachute. With shaking hands, which seemed to lack all dexterity, he fumbled the pack so that the two D rings on the back of it were in front of the two clips on his parachute harness. Then sliding the pack downwards against his chest the rings caught and were held in place by the spring clips. Pulling at the pack to ensure it was firmly attached he turned back towards Freddy's nose and, pushing more bundles of window aside, he lifted up his bomb aimer's padded cushion to expose the forward escape hatch.

"Hurry up!" yelled Doug, in his earphones. "The wing's going to go! Get out!"

Bob turned the handle on the hatch and pulled it inwards being met by an icy 200 mph wind, which tore at his clothes as he threw the hatch out into the night. Then, taking a deep breath, he forward rolled into the darkness and was whipped back in the slipstream along Freddy's belly until his head impacted the H2S blister and his world went black.

Jimmy didn't feel the shells hit. He was just thrown off balance when Freddy dipped a wing and as he grabbed the back of Doug's seat for support his nightmare appeared before his eyes. Looking behind the seat, along the wing, all he could see were brilliant yellow flames. They stretched out behind Freddy as far as Jimmy could see. The slipstream was tearing them backwards into the night and whipping them over the top of the fuselage so that he couldn't see the mid-upper turret for flames. Jimmy's world was now in slow motion as his mind went into overdrive but his body couldn't seem to keep up. He could hear Doug ordering them to bale out and he moved his foot to where his parachute was stowed, but he already knew it wouldn't be there. His foot found space and he knelt down behind Doug's seat to try and find it, but it had gone. The curtain, which separated Ron's navigation compartment from the cockpit, was on the floor. Ron had got himself wrapped up in it and was struggling to get out from underneath. Sod him, he'll have to help himself, thought Jimmy, his eyes wide with fear as he searched for the missing chute. Where the hell could it be? He had looked everywhere behind the seat and he was blocking the way to the forward hatch. It was only because Ron was caught in his curtain that he wasn't fighting to get past.

Suddenly there was a blue flash to his left, down the tunnel of the fuselage, followed swiftly by a flare of yellow flame. The fire was now inside the mid section between the spars. Jimmy stood and stared at it for what seemed a lifetime, but was only a second, before Doug grabbed his arm.

"Hurry up! The wing's going to go! Get out!"

Like in his dream, Jimmy knew Doug wouldn't try to bale out until he had gone. The horror of it all seized him so that with his heart in his mouth he couldn't breathe and his head pounded until he thought it would explode. Then he heard a quiet calm Geordie voice in his head. "I know you, Jimmy Wilson, and you won't let us down." He could see George standing in the dim light of the ablution block as he said it and he wondered if George was still alive. No, he wouldn't let anyone down; he glanced into Doug's urgent face and smiled. Then, without his parachute, he made his way forward to the hatch.

The icy gale roared down the fuselage and ripped at his clothes while he pushed against it. He had to twist sideways to get his broad shoulders through the narrow gap under the right side of the instrument panel leading down into the nose compartment. As he got into the compartment his intercom lead was pulled out and the world seemed strangely quiet after the crackling. Bob had already gone and the compartment was empty. He could feel the bundles of window crushing under his weight and a map swirled around the small windblown compartment. Suddenly Freddy dipped to the left and he fell sideways. He would have to hurry, Ron and Doug would be right behind him now and he had to get out of their way. The hatch was just in front of him and at least he knew it would be quick. He would just keep his eyes shut and he wouldn't know anything about it. All he could think of now was Mary and how upset she would be. He would do anything to spare her from that pain but there was nothing he could do. The tears welled up in his eyes and he knew he would never see her again. He pushed himself upright and faced the hatch, then looked at what he had fallen on. A square canvas pack! His parachute! How the hell had it got there! Quickly he clipped it on. He had a chance, just a chance, he might survive, he might see Mary again. He rolled out of the hatch and into the cold night.

The first Ron knew of their being under attack was when there was a loud explosion underneath him and his legs shot upwards to bang hard against the underneath of his navigation table. Freddy dipped and he was flung across the table, then he fell sideways and while he put his leg out to save himself he continued to fall. With arms flailing he grabbed the blackout curtain and it tore away and fell on top of him as he collapsed on the floor. Damn it! he thought. How he hated flying. When he had finished his tour he would never fly again. He struggled to free himself from the curtain but it had caught on something and he kicked his legs, but they were numb and he couldn't feel anything to push against.

"Bale out! Bale out! Quick!" echoed through his earphones.

What the hell was going on? His arms wrestled with the curtain as he started to panic. What was the matter with his legs? He reached down with his right hand to examine where his right leg had been banged against the table and just above the knee his trousers stopped. He felt further, but couldn't comprehend what he had discovered. There was nothing there. Feeling further over, his fingers touched a jelly-like texture and then a hard shard of what he suddenly realized must be bone.

"Help!" he yelped in panic and shock, his hands fighting to rid himself of the curtain with renewed vigour. After what seemed an age he got his head clear and looked up at the yellow glow covering the Perspex of the cockpit. He twisted his head around to look for help but he could see Jimmy disappearing into the nose.

He tried to push himself into a sitting position against the side of the fuselage but without a right leg his hands just slipped on the wet floor. He looked at his hands in the light of the flames. The palms looked black and he realized he was lying in a pool of blood and it was all his. Pushing himself up on his hands he sat looking down at his legs and pulled the curtain aside. His left leg was bent at 90 degrees to the left above the knee and blood was squirting through a hole in his trousers in a narrow jet. His right leg had gone completely and out of the jagged end of his trousers poked a bloody stump with a hideously white splintered bone protruding from the end of it. The sight of his mangled legs made him want to vomit and he slid back down to lie flat on his back and stared up at the flames above the cockpit. He knew he was going to die and he was surprised to find he didn't care. While the sight of his legs turned his stomach he couldn't feel any pain and he supposed he was in shock. He also knew that by the time the shock wore off he would be dead so he could relax and let his life slip away in peace.

There was no point in carrying on anyway, there hadn't been for a while now. Janice had left him during his last leave; he could see her now walking out of the door. She had been the reason he had done everything, but it had just driven them apart. She had told him she had never really been happy and he was never there when she needed him. Now she wasn't there when he needed her. Wherever he had been in the world, no matter how far they had been apart, he had always had a warm glow in his heart knowing that somewhere there was someone who loved him. He had gained a lot of strength from that, but it hadn't been true. Any love she had had for him had died when he left and all she felt for him was emptiness. Now she was with someone else and the thought of it twisted in his stomach like a knife. Tears filled his eyes and ran backwards onto the cold vibrating floor. He could see her walking out of the door. I only wanted you to be proud of me, he'd said. She had fixed him with her hazel eyes, which used to be so warm but were now so cold. What have you ever done for me to be proud of? she had asked icily and then she'd closed the door and was gone.

There was a screech of tearing metal as the fire ate its way through the last of Freddy's already damaged main spar. Then with the groan of an aircraft that had given its crew all the time it could Freddy's left wing folded slowly upwards until the shattered number two engine, with its propeller still turning at 2,000 rpm, smashed into the top of the cockpit and sent a large shard of Perspex straight into Ron's already broken heart.

Sitting just in front of the main spar Harry felt the impact of the shells as if Freddy was going over a cobbled road at speed. Then the intense yellow of the flames shone through the window by his seat and looking out into the furnace Harry instantly knew he wouldn't be going home. His first thought was how Florence would cope with them being posted missing and he had to get back to her as quickly as he could to stop her worrying.

"Bale out! Bale out! Quick!"

Harry swivelled out of his seat and grabbed his parachute pack from its stowage point on the wall opposite. Even he couldn't stand upright at this point of the fuselage, so he struggled to clip on his parachute while bent over forwards. Finally it clipped home and he stepped over the main spar. As he got his second leg over his feet slipped away from under him and he fell back heavily onto the floor by the rest bunk. Squirming on his back with the weight of the parachute on his chest in the narrow space by the bunk, he felt like a tortoise on its back, but he knew he was short of time and he started to panic. The floor was an inch deep in liquid and it had soaked right through all his layers of clothes chilling his skin. Rolling onto his front he soaked himself more and as he finally regained his feet it suddenly dawned on him that the liquid was petrol from Freddy's smashed number one fuel tank. Freddy lurched again and Harry clung on. As he did his eyes fell on the main aircraft batteries, which were stored under the bunk. There was a blue flash as one of the battery terminals arced and then the petrol vapour ignited with a loud whoosh. In the first second Harry was only aware of a wave of heat over his face and he tried to run over the rear spar but he couldn't see for flames. He hit the spar and fell onto his knees. There was an intense pain in his face and legs. He looked down at his arms and was fascinated to see they were a mass of flames. He had to get away from the fire. Grabbing the side frame of the fuselage wall he tried to pull himself up, but his hands slipped and he could see the burnt skin sliding off his fingers. His lips felt like they were being drawn back into a wide grin and his eyes were narrowing into slits. He could feel himself weakening but he had to get away and he pushed himself up and over the rear spar, forward rolling onto the rear of the bomb bay. The pain in his legs was unbearable when he rolled onto his front and tried to stand, but his arms wouldn't work properly and he only got onto his knees. Looking down he saw his arms were still on fire but his heavy leather flying jacket was burnt off and his skin was black and peeling away. The whole of the area around him seemed to be a fiery hell and his vision started to dim. The pain in his arms, legs and face was starting to subside and he felt very tired. Poor Florence, he thought, as he fell onto his chest and sleep crept up on him. He was suddenly in his bed and he could smell pork burning. Must be Sunday, he thought, and nearly time for lunch, coming, Mum.

Alex was scanning the sky, but had not seen another aircraft since the burning bomber ten minutes before, when suddenly his world lit up. He didn't feel the impact of the shells or hear anything and the first he knew of the attack was the flames flying past his turret. He was facing Freddy's 7 o'clock when they were hit and he looked back over his shoulder at the burning wing and found all he could see was a sea of flames rushing past him on both sides of his turret. The heat was building up quickly and he knew he had to get out quickly or get cooked.

"Bale out! Bale out! Quick!"

He turned his turret to face the rear and, standing up, released his seat. He had considered turning the turret forwards and falling out backwards into the fuselage. But it was a long way down and while it would be quicker he didn't like the thought of the fall. So he went for the conventional climbing down into the fuselage, which was slow at the best of times, but with Freddy jumping and dipping he had to cling on every step of the way down. Finally he slipped and dropped onto the floor, falling backwards onto his bottom. Then there was a flash that lit up the whole length of Freddy's rear fuselage and Alex turned to see flames filling the mid section. A wall of heat hit him and he screwed his eyes up against it. The flames were moving and because his eyes were still adjusting to the light he couldn't see what was going on. Then a lump of flames spilled over the rear spar and Alex realised, with horror, it was someone on fire. The mass of flames was less than six feet away from him and it raised itself into its hands and knees and then slumped back down again. Flames four feet high were still flying up from it and Alex suddenly recovered from the shock and scrambled towards the flames to try to put them out. There was a fire extinguisher on the starboard wall just forward of his turret and he grabbed it and turned it on the flames. He could now tell, by the size, that it was Harry, but he was completely black in the glare of the flames. Working from his feet, which were nearest, to his head it took Alex all of the fire extinguisher to put the fuel soaked body out. By the time he finished it was obvious that it was too late and Harry was dead. With tears in his eyes from the heat, shock, horror and fear and a sickening smell in his nose he threw away the extinguisher and clambered down the fuselage. He ducked under his turret. His parachute was stowed just the other side, by the rear entrance door. He had just reached it when he heard the screech of tearing metal and then a massive bang. A whirlwind roared down the fuselage tunnel and the floor fell away from him. He was lifted off his feet and pushed hard up against the ceiling until he was flat on his back looking up at the floor. Freddy was falling and twisting, with only one wing still attached to the fuselage and the centrifugal force holding Alex tightly where he was. He tried to move, but his arms were so heavy he could only just lift them and it would be impossible to drag himself to the door, which was only four feet away. Still he tried; reaching one of Freddy's ribs he pulled himself four inches closer to his parachute. How high were they, he wondered? He made another gigantic effort and got another four inches closer to his chute. He pictured his mother and father getting the telegram telling them he was missing. Then there would be the weeks of hoping, until the silence gave way to resignation. Another straining pull got him a little nearer and he managed to grab the protective bars around the DR compass, which he had banged his head on so many times getting into and out of the aircraft, until he had finally got used to ducking under the obstruction.

Then Freddy smashed into a wooded hilltop overlooking the Rhine and exploded in a ball of flame, sending Alex to eternity.

George was in agony. He wasn't really fit to fly, he knew that, and he was only there because he had lied to the doctor. But there was no way he would have let his crew go without him. Now he was paying for it. Doug was right, seat parachutes were like sitting on concrete and by squeezing one into the rear turret George had robbed himself of the last bits of space in the already cramped turret. From the waist down he was either numb or in agony. Every few seconds he squirmed into a new position to try and ease the pain, but nothing worked. He didn't see the fighter or feel the explosions but the wall of flame from Freddy's port wing reached out past his turret and into the night. Looking quickly around by pressing his head to the Perspex on the side of his turret he could see that the whole wing was alight.

"Bale out! Bale out! Quick!"

It certainly seemed the sensible thing to do and with no hesitation George rotated his turret fully left and, reaching over his shoulder, opened the turret doors. He rolled into a ball and kicked himself backwards out of the turret, giving the briefest of pauses before pulling his ripcord.

"Bale out! Bale out! Quick!" yelled Doug, suddenly snapping out of his shock and turning his attention back to the instruments, while fighting to keep Freddy steady to give his crew best chance to bale out. Both the left engines were obviously losing power and Freddy was yawing violently to the left so that Doug had to push with all his strength on the right rudder pedal to keep the crippled bomber straight. He quickly reached down with his right hand and found the bath taps, as he always thought of the rudder and aileron trim controls, and put on full right rudder trim. It still wasn't enough to hold Freddy straight, but it took a lot of the weight off the amount of push needed on his right leg. He made a quick check of the instruments to be sure he was flying as straight and level as he could. Then he reached over to the right of the cockpit and pushed both the left-hand engines' fire extinguishers, knowing full well there was no way of putting the fire out, but hoping it would buy a little more time. Now all he could do was hold Freddy steady for the others.

What the hell was Jimmy up to? He appeared to be fumbling around behind Doug's seat and now he was staring down the fuselage. There was no time for this, he had to get out quick, Doug reached over and grabbed his arm.

"Hurry up! The wing's going to go! Get out!"

Jimmy's face stared back at him, a picture of pure terror. His eyes were wide and Doug wasn't sure whether he could even hear him. Then his face suddenly changed, he seemed to relax and he gave Doug a quick smile and squeezed his way under the instrument panel into the nose and out of sight. Doug had already felt the rush of air from the nose whipping around his legs so he knew Bob and now Jimmy were out.

He glanced over his shoulder and for the first time saw the flames filling the mid section. Harry was gone and he hoped he had made it to the rear hatch. The two gunners were, as usual, on their own, far away down the other end of the aeroplane and the fire was too intense in the mid section to see beyond it.

Where was Ron? Then he saw him out of the corner of his eye in the flickering light of the flames. He was lying on his back staring blankly upwards into space and at first he thought he was dead. But then he saw he was breathing, but making no attempt to get out. Exasperated Doug turned back to the controls and thought about making a quick dash for the hatch. It would be a very tight squeeze down into the nose wearing a parachute. And the moment he stopped pushing the right rudder pedal Freddy would roll over onto his back and dive vertically for the ground, pinning them all to the floor, walls or ceiling. He resigned himself to the fact that there was no way out and the best he could do was keep Freddy level for anyone else who might still be trying to get out down the back.

He felt sure he would die and while he wasn't religious, he at least took some comfort in knowing he would die as he had always tried to live, doing his best. His father had always said that to him, "It doesn't matter whether you succeed, so long as you do your best." He had enjoyed his twenty years, but he would have liked to have longer. He would have liked to have a family, but he had never even had a girlfriend.

A wave of sadness washed over him as he remembered Sally. She was beautiful and they would have been so happy together. Over the rubber, oil and fuel he could smell her light perfume now, as he had smelt it while he held her waiting for the ambulance. The only girl he had ever held. What had she said as they put her on the stretcher? "No, you can't come with me yet, you have to look after your crew." Yet? he thought. "Some people say I'm psychic." And as they put her in the ambulance, she'd said, "I'll see you soon." She had known! She must have seen it somehow. He smiled, and his tensed body relaxed a little.

A squeal of metal dragged his head instinctively to the sound and he saw Freddy's port wing bend upwards as it started to tear itself free from the fuselage. It bent upwards to 90 degrees and with the right wing still providing lift on the other side it twisted the fuselage towards the folding wing. Doug watched all this in slow motion and saw the huge number two engine getting nearer as the wing folded in and the massive propeller still spinning at 2,000 rpm heading straight for him. His hands reached for the release pin of his seat harness but they were moving very slowly and as the pin came out the propeller cut through the canopy above his head as if it wasn't there and smashed Doug's head to atoms.

Gunter dived clear and swung his fighter out to fly parallel on Freddy's right side at a respectful distance. He wanted a safety margin in case the bomber blew up and it wasn't unknown for gunners to stay in their turrets, even when their aircraft was obviously doomed. The fire was clearly out of control and it was only a matter of time. Gunter wasn't the type to gloat, but he was a professional and he was pleased at another good clean kill, although he was chastising himself at being careless enough to have let his fire stray into the bomb bay. Now he waited to watch for parachutes.

"One parachute!" called Karl. "I think it was the rear gunner."

"Another," called Gunter. "Schize! Did he hit the underneath?"

"I think so, his parachute hasn't opened." There followed a pause of a few seconds, which seemed like minutes.

"Why the hell is it taking them so long? Can't they see the bomber's finished?"

"There goes another! I can see his chute."

"Come on. Come on." The bomber was now in a slight dive and then it started to fold up. The left wing, slowly at first, started to bend upwards. Then, with increasing speed, it twisted up until the two wings met above the fuselage; to Gunter it looked like a butterfly folding its wings. Next the port wing tore completely free while the majority of Freddy plunged nose first to earth, its one remaining wing spinning it as it went and flames spilling from the detached wing route. The port wing followed Freddy down, slowly spinning like a blazing sycamore leaf. Gunter watched until both pieces of bomber fell out of sight into the cloud.

"Two parachutes out of a crew of seven. Why are there hardly ever more than one or two? Okay, Karl, give me a homing for base."

Bob didn't have any idea where he was. Hitting the H2S dome had knocked him cold and he was only just beginning to come around, thanks to the 120 mph ice-cold wind as he fell to earth. It was as if he was awakening from a dream while he slowly started to recover and become aware of his surroundings. Then he reached a level of consciousness where he felt he was falling. He had felt it before in dreams, but this time it was more realistic. An icy blast of wind hit his face as he tumbled over. That had never happened before in a dream and he was suddenly aware that he was actually falling. What had happened? He fumbled for the ripcord with trembling and unfeeling hands. Where was he? How high was he? Hurry! He looked for the handle, but looking down he couldn't see for the oxygen mask and tube, which was still attached over his nose and mouth. Grabbing them, he wrenched them off, then looked down and saw the ripcord.

His hand grasped the cold metal and he pulled with all his strength. It came away with no effort at all and his heart stopped because he thought it must be broken. Then, with a loud rustle a flapping mass of white silk shot upwards past his face. There was a pause and a loud crack and he was flung downwards hard into his harness, which bit deep into his crotch and upper legs winding him. He looked up at the round canopy above him, then around into the darkness. Slowly he started to remember what had happened prior to him being suspended in his parachute. But he was still dazed and not thinking at all clearly when a roof sprang up at him out of the darkness and he landed with a thud in deep mud.

He rolled over onto his back, the mud soaking through his clothes while he grappled with the release box as the chute refilled with air and dragged him through the mud. There was a crash behind him and he stopped. At the same time chickens started squawking and a dog started to bark. His frozen hands turned the release box and hit the locking plate, freeing him from the chute.

His head pounding and spinning, he staggered to his feet and nearly fell as his world spun around. He had to get away from the dog – it would bring people from miles around – but he couldn't see where he was. There appeared to be dull shapes of buildings all around him so he set off in a random direction. From the smell he was in a farmyard and there had to be a gate somewhere. The deep mud was slippery under his feet and his thick fur-lined boots were not designed to cope with these conditions. He felt drunk and, as a boxer, he was well aware that he was concussed.

In his haste to get away from the dog he blundered into a wall knocking something over and it clattered to the ground. Behind him a light came on, a door opened and the white light spread across the small farmyard.

A tall slim figure was outlined in the doorway and it yelled something in German into the darkness. Bob stepped back against the wall and tipped a bucket onto whatever metal tool he had first knocked over. The silhouette spun quickly towards him. It reached out to one side of the door and picked up a pole before switching on an external light. This flooded the yard with a yellow glow, making Bob squint.

Bob was less than 10 yards from the door, standing against a bare barn wall and the man saw him immediately. The pole came swiftly down to the on-guard position for a rifle and bayonet. Bob immediately noticed two things that made his blood run cold. Firstly the pole was a wicked-looking two-pronged pitchfork and secondly the man's left hand was an evil shiny hook. His stunned brain flashed back to his mother reading Peter Pan to him as a child, when Captain Hook had always been his arch villain.

The farmer slowly and deliberately advanced towards Bob, who edged his way further down the barn wall, until he was in a corner with the farm wall. He was staring into the farmer's eyes which didn't blink as they stared back, full of pure hate. Shaking with shock, cold and fear Bob suddenly remembered he still had one card he could play. Reaching quickly inside his leather jacket he felt for his pistol. It wasn't there! He fumbled around in panic, but it had gone, torn free by Freddy's slipstream and his 120 mph fall.

The farmer had reached him and was speaking in low clipped angry tones, spitting neat venom at him.

"Mine daughter unt mine grand kinder," he heard him say, daughter and grand children? Bob didn't understand. "Terror Flieger!" Bob understood this.

"Look mate," he began. "I'm only doing what I'm told to do. Your lot are doing it to us as well, you know."

The farmer aimed the pitchfork, balancing it over his hook while his right hand prepared to thrust forward.

"I've never hurt anyone," yelled Bob, convinced in his own mind it was true. He grabbed at the pitchfork as it came quickly forward, but the old soldier had done this before and knew what Bob would do. He had dipped the prongs to aim at Bob's belly, but as Bob made his grab he raised his aim so that Bob missed and the pitchfork slid quickly through his Irvine jacket and into his chest.

The force of the blow knocked the air out of Bob and pinned him to the wall. He grabbed the shaft of the fork and tried to pull at it, but the farmer was leaning on it with all his weight. He could smell the strong pipe smoke on the farmer's breath and the dusty damp smell of his clothes. There was a sudden cold feeling in his chest and a sharp pain. The farmer was now twisting the pitchfork, the way he had been taught when he was a soldier. But with only one hand he couldn't get a good grip on the shaft so as he withdrew the prongs he put his foot against Bob's chest to help him get the steel out. Bob felt very weak and as the fork came free his knees buckled under him. He was still dazed from hitting the H2S dome which was probably just as well. His hands still loosely held the shaft, but there was no strength in his arms and the farmer thrust again, driving Bob down onto the mud. He looked up at the dark cloud-covered sky and felt very tired. Taking a deep breath he sighed, but the breath came out in a gurgle of blood, which tasted salty and thick in his mouth. As his eyes closed a single star broke through the layer of cloud. Peter Pan, flying, Captain Hook, and now Tinkerbell he thought. "Mum." And he closed his eyes forever.

Jimmy's chute opened with a crack so loud he jumped, but looking up the chute was fully open and he was safe. The first thing he noticed was the cold; it was freezing. He looked down at the clouds below him, then he tried to spot Freddy, but he was alone in the darkness. He undid the clip of his oxygen mask to let it hang from one side of his helmet and breathed deeply. The grey mass below reached up to him and then he was swallowed up in a swirling mist. There was no longer any up or down, just grey and it felt unreal as the cloud seemed to blank out all sound. The descent through the cloud seemed to go on forever, but in truth it was no more than a couple of minutes.

Emerging from the cloud he was about 1,000 feet above the ground and could make out snow covered forests and fields. The wind was blowing him over a wood and he looked ahead to see where he was going to land. It looked as if he would clear the trees and land in a small field. When he got closer to the ground he realised how strong the wind was. He was moving sideways very quickly and swinging wildly from side to side. Suddenly the ground shot up at him and he landed hard, knocking all the air from his body so that he gasped for breath. The parachute immediately started to drag him gasping across a field and he rolled onto his back and struggled to undo the parachute harness. With a click it snapped free and disappeared into the night, while he lay still in the glorious silence of a dark winter's night.

One thought overcame all others in that moment of peace: he had survived! He didn't care he was in an enemy country with little chance of escape; he knew he would probably be captured, but it didn't matter. The Germans looked after their prisoners and he would survive the war. In a year or so it would all be over and he could go home to Mary with his head held high. If Freddy hadn't been shot down he would have had to face danger night after night until he was killed. Now he had a better chance of living than he had had since he volunteered for aircrew. It was one of the happiest moments of his life.

After about five minutes the cold ground convinced him it was time to move, so he stood up and realised he had no boots on. The slipstream had pulled them off and his right knee hurt from his heavy landing. He had no intention of trying to get away and decided to find the nearest house and give himself up.

The cold, hard, rough ground bit into his feet as he walked across the field and soon they were numb with cold. He started to wonder about the rest of the crew and whether they had got out. He felt guilty about Ron and not helping him. He knew he would have helped if it had been any of the others, but it was no excuse leaving Ron just because he didn't like him. He came to a stone wall and climbed over it to find he was in a narrow country lane with stone walls on either side. Beyond the stone wall on the other side of the road was a wood made up of medium-sized fir trees. The snow was hard and compact showing the road was well used by vehicles, but there was no sign as to which way would lead to the nearest town. After a moment's indecision he turned left, because that was down-hill, and slipped and slid his way along the icy track.

He had only gone a few hundred yards when he heard voices. There were quite a few of them and he started to get frightened again. His knee was hurting and he knew without boots he couldn't walk much further without doing his feet serious damage and risking frostbite. So he took a deep breath, gritted his teeth and started walking again. Ahead he could see, in the dull light of the sky reflected in the snow, a bend in the road and as he got to the bend the voices got louder. There were one or two small lights visible through the trees and as he rounded the bend he found himself less than 50 yards from a crowd of about twenty men. They had found something by the road and were examining it in the light of three or four lanterns. Beyond them was a village and on the other side of the road was a small farm. As he stood and watched he realised they were examining a parachute and everything was clear.

When he released his chute it must have blown into the village and they were going to set out and look for him. With renewed confidence he limped towards the group, until he was 20 yards away, and at the same moment they saw him, he saw the body lying in the snow.

It was a moment when time stands still. The Germans stared in silence at Jimmy and Jimmy stared in silence back, his eyes flashing from the group of men to the body in the snow. In an instant the spell was broken and the crowd rushed at him. Jimmy turned and ran. He knew he was running for his life and nothing could have made him run faster, but his soaked woollen socks slipped over the icy surface of the road giving no grip and he had no feeling in his frozen feet. He only had 20 yards' head start and he had to out distance them but, while he couldn't see them behind him, he knew they were gaining. His knee throbbed and he rounded the bend with the mob close behind and started up the shallow incline towards the brow of the hill. The freezing night air burned in his lungs and left his mouth in clouds, like the smoke from a train's chimney when it's pulling hard. In an effort to distract them he ripped off his leather helmet and threw it away, but they ignored it. The mob were shouting and cursing behind him and when he reached the crest of the hill he saw a wagon's headlights coming towards him about 100 yards away. He was trapped.

Still running he glanced quickly over his shoulder to see the nearest man was only 5 yards behind. So, with lungs bursting, Jimmy leapt for the top of the stone wall to his right and rolled neatly over it into the field. This gained him a couple of yards while the pack of smaller men scrambled over behind him. But now he was on rough ground and the rocky field tore his socks and cut his feet.

No matter how hard he drove himself on he limped more and more and got slower and slower until a flying leap by one of his pursuers brought him crashing to the ground. Using all his strength he rolled clear and started to stand up. But he was already surrounded and a kick in the face from a heavy boot knocked him back down. Kicks rained in from all sides and Jimmy rolled himself up into a ball with his head tucked as far in as he could. Then the kicks stopped and he risked a peep out at what was going on. A tall slim man with a hook for a left hand was advancing on him with a pitchfork.

Although Jimmy had baled out after Bob, Bob hadn't opened his chute until he was almost on the ground and while Freddy had flown a few miles west in the time between Bob and Jimmy baling out, the wind was from the west. So while Jimmy was hanging in his parachute the wind had blown him back east, until he landed less than a mile from Bob. Now Jimmy faced the same fate as Bob. He sat up and scrambled backwards away from the pitchfork, but there was no escape.

"NO!" He yelled, but who was there to help him? The farmer's angry eyes stared down coldly at him with no feeling or compassion and Jimmy filled his lungs and yelled, "SOMEBODY HELP ME!" Then he rolled into a ball and tensed himself for the killing thrust.

A burst of submachine gun fire thudded overhead and was echoed back from the trees. There were shouted orders in harsh, guttural and authoritative German. After a few seconds remaining in a tense ball Jimmy glanced up, still expecting death at any time. He saw a freckle-faced boy in his late teens looking down at him. The boy wore the uniform and peaked cap of the German army and he carried an MP40 submachine gun, with smoke rising up from the muzzle and blowing away in the wind. Behind him stood two more boys who looked younger, but were dressed the same and carried rifles.

The boy who was in charge stared at him for a moment and then said, "I am Feldwebel Herget of the Wehrmacht and you are my prisoner. For you zer war is over."

Jimmy sat up, with tears running down his cheeks. He curled up his knees, put his head in his arms and sobbed, "Thank you."

Because George pulled the ripcord as soon as he left his turret he was still doing 200 mph when his chute opened and, as he would have said, it nearly ripped his bollocks off! Gasping for breath he lifted himself up by pulling on the parachute shrouds, taking his weight on his arms. He thought he could feel his wounds bursting open and bleeding into his clothes, but he wasn't sure. He pulled off his oxygen mask, which he always hated wearing, and looked around. Swinging gently from side to side above the clouds he could see no sign of Freddy and he felt sick. He wondered if he had missed something. Had he not seen the fighter because he hadn't been fit to fly and was distracted by the pain in his backside? Had it been a fighter that got them? All he knew was they had been clobbered hard and fast. Had anyone else got out? What would be the chances of meeting up with them on the ground? He knew the chances of that were pretty small. He had seen a film where a bomber crew had been shot down and met up to make their escape, but they had had time to arrange a rendezvous before they baled out, and they were over Holland and the Dutch helped them escape. George wasn't sure where he was, but he knew he was still over Germany and there would be no help for him.

Drifting through the clouds he tried to plan what to do. It was 2.30 so he would have about five hours before it got light. He would have to get as far as he could before then and find a good hiding place for the day, then set off again the next night. One thing he did know was the wind was from the west and all the time he was in his parachute he was being blown further into Germany.

When he came out of the clouds the ground was surprisingly close, but George was not going to be lucky and he was over a large wood. He set himself up to land, bending his knees and covering his face with his arms, then, with a crash of snapping branches, he dropped through the tops of the fir trees and stopped with a jerk. When he had stopped bouncing around he uncovered his face and looked around. The ground was six feet below him, so he readied himself, then released his harness and dropped to the ground. There was no way he was going to get the parachute out of the tree, so he didn't try. Come the morning it would soon be found so he would have to be well on his way by then. Gingerly he sat down on the carpet of pine needles and checked his escape equipment. A button compass, a map and some German marks. On top of this he emptied from his pockets a packet of cigarettes, a lighter and a bar of chocolate. He looked at the chocolate, thought of Alex, and smiled. I wonder what you can get for a bar of chocolate in Germany, he thought, lighting a cigarette. The wood around him was dark and foreboding and he wondered if there were wolves or bears in German woods.

Fear started to rise within him and he wished he had carried a gun, if only for the confidence it would give him. While he smoked he stripped off his heavy gunner's suit, thought about burying it, then decided to carry it. He would walk as far as he could tonight, then find another wood and put the suit on to keep warm and hide during the day. Then he would do the same the next night and so on until he reached the Rhine. Then he would have to find a way across and once over he would be in France and he would try and contact the French resistance. Piece of cake, he thought, knowing full well it wasn't. He finished his cigarette, adjusted his trousers, which he was sure were sticking to his bloody backside, checked his compass, bundled his heated suit under his arm and set off towards the west.

POSTSCRIPT – DEMONS IN THE DARK

106 Squadron was a real squadron, which flew Hampdens, Manchesters and Lancaster Bombers during the Second World War. The commanding officers of the Squadron described in the book were all real people, although my description of Wing Commander Baxter may be wildly inaccurate as I was unable to find any photographs of him.

During the time of this book 106 Squadron was stationed at RAF Metheringham in Lincolnshire. Little of the station now remains because it was built for the war and soon after the war ended the land was handed back to the farmers from whom it had been commandeered. Parts of the perimeter track and runways still remain and there is a visitors' centre in what used to be the station rations store. Group Captain McKechnie was the Station Commander and he was as described. He flew a large number of Ops, far more than he needed too, and was obviously a very brave man. His wife was pregnant during the time of the book and soon after gave birth to a daughter. Sadly, shortly after this, McKechnie was killed on Ops. The descriptions of the station and its buildings are as accurate as I can make them from the maps and photographs I have seen and the descriptions I have had from people who were on 106 Squadron at Metheringham.

All of the other characters of the book are fictitious, although most of the situations they find themselves in are based on real events, which happened to real wartime aircrew. The technical details are again as accurate as I can make them after reading many technical manuals and talking to many wartime heavy bomber crews. Additionally, I have taken guidance from members of the air and ground crew of the Battle of Britain Memorial flight who still work on and fly a Lancaster.

Pilot Officer Jackson's crew was pretty average in that it was mainly made up of sergeants; many crews had no officers at all. They came from all over the country and from all backgrounds. Many came from the commonwealth and 106 Squadron did have a high proportion of Australians in it. The incidents with the toilet doors and the scarecrow really happened, as did most of the other incidents in the book.

Jackson's was certainly not a lucky crew and they went from rough trip to rough trip. But then, if they had been a lucky crew and sailed through their tour without even seeing a German fighter, as some lucky crews did, then it would have been a pretty uninteresting book. That said, the average number of trips a bomber crew made before getting shot down was seven! So as you can see, the chances of getting through a tour were pretty slim and F for Freddy's crew made one more trip than average.

When a heavy bomber was shot down the average number of people to survive was two out of seven. This is a figure averaged from all the heavy bomber losses during the war. In many bombers there were no survivors and in one or two lucky cases whole crews survived, but in most cases only one or two got out.

The Nuremberg raid was the worst night for Bomber Command and including those that crashed in England on their return, or were so badly damaged they were written off, the RAF lost 108 bombers directly involved in that raid. 106 Squadron actually flew 17 aircraft that night and lost 3 crews, plus Pilot Officer Penman's wrecked aircraft at RAF Manston. (Penman's crew were all killed a few weeks later.) I just added F for Freddy on as an additional, fictional extra.

F for Freddy's crew was unlucky in starting their tour towards the end of the campaign later known as the Battle for Berlin. It was the third in the series of strategic bombing campaigns launched by Sir Arthur "Bomber" Harris. The first being the Battle of the Ruhr, which was a victory because it was within the range of the Oboe blind bombing system and targets could be marked accurately in any weather. The second was the Battle of Hamburg, which was a victory because Hamburg had prominent features. These stood, out well on H2S radar, so again the target could be marked accurately. It was also easy to route the bombers over the sea for most of the route to limit the time they were exposed to German fighters. But Berlin was an altogether different prospect. It was a long way away from the bombers' bases, so the bombers had to carry more fuel and fewer bombs. The trip could only be made during long winter nights, if the bombers were to be covered by darkness. And while much of the journey could still be made over water, Berlin was well beyond the range of Oboe and lacked good features for H2S marking. Finally, as a massive target, it was vital to concentrate the attacks to flatten large areas on each raid, but the bombing tended to be scattered thinly over wide areas. During the winter months of 1943/44 the Berlin campaign was waged with Berlin being the main target, but other cities being targeted from time to time to keep the Germans guessing. Nuremberg was the last raid of the campaign, after this, the nights were too short to cover the long flight and Bomber Command was switched to hitting targets in support of the coming invasion of France.

There are a couple of inaccuracies in the book. The first is pigeons were not carried in Bomber Command aircraft after 1943, although they were still carried in Coastal Command aircraft. I included the pigeons because I find it fascinating that now, in the age of pilot locating beacons, where all any downed pilot has to do is activate his beacon and he can be immediately located by satellites and, with luck, rescued within hours, if not minutes. But 60 years ago we were relying on pigeons.

The second is, RAF Metheringham's FIDO didn't become operational until later in 1944 and so would not have been available during the time of this book. I could have altered the time of the book, but I wanted it to cover the Battle of Berlin period, so miraculously, Metheringham's FIDO became operational early. Another couple of minor points are; the bombers usually gained height by circling over their bases before setting course and the more inexperienced crews were usually placed towards the end of the bomber stream. This was to enable more accurate navigation and so that by the time the inexperienced crews got to the target it would, hopefully, be well lit by the fires of the more experienced crews incendiaries. For the purpose of the story Jackson's crew jumped around over the whole length of the bomber stream but I don't believe it detracts from the story, so I hope you'll forgive my indulgence.

I am sure there are a few other inaccuracies, which sharp-eyed experts will point out, but I have done all I can to make this book as technically accurate and realistic as possible, while at the same time being an interesting and exciting read.